Register of New

Fruit and Nut Varieties 1920 - 1950

Register of New

Fruit and Nut Varieties

1920-1950

by Reid M. Brooks and H. P. Olmo

with the assistance of cooperating horticulturists

Berkeley and Los Angeles, 1952

University of California Press

Originally published in the *Proceedings* of the American Society for Horticultural Science, Volumes 45 (1944), 47 (1946), 50 (1947), 53 (1949), and 56 (1950).

University of California Press

Berkeley and Los Angeles, California

Cambridge University Press, London, England

Printed in the United States of America

Preface

The compilers of the REGISTER OF NEW FRUIT AND NUT VARIETIES have as their objectives the collection and publication of accurate information on the origin, parentage, and most valuable characteristics of new fruits and nuts originating in North America for the period 1920-1950, inclusive. Five lists have been published at intervals in the *Proceedings* of the American Society for Horticultural Science, the first in 1944.

The present summary incorporates the material heretofore published in separate lists of the REGISTER and is designed primarily for those who wish to have the information available under one cover. A unique feature is the complete list of patented varieties. Indexes are arranged so that a variety may be easily located, either by name, species, place of origin, or patent number. There are short descriptions of 1,106 varieties, comprising 49 species of fruit plants.

No attempt has been made to include all new varieties, but only those which have shown promise of becoming important commercially, or that appear to have unusual characteristics useful to the breeder of new forms. Ornamental species that do not bear edible fruits are not included. The compilers are not passing judgment on nomenclature but simply recording the description of the variety as it has been received by us from the originator, the introducer, or an interested horticulturist, and checked by at least one of the cooperators.

It would have been impossible to present this summary without the continued assistance of the many cooperators listed elsewhere. Many others too numerous to mention have contributed and we wish to thank them all. The compilers assume full responsibility for omissions and errors in the text and would appreciate having any oversights reported.

Reid M. Brooks

H. P. Olmo

September 1, 1951
Davis, California

Cooperating Horticulturists

CANADA

British Columbia: A. J. Mann. **Manitoba**: W. R. Leslie, C. R. Ure. **Nova Scotia**: E. L. Eaton. **Ontario**: A. W. S. Hunter, E. F. Palmer.

UNITED STATES OF AMERICA

Alabama: T. B. Hagler. **Arizona**: A. H. Finch, Robert H. Hilgeman, Harvey Tate. **Arkansas**: J. E. Vaile, Roger S. Young. **California**: Claron O. Hesse, W. E. Lammerts, B. Rounds, C. A. Schroeder, Herbert C. Swim. **Colorado**: Ferris M. Green. **Connecticut**: D. F. Jones, E. M. Stoddard. **Delaware**: L. R. Detjen. **Florida**: F. E. Gardner, S. J. Lynch, Geo. D. Ruehle. **Georgia**: M. M. Murphy, J. H. Weinberger. **Idaho**: Leif Verner. **Illinois**:

J. C. McDaniel, R. L. McMunn. **Indiana**: C. E. Baker, C. L. Burkholder, Laurenz Greene. **Iowa**: H. L. Lantz. **Kentucky**: W. D. Armstrong. **Louisiana**: P. L. Hawthorne, Julian C. Miller. **Maryland**: Harley L. Crane, George M. Darrow, C. A. Reed*. **Massachusetts**: John S. Bailey, F. W. Southwick. **Michigan**: Stanley Johnston. **Minnesota**: W. H. Alderman, A. N. Wilcox. **Mississippi**: E. A. Currey, N. H. Loomis. **Missouri**: Paul H. Shepard. **Montana**: F. M. Harrington. **New Hampshire**: L. P. Latimer. **New Jersey**: M. A. Blake*, L. F. Hough. **New Mexico**: J. V. Enzie. **New York**: John Einset, G. H. Howe, George L. Slate, Richard Wellington. **North Carolina**: M. E. Gardner, C. F. Williams. **North Dakota**: Harold Mattson. **Ohio**: C. W. Ellenwood, Freeman S. Howlett. **Oklahoma**: F. B. Cross. **Oregon**: Henry Hartman, C. E. Schuster*, George F. Waldo. **Pennsylvania**: F. N. Fagan, J. U. Ruef, D. G. White. **South Carolina**: John T. Bregger. **South Dakota**: N. E. Hansen*, S. A. McCrory. **Tennessee**: Brooks D. Drain. **Texas**: F. R. Brison, E. Mortenson. **Utah**: Francis M. Coe, S. W. Edgecombe. **Vermont**: M. B. Cummings. **Virginia**: R. C. Moore, George Oberle. **Washington**: Harold W. Fogle, C. D. Schwartze. **West Virginia**: W. H. Childs, Edwin Gould. **Wisconsin**: Franklin A. Gilbert, James G. Moore. **Wyoming**: W. O. Edmondson.

*Deceased.

Contents

Register of Varieties

ALMOND

Harpareil.--Originated in Davis, California, by the United States Department of Agriculture (M. N. Wood) and the California Agricultural Experiment Station (W. P. Tufts). Introduced commercially in 1938. Nonpareil x Harriott; cross of 1926, first crop 1930. Nut: large; color good; softshell; superior to Ne Plus Ultra, which it most nearly resembles. Tree: blossoms early; foliage and bearing habits good.

Jordanolo.--Originated in Davis, California, by the United States Department of Agriculture (M. N. Wood) and the California Agricultural Experiment Station (W. P. Tufts). Introduced commercially in 1938. Nonpareil x Harriott; cross of 1926, first crop 1930. Nut: large, smooth; attractive; quality high; softshell; kernel most nearly resembles Jordan. Tree: bears early and heavily; foliage dense; considerable resistance to spider.

ALMOND-PEACH

Manitou *(Minnesota 7)*.--Originated in Excelsior, Minnesota, by the University of Minnesota Fruit Breeding Farm. Introduced commercially in 1923. *Prunus nana* x Bokhara peach. Tree: small flowering ornamental; sterile, does not set any fruit; produces mass of light pink flowers early just ahead of *P. triloba*.

Minnesota 7.--See **Manitou.**

APPLE

Acheson.--Originated in Edmonton, Alberta, Canada, by Mrs. J. H. Acheson. Introduced commercially in 1941. Open pollinated seedling of Delicious. Fruit: large; ovate; greenish yellow; flesh fine textured; subacid; quality above medium; season mid-August and September. Tree: hardy; productive.

Alaska.--Originated in Ettersburg, California, by Albert F. Etter. Introduced commercially in 1944. Patent no. 699; June 18, 1946; assigned to George C. Roeding, Jr., California Nursery Company, Niles, California. Open pollinated seedling of Bedfordshire Foundling; selected in 1944. Fruit: flesh snow white; skin shiny; medium sized. Tree: heavy producer.

Almeda.--Originated in Sumner County, Tennessee, by J. W. Savely. Introduced commercially in 1939. Patent no. 327; April 18, 1939. Mutation of Rhode Island Greening (?); discovered in 1927. Fruit: large; green; subacid; ripens July 25 to August 5; keeps exceptionally well; excellent for cooking.

Alton.--Originated in Geneva, New York, by the New York State Agricultural Experiment Station (Richard Wellington). Introduced for trial in 1938. Early McIntosh x New York 845 (Red Canada x Yellow Transparent); cross made in 1923, first full crop in 1935. Fruit: similar to Crimson Beauty; flavor mild, subacid; ripens just after Crimson Beauty; eating and cooking apple, for home and roadside markets. Tree: most nearly resembles Crimson Beauty.

Astrachan 2391.--See **Carlton.**

Atha.--Originated in Cullman County, Alabama, by Miss Atha

Warnick. Introduced commercially about 1930. Open pollinated seedling of Red Astrachan (perhaps x Yellow Transparent); selected about 1915. Fruit: firmer, ripens six weeks later, and less tendency to biennial bearing than Yellow Transparent. Tree: most nearly resembles Yellow Transparent, but more vigorous.

Baxter's Black Winesap.--Originated in Nauvoo, Illinois, by Frederick K. Baxter, Emil O. Baxter, and Cecil J. Baxter, Jr. Introduced commercially in 1944. Patent no. 619; March 21, 1944. Parentage unknown; selected in 1930. Fruit: size large; color deep red approaching black; ripens 10 days later than Winesap; holds well on tree; excellent keeper in common storage. Tree: rapid grower; very hardy; early bearer.

Beacon *(Minnesota 423)*.--Originated in Excelsior, Minnesota, by the University of Minnesota Fruit Breeding Farm. Introduced commercially in February, 1936. Open pollinated seedling of Malinda; seed planted in 1908. Fruit: skin solid red; quality good; matures early. Tree: productive.

Beverly Hills.--Originated in Berkeley, California, by the University of California (W. H. Chandler) and fruited at Los Angeles, California, as seedling 302. Introduced commercially in 1945. Melba x Early McIntosh; seed planted in 1939; first fruited in 1942. Fruit: flesh white; skin pale yellow with red stripes and splashed with red; quality very good; most nearly resembles McIntosh. Tree: moderately well suited to southern California coastal climate.

Blackjon.--Originated in Wenatchee, Washington, by the Columbia and Okanogan Nursery Company (A. T. Gossman) and trademarked by them. Introduced commercially in 1931. Bud mutation of Jonathan; selected in 1929. Fruit: earlier coloring and more bright red color than Jonathan, which it most nearly resembles.

Blackmack.--Originated in Oliver, British Columbia, Canada, by H. Simpson. Introduced commercially in 1930. Trademarked by Columbia and Okanogan Nursery Company, Wenatchee, Washington. Bud mutation of McIntosh Red; selected in 1928. Fruit: early coloring, permitting earlier picking and thereby eliminating loss by windfalls.

Breakey.--Originated in Morden, Manitoba, Canada, by the Dominion Experimental Station. Introduced commercially in 1935. Open pollinated seedling of Blushed Calville; selected in 1929. Fruit: medium size; round oblate; well colored red and scarlet; flesh white, fine textured, melting, juicy; flavor mild, spicy; quality good as dessert or sauce; season September to November. Tree: vigorous; upright spreading; hardy.

Cal-King.--Originated in Van Nuys, California, by George King. Introduced commercially in 1947. Parentage unknown; discovered in 1942. Fruit: skin colors well; most nearly resembles Beverly Hills. Tree: does well in southern California.

Carlton *(Astrachan 2391)*.--Originated in Geneva, New York, by the New York State Agricultural Experiment Station (Richard Wellington). Introduced for trial in 1923. Montgomery x Red Astrachan; cross made in 1912. Fruit: ripens 1 month later than Red Astrachan; large, round-conic; skin attractive dark red; flesh white, tender, juicy, subacid, of Astrachan flavor; home use and roadside markets. Tree: vigorous; annual bearer.

Cauley.--Originated in Grenada, Mississippi, by the Mississippi Agricultural Experiment Station (J. W. Willis). Introduced commercially in 1942. Parentage unknown. Fruit: extremely large, weighing as much as 1 pound each; flesh yellow when ripe, with red skin stripes barely visible; flesh crisp and juicy; culinary and jelly apple; most nearly resembles Yellow Newtown. Tree: yields heavily, averaging 26 bushels per tree.

Chestnut *(Minnesota 240)*.--Originated in Excelsior, Minnesota, by the University of Minnesota Fruit Breeding Farm. Introduced commercially in November, 1946. Open pollinated seedling of Malinda; selected in 1921. Fruit: crab; large; pleasant nutlike flavor. Tree: vigorous; productive.

Close *(USDA 57)*.--Originated in Arlington, Virginia, by the United States Department of Agriculture (C. P. Close). Introduced commercially in 1938. Parentage uncertain; selected about 1925. Fruit: ripens with or slightly ahead of Yellow Transparent; fairly large, diameter 2½ inches or more; quality fairly good for both dessert and cooking; stands high summer temperatures well; promising as an early red apple for both home and commercial purposes. Tree: widely adapted.

Colora Red York *(Red York Imperial)*.--Originated in Colora, Cecil County, Maryland, by Lloyd Balderson III. Introduced commercially in the fall of 1935. Patent no. 168; March 10, 1936; assigned to Bountiful Ridge Nurseries, Princess Anne, Maryland. Bud mutation of York Imperial; discovered October 10, 1933. Fruit: colors a full bright red without any stripe; colors uniformly in all parts of the tree; other characteristics identical with York Imperial. Tree: identical with York Imperial.

Conard.--Originated in Mountain Grove, Missouri, by the Missouri State Fruit Experiment Station. Introduced commercially in 1935. Ben Davis x Jonathan; selected in 1920. Fruit: large, well colored; quality good; flavor tart; texture fine-grained; ripens about 1 week after Jonathan; not subject to premature dropping. Tree: vigorous; bears regular crops; resistant to disease.

Cortland.--Originated in Geneva, New York, by the New York State Agricultural Experiment Station (S. A. Beach). Introduced for trial in 1915. Ben Davis x McIntosh; cross made in 1898, seed germinated in 1899. Fruit: attractive red, darkly and obscurely striped; bloom heavy; large; flesh white, slow to discolor on exposure to air; hangs well on tree; stands handling well; dessert, cooking, market; most nearly resembles McIntosh. Tree: early and annual bearer; very hardy. Has become an important commercial variety.

Dakota Beauty.--Originated in Brookings, South Dakota, by Carl A. Hansen. Introduced commercially in 1944. Patent no. 648; one-half assigned to Albert C. Fischer; December 19, 1944. Parentage unknown. Fruit: crab; small. Tree: ornamental, with large double red blossoms; hardy.

Dark-Red Staymared.--Originated in Barber, Allegheny County, Virginia, by B. C. Moomaw, Jr. Introduced commercially in 1927. Trademarked by Stark Brothers Nurseries and Orchards Company, Louisiana, Missouri. Bud mutation of Stayman Winesap. Fruit: skin darker red than that of parent.

Davey.--Originated in North Grafton, Massachusetts, by S. Lothrop Davenport. Introduced commercially in January, 1950. Patent no. 906; December 20, 1949; assigned to Kelly Brothers Nurseries, Dansville, New York. Open pollinated seedling of McIntosh; discovered in 1928. Fruit: high color; distinctive flavor; hangs well on the tree; ripens after McIntosh; keeps all winter; quality and flavor equals Baldwin; most nearly resembles Wealthy in shape, but more highly colored. Tree: bears earlier and more regularly than Baldwin; resistant to scab. In 1945 awarded a first class certificate by the Massachusetts Horticultural Society.

Delawine.--Originated in Port Washington, Ohio, by W. F. Hines. Introduced commercially in the Spring, 1948, by the Henry Field Seed and Nursery Company, Shenandoah, Iowa. Delicious x Stayman Winesap. Fruit: shape, size, and color of Delicious; flesh juicy and flavor of Stayman Winesap. Tree: strong grower; spreading; foliage heavy; tendency toward annual bearing.

Delcon.--Originated in Mountain Grove, Missouri, by the Missouri State Fruit Experiment Station (Paul H. Shepard). Introduced commercially in 1948. Conard x Delicious; selected in 1929. Fruit: good flavor; most nearly resembles Delicious. Tree: dwarf tendency; heavy producer; suitable for home orchards.

Double-Red Baldwin.--Originated in Salisbury, New Hampshire, by E. N. Sawyer. Introduced commercially in 1927. Bud mutation of Baldwin; discovered in 1924. Fruit: deep, brilliant red, coloring early; darker red than parental variety.

Double Red Delicious.--See **Starking.**

Double-Red Duchess.--See **Red Duchess.**

Dunning.--Originated in Geneva, New York, by the New York State Agricultural Experiment Station (Richard Wellington). Introduced for trial in 1938. Early McIntosh x Cox Orange; cross made in 1923; first full crop in 1934. Fruit: skin red striped; medium-sized; flesh sweet, excellent quality; very early ripening (early August); for local use and roadside markets.

Early McIntosh.--Originated in Geneva, New York, by the New York State Agricultural Experiment Station (Richard Wellington). Introduced for trial in 1923. Yellow Transparent x McIntosh; seed borne in 1909; fruit first described in 1918. Fruit: ripens in early August; flavor excellent; most nearly resembles McIntosh.

Empire Red.--Originated in Grand Forks, British Columbia, Canada, by Robert Campbell. Introduced commercially in 1942. Patent no. 608; November 23, 1943. Parentage unknown; selected in 1928. Fruit: ripens early; skin all red; flesh streaked with red; ships well; used for cooking and dessert. Most nearly resembles McIntosh.

Erickson.--Originated in Aitkin, Minnesota, by John and Charles Erickson. Introduced commercially in 1923. Parentage unknown; seed planted in 1905; selected in 1910. Fruit: large; commercial value as an early green apple; most nearly resembles Hibernal. Tree: very winter hardy; annual bearer.

Etter's Gold.--Originated in Ettersburg, California, by Albert F. Etter. Introduced commercially in 1944. Patent no. 659; August 28, 1945; assigned to George C. Roeding, Jr., California Nursery Company, Niles, California. Parentage unknown. Fruit: matures in October; skin golden yellow; flesh crisp.

Faurot.--Originated in Mountain Grove, Missouri, by Missouri State Fruit Experiment Station. Introduced commercially in 1935. Ben Davis x Jonathan; selected in 1920. Fruit: ripens with Winesap; color fair; quality fair; size medium; keeps late; less likely to drop than Jonathan, which it most nearly resembles. Tree: resistant to disease.

Fireside *(Minnesota 993).*--Originated in Excelsior, Minnesota, by the Minnesota Agricultural Experiment Station (Charles Haralson). Introduced commercially in 1943. Parentage unknown; selected in 1917; selected for further testing in 1927. Fruit: large (3 inches in diameter); skin medium red, lightly striped with darker red; flesh yellowish, medium coarse, medium tender, medium juicy; flavor mild subacid; quality excellent for dessert purposes; season of use November to April. Tree: hardy; vigorous; resistant to cedar rust but is only slightly less susceptible than Wealthy to apple scab and fire blight.

Flame *(Minnesota 635)*.--Originated in Excelsior, Minnesota, by the University of Minnesota Fruit Breeding Farm. Introduced commercially in February, 1943. Parentage unknown; selected in 1920. Fruit: crab; brightly colored; hangs well on tree. An ornamental variety.

Folwell *(Minnesota 237)*.--Originated in Excelsior, Minnesota, by the University of Minnesota Fruit Breeding Farm. Introduced commercially in June, 1922. Open pollinated seedling of a Malinda seedling grown by T. E. Perkins of Red Wing, Minnesota; selected in 1913. Fruit: large; attractive; quality good. Tree: most nearly resembles Hibernal.

Franklin.--Originated in Wooster, Ohio, by the Ohio Agricultural Experiment Station. Introduced commercially in 1937. McIntosh x Delicious; selected in 1936. Fruit: well colored; flavor mild; dessert quality high; combines flesh characteristics of each parent; extends McIntosh season 1 week; most nearly resembles Delicious in shape.

Frostproof.--Originated in Mineral, Virginia, by Max Bazzanella, of the Max Nursery. Introduced commercially in 1947. Patent no. 722; January 7, 1947. Parentage unknown; discovered in 1930. Fruit: bronze with russet, quality fair; 2¼ to 3 inches; matures with Winesap; most nearly resembles Rustycoat. Tree: blooms 30 days later than most apples usually do.

Fyan.--Originated in Mountain Grove, Missouri, by the Missouri State Fruit Experiment Station. Introduced commercially in 1935. Ben Davis x Jonathan; selected in 1920. Fruit: ripens 2 weeks after Jonathan; large; fairly well colored; attractive; fine keeper; resembles Jonathan. Tree: spreading; very vigorous; regular bearer of large crops; resistant to disease.

Galbraith Baldwin.--Originated in Amherst, Massachusetts, by the Massachusetts Agricultural Experiment Station (Floyd Galbraith). Introduced commercially in 1948. Bud mutation of Baldwin; selected in 1934. Fruit: highly colored; most nearly resembles Baldwin.

Geneva.--Originated in Ottawa, Ontario, Canada, by the Divi-

sion of Horticulture, Central Experimental Farm. Introduced
commercially in 1930. Open pollinated seedling of *Malus niedzwetzkyana;* selected about 1928. Introduced as a 'Rosybloom'
crabapple, but is not as floriferous as other varieties of
this class. Fruit: crab; large, ornamental; of fair eating
quality; excellent for jelly. Tree: hardy; resistant to apple
scab.

Godfrey.--Originated in Morden, Manitoba, Canada, by the Dominion Experimental Station. Introduced commercially in 1931.
Open pollinated seedling of Patten Greening; selected in 1927.
Fruit: medium to small; well washed bright dark red; flesh
white, tinged greenish, crisp, fine textured; sweet, sprightly
flavor; quality good; season October to February. Tree: vigorous, spreading, productive.

Greendale.--Originated in Geneva, New York, by the New York
State Agricultural Experiment Station (Richard Wellington).
Introduced for trial in 1938. McIntosh x Lodi; cross made in
1924; first full crop in 1935. Fruit: skin attractive green;
well shaped; flavor mild; quality good; for dessert and cooking purposes; extends season of Lodi for local and roadside
markets; most nearly resembles McIntosh in shape and Lodi in
color.

Grove.--Originated in Mountain Grove, Missouri, by the Missouri State Fruit Experiment Station. Introduced commercially
in 1935. Ingram x Delicious; selected in 1930. Fruit: attractive; size good; quality good; colors well before ripening;
excellent keeper; ripens a little later than Winesap; most
nearly resembles Delicious. Tree: blooms late; resistant to
scab, blotch, blight.

Haralson *(Minnesota 90).*--Originated in Excelsior, Minnesota,
by the University of Minnesota Fruit Breeding Farm. Introduced
commercially in February, 1923. Open pollinated seedling of
Malinda; selected in 1913. Fruit: good cooking quality; attractive red; stores well. Tree: hardy.

Heyer 12.--Originated in Neville, Saskatchewan, Canada, by A.
Heyer. Introduced commercially about 1940. Seedling of a Rus-
sian apple received from A. P. Stevenson, Morden, Manitoba.
Fruit: 2½ inches; skin greenish yellow; flesh juicy, moderately coarse, acid; quality fair for cooking; season mid-August
to October. Tree: very hardy; productive; late blooming. Chief
value is a hardy, early apple for northern conditions.

Hoosier Seedling.--See **Jongrimes.**

Horace.--Originated in Ottawa, Ontario, Canada, by the Division of Horticulture, Central Experimental Farm. Has not been

introduced commercially. Open pollinated seedling of Langford
Beauty; selected in 1912. Fruit: medium size; skin highly
colored, striped; good quality; season September to November;
most nearly resembles Fameuse.

Humboldt.--Originated in Ettersburg, California, by Albert
Etter. Introduced commercially in 1944. Patent no. 658; June
5, 1945; assigned to George C. Roeding, Jr., California Nursery Company, Niles, California. Open pollinated seedling of
Transcendent which it resembles. Combines quality of fruit
with very large flowers of exceptional beauty; crab.

Idagold.--Originated in Moscow, Idaho, by the Idaho Agricultural Experiment Station (Leif Verner). Introduced commercially in May, 1944. Esopus Spitzenburg x Wagener; selected in
1939. Fruit: high dessert and keeping qualities; most nearly
resembles Esopus Spitzenburg.

Idajon.--Originated in Moscow, Idaho, by the University of
Idaho (Leif Verner). Introduced commercially in June, 1949.
Wagener x Jonathan; selected in 1936. Fruit: ripens 10 days
before Jonathan; dessert quality good.

Idared.--Originated in Moscow, Idaho, by the Idaho Agricultural Experiment Station (Leif Verner). Introduced commercially in 1942. Jonathan x Wagener; selected in 1935. Fruit:
nearly solid red; core small; texture good; good keeper; excellent dessert quality. Most nearly resembles Wagener.

Improved Blaxtayman 201.--Originated in Wenatchee, Washington,
by the Columbia and Okanogan Nursery Company (J. A. Snyder)
and trademarked by them. Introduced commercially in 1944. Bud
mutation of Stayman Winesap; selected in 1942. Fruit: solid
bright red color.

Jonared.--Originated in Peshastin, Washington, by William
Uecher. Introduced commercially in 1934. Patent no. 85; January 16, 1934; assigned to Stark Brothers Nurseries and Orchards Company, Louisiana, Missouri. Bud mutation of Jonathan;
discovered in 1930. Fruit: earlier coloring than parent; all-
over red color.

Jongrimes *(Hoosier Seedling)*.--Originated in Bloomfield, Indiana, by Roland S. Rogers. Introduced commercially in the 19-
20's. Patent no. 794; March 23, 1948; assigned to Stark Brothers Nurseries and Orchards Company, Louisiana, Missouri.
Parentage unknown; resembles Jonathan only in having some red
color; bears no resemblance to Grimes. Fruit: yellow ground
color streaked with red; tart; high dessert cooking quality;
keeps about as well as Duchess; ripens two weeks ahead of
Jonathan at a very favorable season; hangs in dense clusters

unless thinned. Tree: bears well.

Jonwin.--Originated in Ettersburg, California, by Albert F. Etter. Introduced commercially in 1944. Patent no. 710; September 17, 1946; assigned to George C. Roeding, Jr., California Nursery Company, Niles, California. Jonathan x Baldwin; selected in 1944. Fruit: large, size of Baldwin which it most nearly resembles; ripens during Jonathan season.

Jubilee.--Originated in Summerland, British Columbia, by the Dominion Experimental Station (R. C. Palmer). Introduced commercially in 1939. McIntosh x Grimes Golden; cross made in 1926; original tree planted in 1928; first fruited in 1934; selected in 1936 (A. J. Mann). Fruit: size medium; flesh firm, crisp, cream-colored, juicy; quality good; matures three weeks later than McIntosh; stores well until February. Tree: vigorous; as hardy as McIntosh to date. Named in 1939 in honor of the British Columbia Fruit Growers Association's Golden Jubilee Convention.

June Wealthy.--Originated in Findlay, Ohio, by Earl C. Ohl. Introduced commercially in 1947. Patent no. 765; October 14; 1947; assigned to Stark Brothers Nurseries and Orchards Company, Louisiana, Missouri. Open pollinated seedling of Wealthy; discovered about 1937. Fruit: dark red; quality good; ripens early, with Yellow Transparent.

Kendall.--Originated in Geneva, New York, by the New York State Agricultural Experiment Station (Richard Wellington). Introduced for trial in 1932. McIntosh x Zusoff; cross made in 1912. Fruit: skin handsome dark red color; large; whitish, fine-grained flesh of McIntosh; flavor sprightly; season about that of McIntosh, but keeps longer; hangs well on tree.

Lakeland *(Minnesota 978)*.--Originated in Excelsior, Minnesota, by the University of Minnesota Fruit Breeding Farm. Introduced commercially in 1950. Open pollinated seedling of Malinda; selected in 1927. Fruit: all over red color; Wealthy type; very good adherence to tree at harvest time. Tree: annual bearer; non-clustering fruit habit.

Lizakowsky.--See **Saint Clair.**

Lobo.--Originated in Ottawa, Ontario, Canada, by the Division of Horticulture, Central Experimental Farm. Introduced commercially about 1930. Open pollinated seedling of McIntosh; selected in 1906. Fruit: quality not quite as good as McIntosh but earlier in ripening; resembles McIntosh considerably in appearance. Tree: hardy; productive; bears at an early age.

Lodi.--Originated in Geneva, New York, by the New York State Agricultural Experiment Station (Richard Wellington). Introduced for trial in 1924. Montgomery x Yellow Transparent; cross made in 1911. Fruit: does not grow mealy and soften at center as quickly as Yellow Transparent; larger, keeps longer, ripens later than Yellow Transparent; culinary and fresh use; most nearly resembles Yellow Transparent.

Macoun.--Originated in Geneva, New York, by the New York State Agricultural Experiment Station (Richard Wellington). Introduced for trial in 1923. McIntosh x Jersey Black; seed borne in 1909; fruit first described in 1918. Fruit: similar to McIntosh, but smaller; red-skinned; white-fleshed; richly flavored, aromatic; ripens 1 month later than McIntosh.

Manitoba.--Originated in Morden, Manitoba, Canada, by the Dominion Experimental Station. Introduced commercially in 1931. Open pollinated seedling of Duchess of Oldenburg; selected in 1925. Fruit: medium to above; roundish oblate; yellow to yellow amber, slight blush; flesh white, crisp, juicy, fine textured, melting; flavor spicy, subacid; quality very good for cooking; season November through February. Tree: roundish, vigorous; only moderately hardy.

Manitoba Spy.--Originated in Morden, Manitoba, Canada, by the Dominion Experimental Station. Introduced commercially in 1931. Open pollinated seedling of Patten Greening; selected in 1927. Fruit: large; dullish dark red; flesh tender, juicy, somewhat coarse; flavor mild, sprightly, good for cooking; season November to February. Tree: upright spreading, hardy, vigorous, productive. Most nearly resembles Northern Spy.

Mantet.--Originated in Morden, Manitoba, Canada, by the Dominion Experimental Station. Introduced commercially in 1929. Open pollinated seedling of Tetofsky; selected in 1928. Fruit: medium to below; form roundish; heavily washed and striped bright red; flesh fine grained, tender, juicy, aromatic, sweet very pleasant; fresh eating quality excellent; season early-late August. Tree: upright; hardy; productive.

Margaret Pratt.--Originated in Owen Sound, Ontario, Canada, by C. A. Fleming. Introduced commercially about 1938. Parentage unknown; discovered before 1923 in the garden of Margaret Pratt. Fruit: most nearly resembles Red Astrachan but is larger; should be picked early since it breaks down if allowed to take on full color; used for cooking. Tree: growth-habit and performance similar to Red Astrachan; good bearer.

Martin.--Originated in Gorum, Natchitoches Parish, Louisiana, by Charles A. Martin. Introduced commercially in 1943. Patent no. 564; January 5, 1943. Parentage unknown; discovered in

1936. Fruit: matures early; quality fair to good; dessert fruit; skin yellow with red splashing. Tree: grows successfully in Louisiana; apparently fire blight resistant.

Medina.--Originated in Geneva, New York, by the New York State Agricultural Experiment Station (Richard Wellington). Introduced for trial in 1922. Deacon Jones x Delicious; cross made in 1911. Fruit: larger, better colored, more attractive than Delicious because of golden-yellow ground color; prolongs season of Delicious, which it most nearly resembles.

Melred.--See **Red Melba.**

Melrose.--Originated in Wooster, Ohio, by the Ohio Agricultural Experiment Station (Freeman S. Howlett). Introduced commercially in 1944. Jonathan x Delicious; selected in 1937. Fruit: quality better than Rome Beauty; does not develop Jonathan spot; harvesting season 7 to 10 days later than Jonathan; storage season through March into April; resembles Jonathan in color and shape, but less tart. A good late apple to supplement Stayman Winesap and Rome Beauty in regions of long growing season, and in areas where the parents are grown.

Metzger.--Originated in Seattle, Washington, by Ludwig Metzger and Cecil C. Clark. Introduced commercially in 1948. Patent no. 972; August 15, 1950; assigned to May Nursery Co., Yakima, Washington. Open pollinated seedling of Delicious; selected about 1938. Fruit: firm; attractive; good quality; good shipper and canner; ripens early August; susceptible to fire blight; most nearly resembles Red Delicious.

Miami.--Originated in New Carlisle, Ohio, by H. N. Scarff. Introduced commercially in 1935. Bud mutation of Stark; discovered in 1930. Fruit: solid bronze red; flesh fine textured; high quality for eating and culinary use; late keeping. Most nearly resembles Stark.

Milton.--Originated in Geneva, New York, by the New York State Agricultural Experiment Station (Richard Wellington). Introduced for trial in 1923. Yellow Transparent x McIntosh; cross made in 1909. Fruit: color attractive; characteristic McIntosh taste and aroma; sometimes has unattractive bulge on one side; season after Early McIntosh and preceding McIntosh by a month or 6 weeks; most nearly resembles McIntosh.

Minjon *(Minnesota 700)*.--Originated in Excelsior, Minnesota, by the University of Minnesota Fruit Breeding Farm. Introduced commercially in 1942. Parentage unknown, but probably Wealthy x Jonathan; selected in 1923. Fruit: quality good; skin solid dark red; flesh stained red as in Wealthy; most nearly resembles Jonathan in size, shape, and color; for home and commercial use.

Minnehaha *(Minnesota 300)*.--Originated in Excelsior, Minnesota, by the University of Minnesota Fruit Breeding Farm. Introduced commercially in March, 1920. Open pollinated seedling of Malinda; selected in 1914. Fruit: dark red; very attractive; rich flavor; season early winter.

Minnesota 90.--See **Haralson**.

Minnesota 207.--See **Wedge**.

Minnesota 237.--See **Folwell**.

Minnesota 240.--See **Chestnut**.

Minnesota 300.--See **Minnehaha**.

Minnesota 396.--See **Victory**.

Minnesota 423.--See **Beacon**.

Minnesota 635.--See **Flame**.

Minnesota 638.--See **Redwell**.

Minnesota 700.--See **Minjon**.

Minnesota 714.--See **Oriole**.

Minnesota 978.--See **Lakeland**.

Minnesota 993.--See **Fireside**.

Minnesota 1007.--See **Prairie Spy**.

Minnetonka Beauty.--Originated in Excelsior, Minnesota, by I. E. Soderlund. Introduced commercially in 1941. Patent no. 474; June 10, 1941. Parentage unknown; selected in 1928. Fruit: no bunching on branches; used fresh and for cooking; keeps unusually long.

Monroe *(New York 1546)*.--Originated in Geneva, New York, by the New York State Agricultural Experiment Station (Richard Wellington). Introduced for trial as Seedling No. 1546 in 1947; introduced as Monroe in December, 1949. Jonathan x Rome Beauty; seed produced in 1910. Fruit: solid red; excellent quality; late-keeper; most nearly resembles Jonathan. Tree: hardy; an annual bloomer; good cropper, unless frost injures the blossoms.

Morden 347.--Originated in Morden, Manitoba, Canada, by the Dominion Experimental Station. Introduced commercially in 1941. Martha x Dolgo; selected in 1939. Fruit: resembles a large Dolgo; skin color yellow, generally completely washed dark red; flesh orange-yellow, firm, crisp, juicy and sprightly; quality good as dessert and for canning; season late August. Tree: upright; hardy; vigorous.

Morden 352.--Originated in Morden, Manitoba, Canada, by the Dominion Experimental Station. Introduced commercially in 1945. Dolgo x Haralson; selected in 1944. Fruit: resembles a very large Dolgo in form and color; flesh white, tinged with red, firm, crisp, juicy; flavor sweet, sprightly acid; fair to good as dessert or canned; stores well into winter; ripens late September. Tree: medium tall; robust; very hardy; strongly crotched.

Newfane.--Originated in Geneva, New York, by the New York State Agricultural Experiment Station (Richard Wellington). Introduced for trial in 1927. Deacon Jones x Delicious; seed borne in 1911 and germinated in 1912. Fruit: large, oblong-conic; attractive red; flesh tender, medium juicy, mildly flavored with a pronounced Delicious aroma; dessert apple; ripens with Delicious, which it most nearly resembles.

Newtown Delicious.--Originated in White Salmon, Washington, by E. P. Wray. Introduced commercially about 1937. Patent no. 61; April 18, 1933. Yellow Newtown x Delicious; selected about 1930. Fruit: attractive red and yellow color; flavor good; keeps well; superior for culinary use. Tree: growth vigorous; heavy bearer.

New York 1546.--See **Monroe.**

Nu-Jon.--Originated in Entiat, Washington, by A. J. Marr. Patent applied for by Columbia and Okanogan Nursery Company, Wenatchee, Washington. Introduced commercially in 1949. Parentage unknown; discovered in 1945. Fruit: large, deep red, striped; ripens 10 days earlier than Jonathan; good quality. Tree: not subject to mildew.

Ogden.--Originated in Geneva, New York, by the New York State Agricultural Experiment Station (Richard Wellington). Introduced for trial in 1928. Zusoff x McIntosh; cross made in 1912; first full crop in 1924. Fruit: dark red with heavy bloom, similar to McIntosh but with considerable scarfskin; flesh white, often stained, aromatic, sweet; season little earlier than McIntosh; good baking apple; most nearly resembles McIntosh.

Oriole *(Minnesota 714).*--Originated in Excelsior, Minnesota,

by the University of Minnesota Fruit Breeding Farm. Introduced commercially in March, 1949. Parentage unknown; selected
in 1923 from seed planted in 1914. Fruit: very large; roundish; striped and splashed red over yellow-orange; flesh tender, fine grained, juicy, aromatic, subacid; quality excellent for cooking or dessert; an unusually good early summer
variety.

Orleans.--Originated in Geneva, New York, by the New York
State Agricultural Experiment Station (Richard Wellington).
Introduced for trial in 1924. Deacon Jones x Delicious; cross
made in 1911. Fruit: more attractive and larger than Deli-
cious; keeps in common storage 6 weeks longer than Delicious;
similar to Medina but keeps longer; of the Delicious type.
Tree: similar to Medina and thrives in some soils to which
Medina is not adapted.

Patricia.--Originated in Ottawa, Ontario, Canada, by the Division of Horticulture, Central Experimental Farm. Has not
been introduced commercially. Open pollinated seedling of
McIntosh; selected in 1920. Fruit: handsome; small unless
thinned; high quality; about the same season as McIntosh.
Tree: heavy bearer; hardier than McIntosh.

Payette.--Originated in Moscow, Idaho, by the Idaho Agricultural Experiment Station (Leif Verner). Introduced commercially in May, 1944. Ben Davis x Wagener; selected in November, 1936. Fruit: large, good red color high dessert quality
most nearly resembles Ben Davis.

Pink Pearl.--Originated in Ettersburg, California, by Albert
F. Etter. Introduced commercially in 1944. Patent no. 723;
March 4, 1947; assigned to George C. Roeding, Jr., California Nursery Company, Niles, California. Open pollinated seedling of 'Surprise;' selected June 23, 1944. Fruit: transparent skin which glows pink from flesh beneath; outstanding
bouquet when skin is broken; ripens in September.

Prairie Spy (*Minnesota 1007*).--Originated in Excelsior, Minnesota, by the University of Minnesota Fruit Breeding Farm. Introduced commercially in 1940. Parentage unknown; seed planted
in 1914; selected in 1923. Fruit: high dessert and culinary
quality; flesh crisp and juicy; matures in October; most nearly resembles Northern Spy. Tree: hardy; vigorous.

Red Delicious.--See **Redwin.**

Red Duchess (*Van Buren, Double-Red Duchess*).--Originated in
New York by J. P. Van Buren. Introduced commercially in 1937.
Bud mutation of Duchess; discovered in 1914. Fruit: attrac-
tive solid red color.

Redfield.--Originated in Geneva, New York, by the New York State Agricultural Experiment Station (Richard Wellington). Introduced for trial in 1938. Wolf River x *Malus niedzwetzkyana;* cross made in 1924; first full crop in 1935. Fruit: skin dark solid red; flesh deep red. Tree: foliage dark with reddish-green tinge early in season; large, dark pink flowers. An ornamental variety; most nearly resembles *M. niedzwetzkyana,* but larger.

Redford.--Originated in Geneva, New York, by the New York State Agricultural Experiment Station (Richard Wellington). Introduced for trial in 1938. Wolf River x *Malus niedzwetzkyana;* cross made in 1924. Tree: sister seedling of Redfield which it closely resembles, except the flowers are lighter in color, being deep pink. Most nearly resembles *M. niedzwetzkyana.* An ornamental variety.

Redgold.--Originated in Cashmere, Washington, by F. A. Schell. Introduced commercially in 1946. Patent no. 720; December 24, 1946; assigned to Stark Brothers Nurseries and Orchards Company, Louisiana, Missouri. Golden Delicious x Richared Delicious; selected about 1936. Fruit: fine flavor; red; matures fairly early. Tree: bears early.

Red Graham.--Originated in Manistee, Michigan, by the Manistee Orchard Company. Introduced commercially in 1936. Patent no. 278; May 17, 1938; assigned to Greening Nursery Company, Monroe, Michigan. Bud mutation of Northern Spy; discovered in 1926. Fruit: large, shaped like Northern Spy; color brighter than parent; ripens with McIntosh; keeps in cold storage until spring; good pie and general purpose apple. Tree: growth is similar to Northern Spy.

Red Gravenstein.--Originated in San Juan County, Washington, by Van Sent V. Whipple. Introduced commercially in 1924. Bud mutation of Gravenstein; discovered in 1907 or 1908. Fruit: solid dark red; superior in appearance to Gravenstein or to Banks Gravenstein.

Red Hackworth.--Originated in Morgan or Cullman County, Alabama; originator unknown. Introduced commercially by Empire Nursery and Orchard, Baileyton, Alabama, about 1925. Probably an open pollinated seedling of Hackworth; selected before 1900. Fruit: quality good when fully ripe (August); smaller, firmer, and more solid red than Hackworth. Tree: well adapted to Alabama climate and soils; good understock variety in northern Alabama where it is propagated on own roots from suckers. Most nearly resembles Hackworth in tree and in flavor of fruit.

Redhook.--Originated in Geneva, New York, by the New York State Agricultural Experiment Station (Richard Wellington). Introduced for trial in 1938. McIntosh x Carlton; cross made in 1923; first full crop in 1935. Fruit: skin very attractive dark red with heavy bloom; flesh white but sometimes reddish, highly aromatic; season between Milton and McIntosh; dessert apple for home and roadside markets.

Red McIntosh.--Originated in Dansville, New York, by Isaac C. Rogers. Introduced commercially in 1932. Bud mutation of McIntosh. Fruit: color dark solid red; in all other respects similar to its parent.

Red Melba *(Melred)*.--Origin unknown, but first noticed among a lot of nursery trees from the Wellington and Davidson Nurseries, Fonthill, Ontario, Canada. Introduced commercially in the 1940's. Bud mutation of Melba; discovered previous to 1937. Fruit: resembles Melba but is more highly colored, flesh firmer, bruises less easily, and is a few days later in maturity. Apparently identical sports have appeared in several localities in Canada.

Red Sauce.--Originated in Geneva, New York, by the New York State Agricultural Experiment Station (Richard Wellington). Introduced for trial in 1926. Deacon Jones x Wealthy; cross made in 1910; first full crop in 1917. Fruit: skin nearly solid red; roundish conic, large; flesh coarse, briskly subacid, often red to coreline; makes a red sauce when cooked; season October.

Red Spy.--Originated about 1895 in Victor, New York, by Wm. S. Greene. Introduced for trial in 1923. Bud mutation of Northern Spy; sent to the New York State Agricultural Experiment Station in 1910 by C. E. Greene (son of Wm. S. Greene). Fruit: skin solid bright red, otherwise typical of parent.

Red Striped Graham.--Originated in Manistee, Michigan, by the Manistee Orchard Company. Introduced commercially in 1936. Patent no. 293; October 4, 1938; assigned to Greening Nursery Company, Monroe, Michigan. Bud mutation of Northern Spy; discovered in 1926. Fruit: large and shaped like Northern Spy; color brighter than parent but striped; ripens with McIntosh; keeps well in cold storage until spring; good pie and general purpose apple. Tree: growth similar to Northern Spy.

Redwell *(Minnesota 638)*.--Originated in Excelsior, Minnesota, by the University of Minnesota Fruit Breeding Farm. Introduced commercially in November, 1946. Open pollinated seedling of Scott's Winter; seed planted about 1911; selected in 1923. Fruit: color very attractive bright medium red, russet dots; flesh cream, mild; quality good for baking, dessert, and sauce; matures about mid-October and keeps well until January. Tree: annual bearer.

Redwin *(Red Delicious)*.--Originated in Peshastin, Washington, by J. L. Johnson. Introduced commercially in 1928. Bud mutation of Delicious; discovered in 1925. Fruit: colors early, retaining dark red stripes at full maturity.

Red Winesap.--Originated in Washington by the May Nursery Company. Introduced commercially in 1930. Parentage unknown; selected in 1928. Fruit: wine red; long type Winesap. Most nearly resembles Winesap.

Red York Imperial.--See **Colora Red York.**

Red York Imperial.--See **Yorking.**

Red Yorking.--See **Yorking.**

Rescue *(Scott 1)*.--Originated in Scott, Saskatchewan, Canada, by the Dominion Experimental Station. Introduced commercially in 1933. Open pollinated seedling of Blushed Calville. Fruit: 1½ inch diameter and over; round ovate; greenish yellow, washed and striped red; flesh yellowish white, firm; flavor sweet, subacid, pleasant; season late August; quality good. Tree: medium tall; rounded; healthy; very hardy and adapted to northern areas.

Richard Delicious.--Originated in Monitor, Washington, by J. L. Richardson. Introduced commercially in 1926. Trademarked by Columbia and Okanogan Nursery Company, Wenatchee, Washington. Bud mutation of Delicious. Fruit: more and brighter color than Delicious.

Rome Beauty Double Red.--Originated in Wapato, Washington, by E. E. Cowin. Introduced commercially in 1927. Trademarked by Stark Brothers Nurseries and Orchards Company, Louisiana, Missouri. Bud mutation of Rome Beauty; discovered in 1925. Fruit: skin more highly colored than that of parent.

Rosilda.--Originated in Ottawa, Ontario, Canada, by the Division of Horticulture, Central Experimental Farm. Has not been introduced commercially. Prince x McIntosh; selected in 1916. Fruit: crab; large size; attractive; most nearly resembles McIntosh. Tree: hardy.

Saint Clair *(Lizakowsky)*.--Originated in Lebanon, Saint Clair County, Illinois, by Mr. John J. Lizakowsky. Introduced commercially in 1947. Parentage unknown, raised from seed of an apple purchased from a train vendor in 1913 or 1914. Fruit: large; quality good; matures in summer; nearly solid red when grown in Lebanon, Illinois; most nearly resembles Wealthy in fruit quality and in tree; more vigorous under climatic conditions of the Tennessee and Central Mississippi Valleys.

Tree: strong; productive; adaptable to growing in Alabama.

Scarlet Staymared.--Originated in Wenatchee, Washington, by J. H. Dickey. Introduced commercially in 1936. Patent no. 57; March 21, 1933; assigned to Stark Brothers Nurseries and Orchards Company, Louisiana, Missouri. Bud mutation of Stayman Winesap; discovered in 1930. Fruit: solid red, which appears about 30 days before the coloring of Stayman Winesap.

Scott 1.--See **Rescue.**

Secor.--Originated in Ames, Iowa, by the Iowa State Agricultural Experiment Station (S. A. Beach). Introduced commercially in 1922. Salome x Jonathan; cross made in 1906;selected in 1918. Fruit: red striped; juicy; sprightly flavored; matures on tree 10 days later than Jonathan; hangs well; free from soft scald and Jonathan spot in storage; keeps well until April or May; best quality of any variety in its season.

SeeandO Red Rome 262.--Originated in Wenatchee, Washington, by the Columbia and Okanogan Nursery Company (J. A. Snyder) and trademarked by them. Introduced commercially in 1943. Bud mutation of Rome Beauty; selected in 1941. Fruit: solid bright red color, darker than Rome Beauty, which it most nearly resembles.

SeeandO Winesap.--Originated in Wenatchee, Washington, by the Columbia and Okanogan Nursery Company (J. A. Snyder) and trademarked by them. Bud mutation of Winesap; selected in 1928. Fruit: colors earlier than Winesap.

Sharon.--Originated in Ames, Iowa, by the Iowa State Agricultural Experiment Station (S. A. Beach).Introduced commercially in 1922. McIntosh x Longfield; cross made in 1906; selected in 1920. Fruit: red striped; high quality; keeps in storage through January. Tree: vigorous; productive; hardy, drops fruit too freely. For local markets.

Shotwell Delicious.--Originated in Wenatchee, Washington, by Henry Shotwell. Introduced commercially in April, 1934. Patent no. 90; April 3, 1934; assigned to Columbia and Okanogan Nursery Company, Wenatchee, Washington. Bud sport of Delicious; discovered in 1928. Fruit: colors more and earlier than Delicious.

Spartan.--Originated in Summerland, British Columbia, by the Dominion Experimental Station (R. C. Palmer). Introduced commercially in 1936. McIntosh x Newtown; cross made in 1926; original tree planted in 1928; first fruited in 1932; selected in 1936 (A. J. Mann). Fruit: size above medium; highly colored with solid dark red blush; flesh firm, crisp, white, juicy;

quality very good, fully equal to McIntosh; matures two to three weeks later than McIntosh which it most nearly resembles; stores well until February. Tree: of McIntosh type; as hardy as McIntosh to date; picks easily; more resistant to pre-harvest drop than McIntosh.

Starking *(Double Red Delicious)*.--Originated in Monroeville, New Jersey, by Lewis Mood. Introduced commercially in 1924. Trademarked 1930. Bud mutation of Delicious; discovered in 1921. Fruit: similar to Delicious except for added color; perhaps better keeping quality than parent.

Stark Earliest.--Originated in Orofino, Idaho, by Douglas Bonner. Introduced commercially in 1944. Patent no. 642; September 19, 1944; assigned to Stark Brothers Nurseries and Orchards Company, Louisiana, Missouri. Parentage unknown; discovered about 1938. Fruit: ripens August through September; ships well; cooking apple. Tree: bears over a two-months' period of time.

Staymared.--Originated in Covington, Virginia, by B. C. Moomaw. Introduced commercially in 1929. Bud mutation of Stayman Winesap; discovered in 1926. Fruit: solid red.

Stirling.--Originated in Summerland, British Columbia, Canada, by the Dominion Experimental Station (R. C. Palmer). Introduced for limited trial in 1936. Open pollinated seedling of Yellow Newtown; seed collected in 1924 by R. C. Palmer and sown in November, 1924; original tree planted in 1927; first fruited in 1932; selected in 1933 by A. J. Mann; named in 1936. Fruit: above medium size; attractively striped with bright red; flesh moderately firm, crisp, juicy, cream-colored, somewhat coarse in texture; core small; quality good; matures late, with Yellow Newtown and Rome Beauty; most nearly resembles Rome Beauty. Tree: consistent annual bearer; of Rome Beauty type; proved hardy under conditions at Summerland, B. C. As a result of tests which indicate a comparatively short storage life, it is not now (1948) being recommended for commercial planting.

Superior.--Originated near Blaney Park, Michigan, by Joseph E. Lang. Introduced commercially in 1930. Duchess x Wealthy; discovered in 1928. Fruit: fine quality; keeps well until in December; most nearly resembles Duchess. Tree: somewhat blight resistant; inclined to overbear if not thinned; strong crotches.

Sweet Delicious.--Originated in Geneva, New York, by the New York State Agricultural Experiment Station (Richard Wellington). Introduced for trial in 1922. Deacon Jones x Delicious; cross made in 1911. Fruit: large; color attractive; sweet aromatic flavor of Delicious; home use for dessert and baking; season a little later than Sweet McIntosh. Resembles Delicious in shape, but lipping of stem and dull grayish scarfskin over surface are like Deacon Jones.

Sweet McIntosh.--Originated in Geneva, New York, by the New York State Agricultural Experiment Station (Richard Wellington). Introduced for trial in 1922. Lawver x McIntosh; cross made in 1909. Fruit: externally resembles Lawver, but sweet flavor suggests McIntosh; home use (baking and fresh).

Trail.--Originated in Ottawa, Ontario, Canada, by the Division of Horticulture, Central Experimental Farm. Has not been introduced commercially. Northern Queen x Rideau; selected in 1913. Fruit: crab; large; good dessert quality. Tree: hardy and productive.

Turley.--Originated in Orleans, Indiana, by Joe E. Burton, using funds of the Indiana Horticultural Society. Introduced commercially in 1922. An open pollinated seedling of Winesap; selected about 1910. Fruit: good color; does not crack; ripens a week ahead of Stayman, which it most nearly resembles; good quality for cooking, but lacks the high dessert quality of Stayman. Tree: bears annually; very productive; strong scaffold branches; in seasons such as 1950-51, the fruit spurs are susceptible to winter injury.

USDA 57.--See **Close.**

Valmore.--Originated in Visalia, California, by Val Moore. Introduced commercially about 1934. Patent no. 238; March 16, 1937. Parentage unknown; discovered about 1924 as a seedling. Fruit: ripens with White Astrachan; large; striped with red; excellent for cooking. Tree: productive; somewhat resistant to delayed foliation. Most nearly resembles Stayman Winesap.

Van Buren.--See **Red Duchess.**

Vance Delicious.--Originated in Albemarle County, Virginia, by R. G. Vance. Introduced commercially in 1935. Bud mutation of Delicious; discovered in 1930. Fruit: solid red, coloring at least 2 weeks earlier than Delicious.

Victory *(Minnesota 396)*.--Originated in Excelsior, Minnesota, by the Minnesota Agricultural Experiment Station (Charles Haralson). Introduced commercially in January, 1943. Probably an open pollinated seedling of McIntosh; first fruited in 1918. Fruit: holds well on tree; flesh and skin not as tender as McIntosh which it most nearly resembles; skin medium red; flesh white, fine-grained, juicy, aromatic; season of use October 15 to March 15; dessert variety.

Warder.--Originated in Wooster, Ohio, by the Ohio Agricultural Experiment Station (F. S. Howlett). Introduced commercially in 1937. Open pollinated seedling of Rome Beauty. Fruit: attractive, red overcolor; dessert quality somewhat better than that of Rome Beauty; at Wooster, ripens in season of Grimes Golden to Jonathan (October 1); most nearly resembles Ensee.

Wealthy Double Red.--Originated in Sodus, New York, by James G. Case. Introduced commercially in 1940. Trademarked by Stark Brothers Nurseries and Orchards Company, Louisiana, Missouri. Bud mutation of Wealthy; discovered in 1933. Fruit: resembles parent except that the fruit is of a darker red skin color.

Webster.--Originated in Geneva, New York, by the New York State Agricultural Experiment Station (Richard Wellington). Introduced for trial in 1938. New York 26 (Ben Davis x Jonathan) x New York 19 (Ben Davis x Jonathan); cross made in 1912; first full crop in 1921. Fruit: large; skin solid bright red; season late and keeps well into spring; a cooking apple; quality not high enough for dessert variety; most nearly resembles Jonathan in shape, but much larger. A triploid variety.

Wedge *(Minnesota 207)*.--From seed originally planted by Wyman Elliot, Minneapolis, Minnesota, and later selected in 1912 by the University of Minnesota Fruit Breeding Farm. Introduced commercially in June, 1922. Probably an open pollinated seedling of Ben Davis. Fruit: large; attractive; for fall and early winter use.

Western Giant.--Originated in Paskenta, California, by Earl Davies. Introduced commercially in the fall, 1948. Patent pending; to be assigned to United Nurseries, Red Bluff, California. Parentage unknown; discovered in June, 1947. Fruit: skin thick with a deep blush flecked with red; flesh creamy white; 4½ to 5 inches in diameter; weight 12 to 14 ounces; ripens before Astrachan at the 4,000 foot level on the west side of the Sacramento Valley in Tehama County, around July 5 to 12; keeps well in cold storage; most nearly resembles Alexander.

Whetstone.--Originated in Mountain Grove, Missouri, by the Missouri State Fruit Experiment Station. Introduced commercially in 1935. Conard x Delicious; selected in 1930. Fruit: large; well colored; uniform in size and shape; quality fair; stems long. Tree: vigorous; leaves large; twigs thick; fruit does not drop when dry weather occurs in early fall.

Wickson.--Originated in Ettersburg, California, by Albert F. Etter. Introduced commercially in 1944. Patent no. 724; March 4, 1947; assigned to George C. Roeding, Jr., California Nursery Company, Niles, California. Yellow Newtown x 'Spitzen-berg crab'. Fruit: crab; a small apple for eating fresh as well as for pickling, jam, jelly, and cider; brilliant red; juicy; oblong.

Willow Twig Double Red.--Originated in Hardin, Illinois, by C. F. Braden. Introduced commercially in 1929. Trademarked by Stark Brothers Nurseries and Orchards Company, Louisiana, Missouri. Bud mutation of Willow Twig; discovered in 1927. Fruit: resembles parent variety except for darker red skin color.

Wright.--Originated in Mountain Grove, Missouri, by the Miss-ouri State Fruit Experiment Station (Paul H. Shepard). Intro-duced commercially in 1942. Ben Davis x Jonathan; selected in 1935. Fruit: large; attractive; good flavor and keeping qual-ities; most nearly resembles Jonathan. Tree: thrifty grower on mediocre soil; not subject to blight; not as susceptible to scab as Jonathan.

Wrixparent.--Originated in Magnolia, Delaware, by Wrixhem Mc-Ilvaine. Introduced commercially in 1940. Patent no. 388; May 7, 1940; assigned to Bountiful Ridge Nurseries, Princess Anne, Maryland. Open pollinated seedling of Transparent; selected in 1915. Fruit: ripens early; large. Most nearly resembles Transparent.

Yakima Newtown.--Originated in Yakima, Washington, by Curtis C. Aller. Introduced commercially in 1949. Patent no. 819; January 11, 1949; assigned to May Nursery Company, Yakima, Washington. Bud mutation of Yellow Newtown. Fruit: more elon-gate, brighter green, more pronounced cavity and longer stem, more resistant to bitter pit and scald than parent variety. Tree: similar to parent but with long fruit spurs.

York-A-Red.--Originated in Hedgesville, West Virginia, by Paul L. Lingamfelter. Introduced commercially in 1937. Patent no. 258; July 20, 1937; assigned to Stark Brothers Nurseries and Orchards Company, Louisiana, Missouri. Bud mutation of York Imperial; discovered in 1931. Fruit: identical with York Imperial except for allover red color.

Yorking *(Red York Imperial; Red Yorking).*--Originated in Ship-pensburg, Pennsylvania, by the Allison Estate. Introduced commercially in 1932. Patent no. 125; May 28, 1935; assigned to Buntings' Nurseries, Selbyville, Delaware; Waynesboro Nur-series, Inc., Waynesboro, Virginia; and Harrisons' Nurseries, Inc., Berlin, Maryland. Bud mutation of York Imperial; dis-covered about 1925. Fruit: color all red instead of partly red as on parent tree.

Young-Bearing Jonathan. --Originated in Vera, Missouri, by Lloyd C. Stark. Introduced commercially in 1932. Bud mutation of Jonathan; discovered in 1924. Resembles Jonathan in every respect, except that the trees come into bearing at younger age.

Not Named. --Originated in Los Angeles, California, by Marino La Pietra. Introduced commercially in 1948. Patent no. 801; July 6, 1948. Parentage unknown; discovered in 1935. Fruit: large; dull red overall color; flesh crisp, juicy; seedless; ripens late November. Tree: bears well in the coastal regions of southern California.

APRICOT

Anda. --Originated in Brookings, South Dakota, by the South Dakota State College (N. E. Hansen). Introduced commercially in 1936. Seedling of *Prunus sibirica* from seed brought from northern Manchuria in 1924. Fruit: freestone; of good size; firm even when cooked. Tree: productive; season late; winter hardy.

Bowers. --Originated in Yakima County, Washington, by William I. Bowers. Introduced commercially in April, 1943. Patent no. 630; June 27, 1944. Parentage unknown; discovered in 1930. Fruit: early; large; high color; good canner; fine flavor and texture. Tree: heavy bearer; most nearly resembles Riland.

Brooks. --Originated in Homedale, Idaho, by Bert Brooks and Glenn M. Brooks, Lafayette Nursery Co., Lafayette, Oregon. Introduced commercially in 1937. Patent no. 498; December 30, 1941; assigned to Bert Brooks and Glenn M. Brooks. Parentage unknown; discovered in July, 1935, by Messrs. Brooks when seedling tree was six years old; buds from this tree propagated at their Oregon nursery. Fruit: very large; sugar content high; freestone; skin and flesh reddish; cans and ships well.

Doty. --Originated on the farm of Floyd Doty, Oaks Corners, New York; tree was on the farm before Mr. Doty purchased it. Introduced for trial in 1944. Parentage unknown. Fruit: medium-sized; skin attractive light golden yellow with few reddish markings; flesh sweet, nearly free from fiber; home and local market. Tree: large; hardy.

Earle Orange. --Originated in Grandview, Washington, by W. L. Roberts. Introduced commercially in 1945. Patent no. 674; April 2, 1946; assigned to Stark Brothers Nurseries and Orchards Company, Louisiana, Missouri. Parentage unknown; discovered in 1920. Fruit: flesh deep orange in color; crimson

blush on skin; ripens 10 days earlier than Riland at Grandview; ripens evenly. Tree: upright growth; blooms later than
most late-maturing varieties.

Earligold.--Originated in Ontario, California, by W. H. Kem-
ple. Introduced commercially in January, 1938. Parentage unknown; selected in 1928. Fruit: resembles Royal; usually matures about 2 weeks ahead of Newcastle in southern California. Tree: resistant to delayed foliation.

Early Bee.--Originated in McFarland, California, by the Del
Rancho Fortuna Nursery (T. A. Sand). Introduced commercially
in November, 1949. Parentage unknown; discovered in 1947.
Fruit: ripens ten days before Royal or Blenheim, which it
most nearly resembles.

Ernie Fehr.--Originated in Lewiston, Idaho, by Emma Marie
Fehr. Introduced commercially about 1938. Patent no. 503;
February 24, 1942. Parentage unknown. Fruit: large; matures
early; firm; cans well; fine flavor. Tree: quite productive.

Franciscan.--Originated in Fresno, California, by Marshall E.
Francisco. Introduced commercially in 1948. Patent no. 808;
October 12, 1948. Parentage unknown. Fruit: similar to Royal
but shaped like Tilton; flesh firm; good shipping, drying and
canning quality; ripens from the outside skin inwardly to pit;
in Blenheim time, late June or first of July. Tree: large
fruit buds in the dormant stage; vigorous; very tolerant to
heat and cold; heavy producer.

Golden Giant.--Originated in Grand Junction, Colorado, by
David A. Moore. Introduced commercially Spring, 1948. Patent
applied for; to be assigned to Inter-State Nurseries, Hamburg, Iowa. Parentage unknown; discovered about 1907. Fruit:
large; color attractive; quality fine. Tree: very productive,
even in some areas where standard varieties are unfruitful;
most nearly resembles Moorpark.

Hardy.--Originated in Fayetteville, Arkansas, by Mr. Gilson,
Crider Bros. Nursery. Introduced commercially in 1940. Parentage unknown; discovered in 1939. Fruit: most nearly resembles Moorpark. Tree: very hardy; bears in Arkansas where
other varieties often fail to produce.

Harriet.--Originated in Saint Paul, Minnesota, by Carl Weschcke. Introduced commercially in 1942. Patent no. 476; June
24, 1941. Parentage unknown; selected about 1933. Fruit: flavor high; matures in August. Tree: hardy.

Henderson.--Originated in Geneva, New York, by George W. Henderson. Introduced for trial in 1935. Parentage unknown. Fruit:
large; roundish; flesh yellow, slightly fibrous, sweet; quality good; freestone. Tree: strong, vigorous.

Improved Cluster.--Originated in De Leon, Texas, by Stanley Carruth. Introduced commercially in 1937. Open pollinated seedling of Cluster; discovered in 1931. Fruit: quality poor; resembles Cluster; of little value horticulturally. Tree: very productive.

Leslie.--Originated in Morden, Manitoba, by the Dominion Experimental Station; selected at the Dominion Experimental Station (A. J. Mann), Summerland, British Columbia. Introduced commercially in 1943. Cross made in 1936 at Morden; original tree planted in 1938 and selected in 1942 at Summerland; named in honor of W. R. Leslie, Superintendent of the Dominion Experimental Station, Morden. Fruit: color pale; quality fair; inclined to be somewhat soft in handling; most nearly resembles Tilton. Tree: has proved hardy to date. Not recommended for commercial planting.

Manchu.--Originated in Brookings, South Dakota, by the South Dakota State College (N. E. Hansen). Introduced commercially in 1936. Seedling of *Prunus sibirica* from seed brought from northern Manchuria in 1924. Fruit: large, yellow; good quality for cooking. Tree: heavy bearing; winter hardy.

Morden 604.--Originated in Morden, Manitoba, Canada, by the Dominion Experimental Station. Introduced commercially in 1946. Scout x McClure; selected in 1945. Fruit: large; skin golden yellow; flesh thick, deep orange, moderately firm, very fine texture; flavor sweet, pleasing; excellent as dessert, preserves or jam; season mid-August. Tree: hardy, vigorous, upright spreading, rounded.

Ninguta.--Originated in Brookings, South Dakota, by the South Dakota State College (N. E. Hansen). Introduced commercially in 1937. Seedling of *Prunus sibirica* from seed brought from northern Manchuria in 1924. Fruit: large; yellow with red blush; very mild; season late. Tree: heavy bearer; winter hardy.

Perfection.--Originated in Waterville, Washington, by John and Bertha Goldbeck. Introduced commercially in 1937. Parentage unknown; selected from seed planted in 1911. Fruit: large; uniform shape. Tree: hardy.

Phelps.--Originated in the Yakima Valley, Washington, by B. F. Phelps. Introduced commercially about 1938. Parentage unknown; discovered about 1934. Fruit: ripens very early and evenly; very large; quality good; excellent shipper; flesh yellow; skin with red blush.

Reeves.--Originated in Burbank, California, by William H. Reeves. Introduced commercially in 1947. Patent no. 693; June

4, 1946; assigned to Armstrong Nurseries, Inc., Ontario, California. Parentage unknown; discovered about 1939. Fruit: ripens approximately 1 month before Royal and about 2 weeks before Newcastle; superior in flavor, skin color, and size to Newcastle; poor shipper. Tree: chilling requirement similar to that of Newcastle.

Reliable.--Originated in Summerland, British Columbia, by the Dominion Experimental Station (A. J. Mann). Introduced commercially in 1945. Wenatchee Moorpark x Hewetson; cross made in 1937; selected in 1942. Fruit: orange with a blush; fair quality;   texture dry and firm, maintaining its firmness on the tree for about ten days after attaining full color; ships well; a canning variety.

Riland.--Originated in Rock Island, Washington, by H. Yount. Introduced commercially in 1932. Patent no. 74; September 26, 1933, assigned to Andrew T. Gossman, Wenatchee, Washington. Parentage unknown; seed planted in 1923. Fruit: said to keep well.

Robust.--Originated in Morden, Manitoba, Canada, by A. Spangelo, Morden Nursery. Introduced commercially in 1941. Seed brought from Manchuria; seedling selected in 1940. Fruit: size medium; skin yellow; flesh yellow, meaty, smooth texture; flavor mild, sweet, pleasant; very fine as dessert or jam; season late July or early August. Tree: tall, rounded; vigorous; hardy.

Scout.--Originated in Morden, Manitoba, Canada, by the Dominion Experimental Station. Introduced commercially in 1937. Seed sent by the Experimental Station of the Eastern Siberian Railway, Echo, Manchuria; planted in 1930. Fruit: medium to large; flat oblong-cordate, pointed; skin bronzy golden; flesh deep yellow, fine, tender; freestone; quality fair to good as dessert, fair canned, good as jam; season late July and early August. Tree: tall, rounded; vigorous; hardy; productive.

Sing.--Originated in Brookings, South Dakota, by the South Dakota State College (N. E. Hansen). Introduced commercially in 1936. Seedling of *Prunus sibirica* from seed brought from northern Manchuria in 1924. Fruit: large; cooks to a rich yellow sauce. Tree: productive; winter hardy.

Sun Glo.--Originated in Entiat, Chelan County, Washington, by Otto H. Heider. Introduced commercially in May, 1946. Patent no. 751; August 12, 1947; assigned to Columbia and Okanogan Nursery Company, Wenatchee, Washington. Parentage unknown; discovered about 1942. Fruit: ripens uniformly and about seven days before Wenatchee Moorpark.

Sunshine.--Originated in Brookings, South Dakota, by the South Dakota State College. Introduced commercially in 1950. Open pollinated seedling of Siberian apricot; discovered in 1940. Fruit: large; good quality; most nearly resembles Manchu.

Tola.--Originated in Brookings, South Dakota, by the South Dakota State College (N. E. Hansen). Introduced commercially in 1936. Seedling of *Prunus sibirica* from seed brought from northern Manchuria in 1924. Fruit: large, freestone; season early; good for cooking. Tree: heavy bearer; winter hardy.

AVOCADO

Arturo.--Originated in Fallbrook, California, by A. R. Chenoweth. Introduced commercially in 1946. Patent no. 667; January 15, 1946; assigned to the originator. Mexican seedling. Fruit: skin light green; seed small; 6 to 10 ounces; oil content 20%; flavor fine; matures October to April, with bulk of crop in October and November. Tree: symmetrical; more cold resistant than Fuerte; blossoms in February.

Avon.--Originated in Avon Park, Florida, by W. F. Ward. Introduced commercially in 1940. Parentage unknown; hybrid of Guatemalan x West Indian races; seedling discovered about 1927. Fruit: attractive glossy green skin; flesh light yellow; seed very large, 22% of fruit weight. Tree: branches able to stand a great deal of bending without breakage; consistently heavy bearer; not cold resistant.

Blair.--Originated in Naranja, Florida, by J. R. Hickson. Introduced commercially in 1939. Open pollinated seedling of Taylor, of Guatemalan type. Fruit: obovate; medium; not subject to scab; most nearly resembles Lula; season December and January. Tree: bears regularly.

Bonita.--Originated in Homestead, Florida, by C. Santini. Introduced commercially in 1936. Parentage unknown; selected in 1930. Fruit: medium to large; obovate; green; not considered promising for northern United States' markets, but sells well locally; season December and January. Tree: bears heavily. Class 'A' for pollination purposes.

Booth 1.--Originated in Homestead, Florida, by William Booth. Introduced commercially in 1935. Open pollinated seedling of Guatemalan race (probably a West Indian cross); selected in 1927. Fruit: season December and January; withstands cold storage; quality rather poor; seed extremely large. Tree: regular and heavy bearer. Class 'A' for pollination purposes.

Booth 3.--Originated in Homestead, Florida, by William Booth.

Introduced commercially in 1940. Open pollinated seedling of
Guatemalan race (probably a West Indian cross); selected in
1927. Fruit: quality good; season December and January. Tree:
bears heavily. Class 'B' for pollination purposes. Most nearly resembles Booth 7.

Booth 7.--Originated in Homestead, Florida, by William Booth.
Introduced commercially in 1935. Open pollinated seedling of
Guatemalan race (probably a West Indian cross); selected in
1927. Fruit: flavor good; shape round-obovate; season December and January. Tree: bears prolifically. Class 'B' for pollination purposes.

Booth 8.--Originated in Homestead, Florida, by William Booth.
Introduced commercially in 1935. Open pollinated seedling of
Guatemalan race (probably a West Indian cross); selected in
1927. Fruit: medium to small; .marketing season good (November
and December); somewhat resembles Hickson. Tree: very prolific bearer. Class 'B' for pollination purposes.

Choquette.--Originated in Miami, Florida, by R. D. Choquette.
Introduced commercially in 1939. Parentage unknown; hybrid
of Guatemalan x West Indian types; selected in 1934 from seed
sown in 1929. Fruit: 30 to 40 ounces; oval; skin nearly smooth,
glossy, dark green, leathery; flesh thick, yellow; seed medium, tight in cavity; oil content 13%; quality very good;
season January to March. Tree: alternate bearing habit; resistant to common avocado diseases. Chiefly recommended in
Florida for home plantings.

Coit.--Originated in Vista, California, by J. Eliot Coit.
Introduced in 1936. Parentage unknown (but from a Guatemalan
x Mexican cross); registered with the California Avocado Society in 1939. Fruit: light green; thin skin; smooth, pyriform; 10 to 16 ounces; seed medium; flavor good; oil content
15%; season May to August 1 (southern California); most nearly resembles Fuerte.

Collinred Seedling B *(Fairchild 106941)*.--Originated in Coconut Grove, Florida, by the United States Department of Agriculture Plant Introduction Garden. Introduced commercially in
1934. Seedling of Collinred; hybrid of Guatemalan x West Indian types; from seed planted in 1925 and selected in 1930.
Fruit: 16 to 30 ounces; obovate, slightly flattened at the dis-
tal end; skin dull light green, often with deep maroon blush,
thin, tough; flesh light yellow; oil content 6 to 8%; seed medium large, loose in cavity with loose seed coats; season October; does not ship well.

Collinson.--Originated in Miami, Florida, by the United States
Department of Agriculture Plant Introduction Garden. In-

troduced commercially in 1922. Collins x unknown (probably of West Indian race); selected in 1920. Fruit: flavor good. Tree: a very poor bearer; pollen sterile. Class 'A' for pollination purposes.

Courtright.--Originated in Lakeland, Florida, by R. M. Courtright. Introduced commercially in 1942. Parentage unknown; of Mexican race; discovered in 1941.Fruit: 8 to 12 ounces; pyriform; skin purple, thin; flesh yellow; quality fair; oil content 15%; seed fairly large, loose in cavity; season September and October.

Darwin.--Originated in Santa Ana, California, by Mr. Darwin Speck. Introduced commercially in 1946. Parentage unknown; discovered in November, 1941. Fruit: skin black; flavor fair; 6 to 8 ounces; oil content 20.1%; of Mexican type. Tree: hardy; productive.

Edmonds.--Originated near Homestead, Florida, by Tom Edmonds. Not introduced commercially. Parentage unknown; probably a hybrid of Guatemalan x West Indian races; discovered in 1935. Fruit: 24-36 ounces; oval; skin smooth, green; seed rather small; flavor very good; season September and October.

Edranol.--Originated in Vista, California, by E. R. Mullen. Introduced commercially in 1932. Open pollinated seedling of Lyon; selected in 1930; Guatemalan race. Fruit: skin green and thick; pyriform; quality high; flavor excellent; seed small; season early summer. Tree: tall; slender; vigorous; bears heavily.

Elsie.--Originated in Whittier, California, by Charles H. Hamburg. Introduced commercially in 1935. Patent no. 816; December 28, 1948; assigned to Cecil Knowlton. Parentage unknown. Fruit: higher oil content than Fuerte which it most nearly resembles; season from March to August; flavor fine; nearly fiberless. Tree: compact; upright.

Fairchild 106941.--See Collinred Seedling B.

Fuchsia.--Originated in Homestead, Florida, by C. T. Fuchs, Sr. Introduced commercially in 1926. Open pollinated seedling of West Indian race; selected in 1916. Fruit: earliest maturing variety (season from late June to August); flavor good; appearance handsome; does not hold up for distant shipping when fully mature or overmature. Class 'A' for pollination purposes.

Gano.--Originated in Whittier, California, by Jennie C. Gano. Introduced commercially in 1935. Patent no. 100; August 7, 1934. Open pollinated seedling of Colorado; selected in 1918.

Fruit: rather long; dull green; skin tough; averages 1 pound;
little fiber; flavor excellent; oil content about 20%; season
July and August. Tree: vigorous, upright;stands frost slightly better than most Guatemalans.

Gem.--Originated in Fullerton, California, by the Sherwood
Specialty Nursery (Lawrence W. Sherwood). Not introduced commercially as yet. Patent no. 773; December 30, 1947. Open
pollinated seedling of the Mexican race. Fruit: good size for
marketing, 8-12 ounces; skin bright purple, attractive, smooth,
glossy; seed small; oil content high; ripens in September.

Graham.--Originated in La Habra, California, by M. M. Graham.
Introduced commercially in December, 1945. Patent no. 662;
November 27, 1945; assigned to Armstrong Nurseries, Inc.,
Ontario, California. Open pollinated seedling of Lyon; se-
lected in 1944. Fruit: oil content high; flavor excellent;
cut surface of fruit seals over and can be kept for several
days at room temperature. Tree: more easily propagated than
Lyon; slender; suitable for home planting; upright growing.

Hall.--Originated in Miami, Florida, by Willis Hall. Introduced commercially in 1938. Parentage unknown (probably a
West Indian x Guatemalan hybrid); selected in 1937. Fruit:
large; bright green; handsome; season November to March. Tree:
alternate but heavy bearer. Resembles Monroe in being excellent for the limited fancy-fruit market: Class 'B' for pollination purposes.

Harris.--Originated in Homestead, Florida, by W. K. Walton.
Introduced commercially in 1940. Open pollinated seedling of
Wagner; selected in 1935. Fruit: season desirable, from De-
cember to February; small to medium; dull, dark green; resem-
bles Booth 7, but has more rippled skin. Tree: heavy bearer.
Class 'A' for pollination purposes.

Hass.--Originated in La Habra Heights, California, by Rudolph
G. Hass. Introduced commercially in 1936. Patent no. 139; August 27, 1935. Parentage unknown (but of Guatemalan race); selected in 1934. Fruit: flavor excellent; no fiber; oil content
23.7%; size 10 ounces; skin leathery, purple when ripe, thick,
rough; seed small; keeping qualities excellent; good shipper.
Tree: heavy bearer; starts bearing second year; thriftygrow-
er; buds and grafts readily.

Hellen.--Originated in Santa Monica, California, by Mrs. S.
L. Duey. Introduced commercially in December, 1941. Parentage
unknown. Fruit: dark green; pyriform; 9.5 ounces; seed tight;
oil content 21%; season June to September.

Henry Select.--See **Henry's Select.**

Henry's Select *(Henry Select)*.--Originated in Escondido, California, by Jesse L. Jones and Charles C. Henry. Introduced commercially in 1937. Patent no. 234; February 9, 1937; one-half assigned to Jesse L. Jones, Escondido. Parentage unknown; discovered in 1931. Fruit: deep maroon-purple; skin smooth and glossy; 9 ounces; season September to November at Escondido; oil eontent 18%; seed small, conical, loose when mature. Tree: does not bear well nor consistently.

Herman.--Originated in South Miami, Florida, by Fred Herman. Introduced commercially in 1940. Parentage unknown; selected in 1937. Fruit: quality good; season November through January; most nearly resembles Lula, but has smoother skin. Tree: precocious and heavy bearer. Class 'A' for pollination purposes.

Hickson.--Originated in Navanja, Florida, by J. R. Hickson. Introduced commercially in 1936. Parentage unknown; selected in 1934. Fruit: flavor excellent; ships well; season desirable, November to January; similar to Booth 8 in shape, but brighter green in color. Tree: fair bearing ability. Class 'B' for pollination purposes.

Itzamna *(P. I. 43486; P. I. 55736)*.--Originated in Santa Maria de Jesus, Guatemala, and introduced by the United States Department of Agriculture (F. W. Popenoe) in 1916. Introduced commercially in 1923. Parentage unknown; of Guatemalan race. Fruit: light green; coarse; pyriform; 12 to 18 ounces; skin thick; seed small; oil content 15%; quality excellent; season September to December in southern California, February 15 to April 15 in Florida; storage quality sometimes poor.

Jalna.--Originated in Vista, California, by J. Eliot Coit. Introduced commercially in 1936. Parentage unknown (but of Mexican race); selected in 1933. Fruit: thin skin; green. Tree: heavy bearer, being one of the few green-fruited Mexican avocados that produces well on the Pacific Coast.

Kilgore Special.--Originated in Clearwater, Florida, by Barnard Kilgore. Introduced commercially in 1936. Open pollinated seedling of Fuerte, selected in 1930 from seed sown in 1927. Fruit: 12-18 ounces; obovate; skin green, smooth, leathery; flesh pale yellow; seed medium size; flower only fair; season December and January. Tree: bears heavily; blossoms very early; appears more resistant to anthracnose than Fuerte.

Leucadia.--Originated in Encinitas, California, by J. Eliot Coit. Introduced commercially in 1932. Parentage unknown (but of Mexican type); selected in 1929. Fruit: size good; skin handsome, purple, thin, smooth; most nearly resembles Puebla.

Lindgren.--Originated in Goulds, Florida, by A. Lindgren. Introduced commercially in 1940. Parentage unknown; selected in 1935. Fruit: small; attractive; bright green; season November and December; seed moderately large. Class 'A' for pollination purposes.

Lula.--Originated in Miami, Florida, by George B. Cellon. Introduced commercially in 1921. Open pollinated seedling of Taft (probably crossed with Mexican race); selected in 1919. Fruit: flavor good; very susceptible to avocado scab; pyriform. Tree: prolific and regular bearer. Class 'A' for pollination purposes.

Macpherson.--Originated in Encinitas, California, by James H. Macpherson. Introduced commercially in 1942. Patent no. 433; November 26, 1940. Parentage unknown; selected in 1936. Fruit: appearance and flavor good; skin green, smooth; flesh deep, golden color; seed small; season December to April. Tree: large; vigorous grower.

Major.--Originated in Katz Grove, Florida, by Herbert Katz. Introduced commercially in 1942. Parentage unknown; selected in 1942. Fruit: attractive, good quality; season October and November.

Marfield.--Originated in Marfield Grove, Florida, by H. A. Marsh. Introduced commercially in 1943. Parentage unknown; selected in 1940. Fruit: season July.

Mary Martin.--Originated in San Diego, California, by John Martin Reinecke. Introduced commercially in January, 1943. Patent no. 576; April 20, 1943; assigned to Armstrong Nurseries, Inc., Ontario, California. Open pollinated seedling of Linscott; selected about 1938. Fruit: high quality; medium size; most nearly resembles Nabal. Tree: produces regularly and heavily.

Middleton.--Originated in Pomona, California, by E. E. Middleton. Introduced commercially in 1941. Parentage unknown; of Mexican race; selected about 1932. Fruit: dark purple; pyriform; 8 ounces; oil content about 15%; flavor excellent and of high quality; season just before Fuerte. Tree: tall, slender; some frost resistance.

Mitchell.--Originated on Mitchell place between Cutler and South Miami, Florida. Introduced commercially in 1930. Parentage unknown, of West Indian race. Fruit: 2 to 3 pounds; short obovate; skin very smooth, dark green, pliable; flesh yellow; seed medium; season August and September. Tree: mentioned as bearing well.

Monroe.--Originated in Homestead, Florida, by J. J. L. Phillips. Introduced commercially in 1937. Patent no. 261; August 24, 1937; assigned to Redland Avocado Grove, Homestead, Florida. Parentage unknown (very likely a West Indian x Guatemalan hybrid); selected in 1935. Fruit: large; handsome; shiny green; season December and January. Tree: heavy bearer. Class 'B' for pollination purposes.

Nabal.--Originated in Guatemala; budwood introduced into California in 1917 by the United States Department of Agriculture (F. W. Popenoe). Introduced commercially in California in 1927, in Florida in 1937. Parentage unknown; of Guatemalan race. Fruit: medium, 16 to 24 ounces; almost round; skin smooth, dark green; flesh yellow; good flavor; oil content 10 to 15%; seed medium small, tight in cavity; season January and February. Tree: heavy and consistent producer.

P. I. 43486.--See **Itzamna**.

P. I. 55736.--See **Itzamna**.

Rusterholz.--Originated in Whittier, California, by Mrs. Katharine L. Rusterholz. Introduced commercially in May, 1950. Patent no. 969; July 25, 1950. Parentage unknown, probably a seedling of Lyon; discovered in 1924. Fruit: medium to large; skin purple, thin, pliant; seed medium, tight to flesh; flesh smooth, creamy, light green, no fiber; season late November to January; most nearly resembles Lyon. Tree: upright; has some frost resistance.

Ryan *(Summer Fuerte)*.--Originated in Whittier, California, by A. R. Rideout. Introduced commercially in 1936. A hybrid between Guatemalan and Mexican races; possibly an open pollinated seedling of Amigo. Fruit: green; slightly rough; pyriform; 10 to 14 ounces; skin leathery; seed large; quality fair to good; oil content 20 to 25%; season May to September. Tree: vigorous; propagates readily.

Schmidt.--Originated in Mexico; imported as budwood in 1911 by Carl Schmidt for the West India Gardens, Altadena, California. Introduced commercially in Florida in 1922. Parentage unknown; of Guatemalan type. Fruit: medium to large, 16 to 26 ounces; pyriform; skin rough, pebbled, dark green; flesh light yellow, good flavor; oil content 12 to 16%; seed medium size, adheres tightly; season February 1 to April 1; does not store well; easily injured by frost. Tree: weak grower and poor bearer; not generally recommended.

Simpson.--Originated in Richmond, Florida, by Robert Simpson. Introduced commercially in 1933. Parentage unknown (very likely West Indian x Guatemalan hybrid); selected in 1925. Fruit:

large, obovate; light green; skin smooth; season November to December. Class 'B' for pollination purposes.

Summer Fuerte.--See Ryan.

Tomko.--Originated in Carlsbad, California, by Sam Thompson. Introduced commercially in 1944. Patent no. 628; June 6, 1944. Parentage unknown (but probably a seedling of Cantel x Fuerte). Fruit: ripens after Fuerte; 10 or 11 ounces; green, leathery skin which peels easily; stem offset; oil content 24%.

Tonnage.--Originated in Homestead, Florida, by Dan Roberts. Introduced commercially in 1930. Open pollinated seedling of Taylor, of Guatemalan type; selected in 1921. Fruit: 16 to 24 ounces; pyriform with stem placed obliquely, often necked; skin dark green, pebbled, rather glossy, thick; flesh pale yellow; oil content 8 to 10%; seed medium, fairly tight; season October 15 to December 1. Tree: the original tree very productive.

Winter Mexican.--Originated in Palm Beach, Florida. Introduced commercially in 1936. Parentage unknown; hybrid of Guatemalan x Mexican races; discovered in 1922. Fruit: 12 to 18 ounces; oblong to pyriform; skin thick, leathery, dark green; seed medium size, tight in cavity; season December and January. Tree: very vigorous, bearing heavily and regularly; very hardy to cold; resistant to scab; considered promising for the West Coast of Florida.

Yon.--Originated in Orlando, Florida, by J. Hugh Yon. Introduced commercially in 1937. Parentage unknown; hybrid of Guatemalan x West Indian races; selected in 1932 from seed planted in 1926. Fruit: 2 to 4 pounds, oval-oblong; skin dark bronzed green, almost smooth, thick, leathery; seed medium small; flesh very thick; season December to February in Florida. Tree: very hardy to cold and of promise for Central Florida.

Zutano.--Originated in Fallbrook, California, by W. L. Truitt. Introduced commercially in 1941. Parentage unknown; probably a hybrid between Mexican and Guatemalan races; selected in 1926. Fruit: light green; pyriform; 8 to 12 ounces; skin very thin; oil content about 16%; flavor good; season December and January. Tree: consistent producer; more hardy than Fuerte.

BLACKBERRY

Acme Thornless Young.--Originated in Chino, California, by Elmer L. Pollard and Jubal E. Sherrill. Introduced commercially in 1930. Patent no. 4; October 20, 1931. Bud mutation of Young; discovered in 1928. Plant: thornless; has all the other characteristics of parent, but is more susceptible to disease.

Bailey.--Originated in Geneva, New York, by the New York State Agricultural Experiment Station (George L. Slate). Introduced commercially during the Fall of 1950. Parentage unknown, as the label was lost; selected about 1929. Fruit: large, medium firm, quality good, subacid; less trouble from imperfect berries than with many varieties. Plant: reliable productivity.

Bauer Thornless Logan.--Originated in San Gabriel, California, by Beulah E. Bauer and Gordon R. Bauer. Introduced commercially in 1934. Patent no. 82; November 14, 1933. Bud mutation of Logan; discovered in 1929. Plant: canes and leaves entirely thornless; canes strong; season earlier and longer than that of parent.

Big-Ness *(Texas R40-51)*.--Originated in College Station, Texas, by the Texas Agricultural Experiment Station (S. H. Yarnell). Introduced commercially October 31, 1946. Plant selected in 1940 from F_3 of *Rubus rubrisetus* x Nessberry. Fruit: large; season early; most nearly resembles Mammoth. Bush: vigorous; resistant to little-fruit.

Bowen.--Originated in Burlingame, California, by J. C. Bowen. Introduced commercially in 1944. Patent no. 635; August 1, 1944. From a wild thornless blackberry; discovered in 1940. Fruit: large; matures early; seeds very small. Bush: thornless; does not sucker or propagate from root cuttings; quite productive. The variety may be identical with Cory Thornless.

Brainerd.--Originated in Atlanta, Georgia, by the United States Department of Agriculture (Geo. M. Darrow). Introduced commercially in 1932. Himalaya x Eastern erect-growing variety (possibly Georgia Mammoth); selected in 1920. Fruit: large; quality high; good for canning, preserving, and the frozen-pack trade. Bush: extremely productive and vigorous; very hardy.

Cameron.--Originated in Raleigh, North Carolina, by the North Carolina Agricultural Experiment Station (Carlos F. Williams). Introduced commercially in 1938. Young x Lucretia; selected from a cross of 1930. Fruit: shiny black; larger and sweeter than Lucretia which it most nearly resembles. Bush: productive; vigorous; disease resistant; dewberry-type.

Cascade.--Originated in Corvallis, Oregon by the United States Department of Agriculture (George M. Darrow and George F. Waldo). Introduced commercially in 1940. Zielinski x Logan; selected in 1935. Fruit: excellent for canning or in frozen pack; flavor characteristic of the native blackberry (*Rubus* *macropetalus)*. Bush: vigorous and productive.

Chehalem *(Oregon 731)*.--Originated in Corvallis, Oregon, by the United States Department of Agriculture and the Oregon Agricultural Experiment Station (George F. Waldo). Introduced commercially in 1948. Santiam x Himalaya; cross made in 1936; seedling planted in 1937; selected in 1939. Fruit: bright black: excellent for frozen products; size smaller than Logan. Plant: probably limited range of adaptation; vigorous and productive in moist and rich soils.

Earli-Ness *(Texas R40-4)*.--Originated in College Station, Texas, by the Texas Agricultural Experiment Station (S. H. Yarnell). Introduced commercially October 31, 1946. Plant selected in 1940 from F_3 of *Rubus rubrisetus* x Nessberry. Fruit: earliest maturing variety known. Bush: vigorous; re- sistant to little-fruit; most nearly resembles Early Wonder.

Hedrick.--Originated in Geneva, New York, by the New York State Agricultural Experiment Station (George L. Slate). In- troduced commercially in the Fall of 1950. Eldorado x Brewer; cross made in 1929. Fruit: large; medium firm; pleasantly tart; most nearly resembles Eldorado but more irregular. Plant: reliably productive; less trouble from imperfect berries than many varieties.

John Innes.--Originated in Merton Park, London, England, by the John Innes Institute (M. B. Crane). Introduced commer- cially in the United States in January, 1944. *Rubus rusti- canus* x *R. thyrsiger;* selected about 1926 or 1927. Fruit: very firm; sweet; late ripening; might be valuable for home use as a late-ripening variety. Most nearly resembles Oregon Evergreen.

Kayberry.--Originated in Chehalis, Washington, by Mrs. Maggie Phillips Kelly. Introduced commercially in 1948. Fruit: small seeds; soft core; good shipper and freezer; excellent for pies, jam, and jelly; most nearly resembles California Mam- moth. Bush: heavy producer.

Kosmo.--See **Kosmos**.

Kosmos *(Kosmo)*.--Originated in Oregon City, Oregon, by Percy W. Meredith. Not introduced commercially. Patent no. 39; Oc- tober 25, 1932. Parentage unknown. Fruit: berry very soft. Bush: very susceptible to leaf spot.

Lowden.--Originated in Hamilton, Ontario, Canada, by Edward Lowden. Introduced commercially in 1939. Possibly a mutation of Snyder; discovered about 1926 or 1927. Fruit: core small; colors uniformly. Bush: hardy; productive; resistant to orange rust.

Merton Thornless.--Originated in Merton Park, London, England, by the John Innes Institute (M. B. Crane). Not introduced commercially in the United States; on trial in various states. Patent no. 571; March 9, 1943; assigned to Armstrong Nurseries, Inc., Ontario, California. John Innes x a thornless selfed-John Innes seedling. Fruit: large, round; large drupelets; long midseason ripening. Bush: thornless; tetraploid; vigorous grower; crop production in this country has not been very high.

Nectar *(Nectarberry).*--Originated in El Monte, California, by Howard G. Benedict. Introduced commercially in 1937. Said to have been a seedling of Young but thought by many to be a chimera of Boysen which it most nearly resembles; discovered before 1936. Fruit: diameter greater than Boysen; many claim the berry is sweeter than Boysen; about 9 drupelets around the core at the calyx end instead of 10 or usually 11 as in Boysen; drupelets larger than those of Boysen; drupelets not acute; base of style usually set in a depression. Bush: trailing; production and habit almost if not identical with Boysen.

Nectarberry.--See **Nectar.**

Olallie *(Oregon 609).*--Originated in Corvallis, Oregon, by the United States Department of Agriculture (George F. Waldo) in cooperation with Oregon Agricultural Experiment Station. Introduced commercially in January, 1950. Black Logan x Young; selected in July, 1938. Fruit: shiny black; firm; large; most nearly resembles Mammoth blackberry. Plant: productive. Adaptable to California and western Oregon conditions.

Olympic.--Originated in Vashon, Washington, by Peter Erickson. Introduced commercially in 1930. Patent no. 247; April 20, 1937; assigned to H. F. Greider, Vashon, Washington. Young x Plum Farmer?; selected about 1929. Fruit: claimed to be larger, darker, and sweeter than Young; but similar if not identical with it.

Oregon 609.--See **Olallie.**

Oregon 731.--See **Chehalem.**

Pacific.--Originated in Corvallis, Oregon by the United States Department of Agriculture (George M. Darrow and George F. Waldo). Introduced commercially in 1940. Zielinski x Logan; selected in 1935. Fruit: excellent for canning and frozen pack; firmer than Cascade, and with more acid; flavor characteristic of the native blackberry *(Rubus macropetalus).* Bush: vigorous and productive.

Regal-Ness *(Texas R40-202)*.--Originated in College Station, Texas, by the Texas Agricultural Experiment Station (S. H. Yarnell). Introduced commercially October 31, 1946. Plant selected in 1940 from F_3 of *Rubus rubrisetus* x Nessberry. Fruit: matures early; most nearly resembles Earli-Ness. Bush: vigorous; resistant to little-fruit.

Texas R40-4.--See **Earli-Ness**.

Texas R40-51. See **Big-Ness**.

Texas R40-202.--See **Regal-Ness**.

Thornless Boysen.--Originated in El Monte, California, by D. L. Duffin. Introduced commercially in 1938. Bud mutation of Boysen; discovered in 1936. May be identical with Acme Thornless Young.

BLUEBERRY

Atlantic.--Originated in Whitesbog, New Jersey, by the United States Department of Agriculture (F. V. Coville). Introduced commercially in 1941. Jersey x Pioneer; selected in 1925. Fruit: flavor good; size superior; no cracking in wet weather; ripens late.

Berkeley.--Originated in Weymouth, New Jersey, by the United States Department of Agriculture (F. V. Coville and George M. Darrow) and the New Jersey Agricultural Experiment Station (Franklin A. Gilbert). Introduced commercially September 20, 1949. Stanley x GS-149 (Jersey x Pioneer); selected in 1938. Fruit: light blue color; largest of any in the trade; berries not subject to cracking; ripen about a week after Stanley and a week before Jersey. Bush: productive; easy to propagate.

Burlington.--Originated in Whitesbog, New Jersey, by the United States Department of Agriculture (F. V. Coville). Introduced commercially in 1941. Rubel x Pioneer; selected in 1916. Fruit: matures late; dessert quality very good. Bush: vigorous; healthy.

Cabot.--Originated in Whitesbog, New Jersey, by the United States Department of Agriculture (F. V. Coville). Introduced commercially in 1920. Brooks x Chatsworth. Fruit: early; season long.

Callaway.--Originated in Tifton, Georgia, by Georgia Coastal Plain Experiment Station and the United States Department of Agriculture (W. T. Brightwell). Introduced commercially in December, 1949. Myers x Black Giant; selected in 1943.

Fruit: large; flavor high. Plant productive.

Catawba.--Originated in Whitesbog, New Jersey, by the United States Department of Agriculture (F. V. Coville). Introduced as a novelty in 1932. F_2 of (Brooks x Russell). Fruit: Catawba-grape color. Bush: half-high.

Coastal.--Originated in Tifton, Georgia by the Georgia Coastal Plain Experiment Station and the United States Department of Agriculture (W. T. Brightwell). Introduced commercially in December, 1949. Myers x Black Giant; selected in 1943. Fruit: large; color attractive. Plant: vigorous; productive.

Concord.--Originated in Whitesbog, New Jersey, by the United States Department of Agriculture (F. V. Coville). Introduced commercially in 1928. Brooks x Rubel. Fruit: midseason. Bush: productive.

Coville.--Originated in Weymouth, New Jersey, by the United States Department of Agriculture (F. V. Coville and George M. Darrow) and the New Jersey Agricultural Experiment Station (Franklin A. Gilbert). Introduced commercially September 20, 1949. GM-37 (Jersey x Pioneer) x Stanley; selected in 1936. Fruit: very large; ripens latest of any in the trade; firm; tart flavor; high aroma. Bush: vigorous; productive; easy to propagate.

Dixi.--Originated in Weymouth, New Jersey, by the United States Department of Agriculture (F. V. Coville). Introduced commercially in 1936. (Jersey x Pioneer) x Stanley. Fruit: very large. Bush: productive.

Ethel.--Originated near Brunswick, Georgia, by W. M. Walker. Introduced commercially in 1944. Parentage unknown. Fruit: good size and color.

Greenfield.--Originated in Whitesbog, New Jersey, by the United States Department of Agriculture (F. V. Coville). Introduced commercially in 1926. Brooks x Russell. Fruit: early. Bush: half-high.

Jersey.--Originated in Whitesbog, New Jersey, by the United States Department of Agriculture (F. V. Coville). Introduced commercially in 1928. Rubel x Grover. Fruit: late; large; fine blue; good keeper. Bush: easily pruned.

June.--Originated in Whitesbog, New Jersey, by the United States Department of Agriculture (F. V. Coville). Introduced commercially in 1930. (Brooks x Russell) x Rubel. Fruit: early; short season.

Katharine.--Originated in Whitesbog, New Jersey, by the United States Department of Agriculture (F. V. Coville). Introduced commercially in 1920. Brooks x Sooy. Fruit: flavor pronounced; berry large.

Murphy *(North Carolina 262)*.--Originated in Atkinson, North Carolina, by the North Carolina Agricultural Experiment Station and the United States Department of Agriculture (F. V. Coville). Introduced commercially in June 1950. Weymouth x F-6 (Stanley x Crabbe 4); planted in 1935; selected in 1940. Fruit: round to round-oblate; firm; good flavor; earlier than the June or Stanley. Bush: low; spreading; high resistance to canker; as productive as Weymouth; excellent cluster type.

North Carolina 255.--See **Wolcott.**

North Carolina 262.--See **Murphy.**

Pemberton.--Originated in Whitesbog, New Jersey, by the United States Department of Agriculture (F. V. Coville). Introduced commercially in 1941. Katharine x Rubel; selected in 1921. Fruit: matures late; large. Bush: very productive; extremely vigorous.

Pioneer.--Originated in Whitesbog, New Jersey, by the United States Department of Agriculture (F. V. Coville). Introduced commercially in 1920. Brooks x Sooy. Fruit: flavor pronounced; size large; midseason.

Rancocas.--Originated in Whitesbog, New Jersey, by the United States Department of Agriculture (F. V. Coville). Introduced commercially in 1926. (Brooks x Russell) x Rubel. Fruit: early midseason. Bush: productive; resistant to stunt virus disease and canker.

Redskin.--Originated in Whitesbog, New Jersey, by the United States Department of Agriculture (F. V. Coville). Introduced commercially in 1932. F_2 of (Brooks x Russell). Fruit: red. Bush: half-high.

Satilla.--Originated near Brunswick, Georgia, by W. M. Walker. Introduced commercially in 1944. Parentage unknown. Fruit: good color and size; texture firm.

Scammell.--Originated in Whitesbog, New Jersey, by the United States Department of Agriculture (F. V. Coville). Introduced commercially in 1931. (Brooks x Chatsworth) x Rubel. Bush: productive, especially in North Carolina; resistant to canker.

Stanley.--Originated in Whitesbog, New Jersey, by the United States Department of Agriculture (F. V. Coville). Introduced

commercially in 1930. Katharıne x Rubel. Fruit: midseason;
flavor very pronounced. Bush: easy to prune.

Walker.--Originated near Brunswick, Georgia, along the Satilla
River by W. M. Walker. Introduced commercially in 1944. Parentage unknown. Fruit: color good. Bush: disease resistant.

Wareham.--Originated in East Wareham, Massachusetts, by the
United States Department of Agriculture (F. V. Coville). Introduced commercially in 1936. Rubel x Harding. Fruit: very late;
flavor pronounced.

Weymouth.--Originated in Weymouth, New Jersey, by the United
States Department of Agriculture (F. V. Coville). Introduced
commercially in 1936. June x Cabot. Fruit: very early; large.
Bush: very productive.

Wolcott *(North Carolina 255).*--Originated in Atkinson, North
Carolina, by the North Carolina Agricultural Experiment Sta-
tion and the United States Department of Agriculture (F. V.
Coville). Introduced commercially in June, 1950. Weymouth x
F-6 (Stanley x Crabbe 4); planted in 1935; selected in 1940.
Fruit: generally round; firm to slightly soft but firmer than
Weymouth; good flavor; early as Weymouth. Bush: semi-upright;
large; high resistance to canker; productive as Weymouth.

BUTTERNUT

Weschcke.--Originated in River Falls, Wisconsin, by Carl Weschcke. Introduced commercially in 1938. Open-pollinated seedling of a wild tree; discovered about 1934. Nut: claimed to
crack out in whole halves. Tree: hardy.

CARISSA

Chesley.--Originated in Carlsbad, California, by Chesley Alles.
Introduced in 1929. Parentage unknown; selected in 1928. Fruit:
size large; flavor and texture not too good.

Serena.--Originated in Santa Barbara, California, by J. Eliot
Coit. Introduced commercially in 1932. Parentage unknown; selected in 1929. Fruit: ripe 8 months of the year; stem long,
making it possible to pick with buttons on; good keeper.

CAROB

Santa Fe.--Originated in Santa Fe Springs, Los Angeles County,
California, by Lawrence Holmes of the California Carob Planta-

tions. Introduced commercially in 1922. Selection made from a
wild tree in 1920; this original tree was still alive in 1946.
Fruit: large. Two plantings were made: one at Riverside,
California, now completely submerged by the Los Angeles
Metropolitan Water District lake; the other at Pasadena,
California, which was abondoned when the land was subdivided
for residences.

CHERIMOYA

Bays.--Originated on the James H. Bays ranch in Ventura, California. Introduced commercially in 1920. Parentage unknown.
Fruit: round; fingerprinted surface; quality good. Tree: good
bearer.

Booth.--Originated in Hollywood, California, by John S.
Armstrong. Introduced commercially in 1921. Parentage unknown;
discovered on the A. F. Booth Ranch. Fruit: quality good; skin
moderately smooth; season late. Tree: bears well in certain
areas.

Carter.--Originated in Encinitas, California, by James H. Macpherson. Introduced commercially in February, 1940. Parentage
unknown; discovered in January, 1938. Fruit: long, conical;
smooth; ripens in June in San Diego County; keeps well; may be
a good shipper. Tree: heavy bearer; sets fairly well without
pollination in some areas. Most nearly resembles Ryerson.

Chaffey *(P. I. 44841)*.--Originated in West Los Angeles, California, by Mrs. A. M. Chaffey. Introduced commercially in 1945.
Seedling from a seed lot bearing P. I. 44841 collected in
Oran, Salta, Argentina, by Mr. W. S. Damon; seedling received
by Mr. Chaffey June 9, 1917, from the United States Department
of Agriculture. Fruit: flesh light cream color; 3/4 to 1
pound; seeds small, 30 to 60 per fruit; quality excellent;
season December to March along the coast of California; does
not bruise easily; short, conical, 4 inches long. Tree: bears
crops regularly.

Dr. White.--See **White.**

McPherson.--Originated in Orange, California, by Bill Weber.
Introduced commercially in 1933. Parentage unknown; original
tree still growing in the McPherson Brothers' orchard, after
whom the variety was named. Fruit: quality good; moderate
size; skin smooth but with some development of tubercles; midseason to late in maturity. Tree: vigorous and quite productive even without hand pollination.

Ott.--Originated in Mexico City, Mexico, and fruited at Whittier, California, by Wm. H. Ott. Introduced commercially in 1946. Patent no. 656; March 27, 1945; assigned to Armstrong Nurseries, Inc., Ontario, California. An open pollinated seedling of unknown parentage. Fruit: flavor very pronounced and distinct; high sugar content; skin tough but thin. Tree: fairly self-fruitful. A prospective shipping variety.

P. I. 44841. --See **Chaffey.**

Ryerson. --Originated in Chula Vista, California, by William H. Sallman. Selected in 1928 by J. Eliot Coit, who named it for Knowles A. Ryerson. Introduced commercially in 1935. Parentage unknown. Fruit: shape regular; skin smooth and tough; ships well.

Sallmon. --Originated in Chula Vista, California, by J. Eliot Coit. Introduced commercially in 1931. Seeds came from the William Sallmon ranch; parentage unknown. Fruit: large; skin smooth and tough; quality poor. No longer being planted.

Whaley. --Originated in Hollywood, California, by John S. Armstrong. Introduced commercially in 1927. Parentage unknown. Fruit: tuberculate; large; quality good; light green; tends to develop a membrane around the seed.

White *(Dr. White).* --Originated on the Dr. White ranch, Lemon Grove, California, by James H. Macpherson. Introduced commercially in 1930. Parentage unknown; discovered in 1928 from a tree planted in 1912. Fruit: large; flavor fine, even after fruit is quite soft.

CHERRY

August Supreme. --Originated in Wayne County, Ohio, by Menno Gerber. Introduced commercially in 1936. Patent no. 164; January 21, 1936; assigned to W. N. Scarff's Sons, New Carlisle, Ohio. Parentage unknown; discovered in 1932. Fruit: sweet; ripens very late, August 1 to 15 in region of origin; firm; juicy; juice does not exude when the stem is removed.

Black Giant. --Originated in Sebastopol, California, by Luther Burbank. Introduced by Stark Brothers Nurseries and Orchards Company, Louisiana, Missouri; trademarked by this company. Parentage unknown. Fruit: sweet; skin black; flesh firm, blood red; pit small; large; ships well. Tree: fairly hardy.

Black Sour. --Originated in Rahway, New Jersey, by a Mrs. Dolechek who imported seeds from Rumania. Introduced commercially in 1949 by The Ackerman Nurseries, Bridgman, Michigan. Parentage unknown; selected in 1935. Fruit: sour; skin color dark red; most nearly resembles May Duke but darker in color.

Burbank's Hearthoney.--See **Honey Heart.**

Coronation *(Morden 500).*--Originated in Morden, Manitoba, Canada, by the Dominion Experimental Station. Introduced commercially in 1937. Open pollinated seedling of Shubianka; selected in 1933. Fruit: large, up to 15/16 inch on young bushes; round obovate in form; skin dark red; flesh yellowish, firm, acid; juice pink, plentiful; quality fair to good as Morello for canning; season late July and early August. Bush: upright, round-headed; moderately productive.

Early Montmorency.--See **Richmorency.**

Ebony.--Originated in Moscow, Idaho, by the Idaho Agricultural Experiment Station (Leif Verner). Introduced commercially in 1946. Lambert x Black Republican (probably); selected in 1940. Fruit: good dessert quality; most nearly resembles Black Republican. Tree: bears heavily.

Gil Peck.--Originated in Geneva, New York, by the New York State Agricultural Experiment Station (Richard Wellington). Introduced for trial in 1936. Napoleon x Giant; cross made in 1925; first full crop in 1933. Fruit: skin dark purplish-black; large; firm-fleshed; rich flavor; cracks less than Napoleon; season between Noble and Geant d'Hedelfingen; most nearly resembles Giant.

Honey Heart *(Burbank's Hearthoney).*--Originated in Santa Rosa, California, by Luther Burbank. Introduced commercially in 1934. Patent no. 41; November 8, 1932; assigned to Stark Brothers Nurseries and Orchards Company, Louisiana, Missouri. Parentage unknown. Fruit: sweet; skin yellow with a red blush; flesh firm, cream colored; most nearly resembles Napoleon.

Lamida.--Originated in Moscow, Idaho, by the Idaho Agricultural Experiment Station (Leif Verner). Introduced commercially in 1946. Open pollinated seedling of Lambert; selected in 1940. Fruit: resists cracking; large; good dessert quality; most nearly resembles Lambert.

Late Lambert.--See **Stark Royal Purple.**

Meyer.--See **Starking Hardy Giant.**

Minnesota 58.--See **Northstar.**

Minnesota 63.--See **Orient.**

Montearly.--Originated in East Jordan, Michigan, by Levi R.

Taft. Introduced commercially in 1932. Patent no. 30; October 4, 1932; assigned to Stark Brothers Nurseries and Orchards Company, Louisiana, Missouri. Parentage unknown; selected in 1928. Fruit: sour; one-third larger than Early Richmond; ripens 10 days to 2 weeks earlier than Montmorency, which it resembles.

Montlate.--Originated in East Jordan, Michigan, by Levi R. Taft. Introduced commercially in 1932. Patent no. 29; October 4, 1932; assigned to Stark Brothers Nurseries and Orchards Company, Louisiana, Missouri. Mutation of Montmorency; selected in 1927. Fruit: sour; identical with Montmorency except that it ripens 10 days to 2 weeks later than its parent.

Morden 500.--See **Coronation.**

Noble *(St. Margaret, Tradescant Heart).*--An old English variety of unknown origin. Introduced for trial in the United States in 1943 by the New York State Agricultural Experiment Station. Parentage unknown. Fruit: sweet; flesh firm; color dark purplish red; cracks less than most late varieties; season between Schmidt and Geant d'Hedelfingen; heart-shaped.

Northstar *(Minnesota 58).*--Originated in Excelsior, Minnesota, by the University of Minnesota Fruit Breeding Farm. Introduced commercially in 1950. English Morello x Serbian Pie 1 (a selection from seed of sour cherry obtained in Serbia in 1918); cross made in 1933; selected in 1942. Fruit: English Morello type. Tree: small; very hardy in wood and fruit bud; resistant to leaf spot.

Orient *(Minnesota 63).*--Originated in Excelsior, Minnesota, by the University of Minnesota Fruit Breeding Farm. Introduced commercially in March, 1949. Self-pollinated seedling of a Nanking cherry *(Prunus tomentosa)* originally obtained from O. M. Jenson of Albert Lea, Minnesota, in 1925; selected in 1940. Fruit: good quality. Tree: vigorous; self-fertile.

Rainbow Stripe.--Originated in Yakima, Washington, by E. Remy & Son. Introduced commercially in 1930. Bud mutation of Lambert; discovered in 1925. Fruit: sweet; white with a narrow blood-red stripe from stem to tip, extending through the flesh; most nearly resembles Lambert.

Richmorency *(Early Montmorency).*--Originated in Saint Joseph, Michigan, by L. B. Reber. Introduced commercially in 1938. Patent no. 316; February 28, 1939; assigned to The Greening Nursery Company, Monroe, Michigan. Bud mutation of Montmorency; discovered in 1929. Fruit: sour; ripens 1 week or more before its parent.

Seneca.--Originated in Geneva, New York, by the New York State Agricultural Experiment Station (Richard Wellington). Introduced for trial in 1924. Early Purple Guigne x unknown; cross made in 1911; first full crop in 1922. Fruit: sweet; early, ripening 2 weeks earlier than Black Tartarian; large, round-cordate; skin purple-black; flesh soft, juicy, melting, rich flavor; pit free; skin does not crack. Tree: vigorous; productive; most nearly resembles Black Tartarian.

Sodus.--Originated in Geneva, New York, by the New York State Agricultural Experiment Station (Richard Wellington). Introduced for trial in 1938. Napoleon x Giant; cross made in 1925; first full crop in 1935. Fruit: sweet; skin light-colored; resistant to cracking; large; flesh firm, white; ripens between Emperor Francis and Napoleon; most nearly resembles Victor.

Spalding.--Originated in Moscow, Idaho, by the Idaho Agricultural Experiment Station (Leif Verner). Introduced commercially in 1946. Bing x Deacon (probably); selected in 1942. Fruit: large; very firm; good luster; most nearly resembles Bing.

Sparkle.--Originated in Summerland, British Columbia, Canada, by the Dominion Experimental Station (A. J. Mann). Introduced commercially in 1944. Open pollinated seedling of Empress Eugenie; cross made in 1936; selected in 1942. Fruit: flavor sweet, sprightly; flesh white, firm; size medium to small; appearance attractive; skin has a bright luster which suggested the varietal name; fairly resistant to cracking; rounder and less conical than Napoleon which it most nearly resembles; matures one week earlier than Napoleon. Tree: vigorous; upright grower; a pollinator for Bing, Lambert, Napoleon, and Van; pollinated by Bing, Deacon, Lambert, Napoleon, and Van. Not recommended for commercial planting, but is a good variety for the home garden.

St. Margaret.--See Noble.

Star.--Originated in Summerland, British Columbia, Canada, by the Dominion Experimental Station (A. J. Mann). Introduced commercially in January, 1949. Open pollinated seedling of Deacon; selected in 1944. Fruit: dark red; resembling Deacon in shape, and Bing in size, firmness, and quality; ripens a week earlier than Bing. Tree: moderately heavy bearer; hardy.

Starking Hardy Giant *(Meyer)*.--Originated in Cedarburg, Wisconsin, by Mrs. Ottilie R. Meyer. Introduced commercially in 1948. Patent no. 764; October 7, 1947; renamed in 1949 by Stark Brothers Nurseries and Orchards Company, Louisiana, Missouri, assignee and introducer. Parentage unknown; discovered in 1925. Fruit: sweet; color deep red; larger size

than most stardard varieties including Schmidt, Bing, and
Lambert; not quite as firm as Bing, but ships well; quality
very high; most nearly resembles Schmidt. Tree: very hardy and
productive.

Stark Royal Purple *(Late Lambert)*.--Originated in Charlevoix,
Michigan, by C. Fairman. Introduced commercially in 1944.
Patent no. 627; May 9, 1944; renamed in 1948 by Stark Brothers
Nurseries and Orchards Company, Louisiana, Missouri, assignee
and introducer. Bud mutation of Lambert; discovered in 1933.
Fruit: ripens 10 to 14 days after Lambert, which it most
nearly resembles.

Sweet September.--Originated in Wayne County, Ohio, by Menno
Gerber. Introduced commercially in 1936. Patent no. 94; April
17, 1934. Parentage unknown; selected in 1930. Fruit: sweet;
ripens latter part of August; keeps in good condition on tree
for a long time.

Tradescant Heart.--See Noble.

Unark.--Originated in Fayetteville, Arkansas, by H. R. Rosen.
Introduced commercially in 1930. Parentage unknown; discovered
in September, 1918. Fruit most nearly resembles Saylor and
Yellow Spanish. Tree: partially resistant to brown rot; good
winter hardiness; late in blossom.

Van.--Originated in Summerland, British Columbia, Canada, by
the Dominion Experimental Station (A. J. Mann). Introduced
commercially in 1944. Open pollinated seedling of Empress
Eugenie; cross made in 1936; selected in 1942. Fruit: Bing
type; sweet; black; bright luster to skin; somewhat resistant
to cracking; as large as Bing and slightly firmer and quite
as good in quality as Bing; slightly earlier in season than
Bing. Tree: vigorous; upright grower; a pollinator for Bing
and Lambert; pollinated by Bing, Deacon, Lambert, and Napoleon.
Variety named in honor of J. R. Van Haarlem, Horticultural
Emperiment Station, Vineland, Ontario, Canada.

Velvet.--Originated in Vineland, Ontario, Canada, by the Ontario Horticultural Experiment Station. Introduced commercially
in 1937. Open pollinated seedling of Windsor; selected in
1925. Fruit: sweet; black; ripens late; best variety in Station quick-freezing tests. Most nearly resembles Schmidt.

Vernon.--Originated in Vineland, Ontario, Canada, by the Ontario Horticultural Experiment Station. Introduced commercially
in 1937. Open pollinated seedling of Windsor; selected in
1925. Fruit: sweet; black; ripens in midseason; quality good;
firm. Tree: yields heavy crops. Most nearly resembles Windsor.

Victor.--Originated in Vineland, Ontario, Canada, by the Ontario Horticultural Experiment Station. Introduced commercially in 1925. Open pollinated seedling of Windsor; selected in 1923 from crosses made in 1916. Fruit: sweet; ripens early; white, heavily blushed, therefore outsells Napoleon; processes well. Most nearly resembles Napoleon.

York Imperial.--Originated in York, Pennsylvania, by H. B. Faber and J. A. C. Ziegler, Jr. Introduced commercially in 1940. Patent no. 421; September 17, 1940; assigned to White Rose Seed & Nursery Company, York, Pennsylvania. Napoleon x Schmidt. Fruit and tree: similar to or identical with Napoleon.

CHERRY PLUM

Convoy.--Originated in Valley River, Manitoba, Canada, by W. J. Boughen. Introduced commercially in 1941. Parentage unknown. Fruit: somewhat larger than Compass; skin scarlet red; flesh yellowish; little harsh for dessert use, good for canning; season end of August. Tree: very upright, narrow; hardy; productive.

Dura *(Morden 116)*.--Originated in Morden, Manitoba, Canada, by the Dominion Experimental Station. Introduced commercially in 1940. Open pollinated seedling of Sapa; selected in 1936. Fruit: oblong; skin dark green, mottled purplish; flesh maroon-purple, crisp, tender, meaty, sweeter and less clingstone than Sapa; quality very good as dessert or canned. Bush: low, spreading; very hardy; productive.

Heaver.--Originated in Baljennie, Saskatchewan, Canada, by K. N. Heaver. Introduced commercially in 1944. Open pollinated seedling of Opata. Fruit: roundish; large; skin purplish-black; flesh greenish, firmer than Opata, juicy, sweet; quality good as dessert, very good when canned; season mid-August. Bush: low; spreading; hardy; productive.

Honey Dew.--Originated in Brookings, South Dakota, by the South Dakota State College. Introduced commercially in 1950. *Prunus besseyi* x Gold plum; discovered in 1930. Fruit: early; high quality; most nearly resembles Opata.

Manor *(Morden 119)*.--Originated in Morden, Manitoba, Canada, by the Dominion Experimental Station. Introduced commercially in 1945. Open pollinated seedling of Sapa; selected in 1937. Fruit: roundish; skin purplish; flesh dark red to purplish, meaty, tender, juicy, sweet; good as dessert, fair for canning; season mid-August; particularly adapted to northern prairies. Bush: hardier and more upright than Sapa at Morden.

Minnesota 144.--See Nicollet.

Minnesota 145.--See St. Anthony.

Morden 116.--See Dura.

Morden 119.--See Manor.

Mordena.--Originated in Morden, Manitoba, Canada, by the Dominion Experimental Station. Introduced commercially in 1930. Open pollinated seedling of Compass. Fruit: smallish; skin red to dark purplish-red; flesh yellow, juicy, sweet, sprightly; quality good for canning, excellent for jelly; season early September. Tree: spreading; vigorous; hardy; productive; late blooming.

Nicollet *(Minnesota 144).*--Originated in Excelsior, Minnesota, by the University of Minnesota Fruit Breeding Farm. Introduced commercially in February, 1925. *(Prunus avium x P. pennsylvanica)* x *P. besseyi;* seed planted in 1912; selected in 1916 or 1917. Fruit: cherry plum; small, round; sour cherry flavor. Tree: dwarf, bushlike.

Red Cortland.--Originated in Blaney Park, Michigan, by J. E. Lang. Introduced commercially in 1934. Sapa x Superior; discovered in 1933. Fruit: larger than Sapa; skin purplish-black; flesh reddish purple; good quality. Tree: strong grower for a sand cherry hybrid; rapid grower; heavy bearer.

St. Anthony *(Minnesota 145).*--Originated in Excelsior, Minnesota, by the University of Minnesota Fruit Breeding Farm. Introduced commercially in 1923. *Prunus besseyi* x *P. salicina* hort. var. Satsuma; selected in 1915. Fruit: cherry-plum type; rich flesh color; semi-freestone; for culinary use only. Tree: vigorous; early and prolific bearing habit.

Zumbra.--Originated in Excelsior, Minnesota, by the University of Minnesota Fruit Breeding Farm. Introduced commercially in 1920. *(Prunus avium* x *P. pennsylvanica)* x *P. besseyi;* selected in 1916. Fruit: flesh firm and crisp; quality good for cooking. Tree: vigorous; dwarf; bushy; hardy.

CHESTNUT

Abundance.--Originated in Eagle Creek, Oregon, by Carroll D. Bush. Introduced commercially in 1941. Parentage: scions were cut from most vigorous seedlings resulting from planting of imported seed of *Castanea mollissima.* Nut: appearance attractive; cleans well; sweet; larger and more prolific than Honan which it most nearly resembles.

Carr *(Carrissima)*.--Originated in Magnolia, North Carolina.
Introduced commercially in 1935. Parentage unknown; grown from
seed *(Castanea molissima)* procured from Tientsin, China, and
the small tree sent to R. D. Carr by the United States Department of Agriculture in 1915; selected in 1930; first grafted
in 1932 by H. F. Stoke of Roanoke, Virginia. Nut: size good;
very sweet; too gray to be as attractive as some others;
quality excellent.

Carrissima.--See **Carr.**

Connecticut Yankee.--See **Yankee.**

Hobson.--Originated from seed procured by the United States
Department of Agriculture northwest of Peiping, China, and
sent to James Hobson, Jasper, Georgia, as a small seedling in
1917. First grafted in 1932 by H. F. Stoke, Roanoke, Virginia,
although named in 1930. Introduced commercially in 1935.
Parentage unknown. Fruit: smaller than Carr; more attractive
in appearance than Carr, but no sweeter. Tree: thought by some
to be more prolific than Carr.

Honan.--Originated in Eagle Creek, Oregon, by Carroll D. Bush.
Introduced commercially about 1935. A vigorous seedling selected from a planting of imported seed of *Castanea mollissima.* Nut: not as large or as good a producer as Abundance,
which it most nearly resembles.

Kuling.--Originated in Philema, Georgia, by the United States
Department of Agriculture. Introduced commercially in June,
1949. Grown as a nursery seedling resulting from nuts *(Castanea mollissima)* imported from South Central China, in 1938.
Nuts: 35 to 40 per pound; dropping free from burr; midseason;
keeping quality very good. Tree: medium large, vigorous; shoot
growth slightly willowy; moderate upright in form.

Mayseptjan.--Originated in Nevada County, California, by the
Felix Gillet Nursery (C. E. Parsons). Introduced commercially
in 1932. Parentage unknown; from a seedling brought in from
the Reihl orchard, Alton, Illinois; selected in 1930. Nut:
large; quality good; matures in early fall. Tree: bears well.

Meiling.--Originated in Philema, Georgia, by the United States
Department of Agriculture. Introduced commercially in June,
1949. Grown as a nursery seedling resulting from nuts *(Castanea mollissima)* imported from South Central China in 1938.
Nuts: 35 to 40 per pound; dropping free from burr; midseason;
good keeping quality. Tree: vigorous; upright; shoot growth
fairly stocky; early and heavy bearer.

Nanking.--Originated in Philema, Georgia, by the United States

Department of Agriculture. Introduced commercially in June, 1949. Grown from seed *(Castanea mollissima)* imported directly from South Central China in 1938. Nuts: 30 to 43 per pound; uniform in shape; few with split shells. Tree: vigorous; precocious; heavy bearer of annual crops; midseason pollination; medium late harvest.

Reliable.--Originated in Roanoke, Virginia, by H. F. Stoke. Introduced commercially in 1936. Seedling of *Castanea mollissima* selected in 1932. Nut: small. Tree: blooms late; bears regularly. Going out of production because nuts are too small.

Stoke *(Stoke Hybrid).*--Originated in Roanoke, Virginia, by H. F. Stoke from mixed seed sent to him for stock purposes by the Division of Forest Pathology, U. S. Plant Industry Station, Beltsville, Maryland. The seed was produced at the Plant Propagating Garden (Bell Station), Glenn Dale, Maryland. Introduced commercially by Mr. Stoke in 1936. Parentage largely or altogether Japanese, although possibly part Chinese. Nut: ripens at Roanoke very early, usually beginning during the third week in August. Tree: extremely precocious; prolific; little else to commend it. Probably obsolete.

Stoke Hybrid.--See **Stoke.**

Yankee *(Connecticut Yankee).*--Originated in Riverside, Connecticut, on land now owned by E. E. Hunt; first propagated by Dr. J. Russell Smith, Swarthmore, Pennsylvania, in the Sunny Ridge Nurseries of northern Virginia in 1935. Introduced commercially in 1935. Parentage unknown, but probably indirectly from the United States Department of Agriculture. Nut: choice. Tree: hardy in eastern United States; *Castanea mollissima.*

Zimmerman.--Originated in Linglestown, Pennsylvania, by Dr. G. A. Zimmerman. Introduced commercially in 1935. Grown as a nursery seedling resulting from nuts *(Castanea mollissima)* imported from Nanking; selected in 1930; first propagated by H. F. Stoke, Roanoke, Virginia, in 1933; first catalogued by Dr. J. Russell Smith in 1938. Nut: appearance attractive; cleaning quality good; sweet; trifle small; may be supplanted by other varieties that have larger fruits.

CRANBERRY

Beckwith.--Originated in Beltsville, Maryland, by the United States Department of Agriculture (H. F. Bain and H. F. Bergman). Introduced commercially in 1950. McFarlin x Early Black; selected 1938 to 1940. Fruit: large; late maturing. Vine: productive; resistant to rot and false blossom. Promising in New Jersey.

Stankavich.--Originated in Bandon, Oregon, by Joseph F. Stan-kiewicz. Introduced commercially in 1926. Trademarked Original Stankavich. Oregon native x an Eastern variety; selected between 1914 and 1917. Fruit: size averaging 3/4 to 5/8 inch; global; high color; low acid content, good sugar content; ripens early. Plant: produces well. Most nearly resembles Michigan Bennett.

Stevens.--Originated in Beltsville, Maryland, by the United States Department of Agriculture (H. F. Bain). Introduced commercially in 1950. McFarlin x Potter; selected 1938 to 1940. Fruit: very large; medium late; firm. Vine: vigorous; very productive.

Wilcox.--Originated in Beltsville, Maryland, by the United States Department of Agriculture (H. F. Bain). Introduced commercially in 1950. Howes x Searles; selected in 1938 to 1940. Fruit: very early ripening. Vine: very productive; vigorous.

CURRANT

Cascade *(Minnesota 70)*.--Originated in Excelsior, Minnesota, by the University of Minnesota Fruit Breeding Farm. Introduced commercially in 1942. Open pollinated seedling of Diploma; selected in 1926. Fruit: larger than Red Lake, and matures one week later. Bush: productive; erect; medium vigor.

Coronet *(Ottawa 393)*.--Originated in Ottawa, Ontario, Canada, by the Division of Horticulture, Central Experimental Farm. Introduced commercially in 1948. *Ribes ussuriense* Jancz. x Kerry; selected July 22, 1943. Fruit: black; most nearly resembles standard black currant varieties. Bush: immune from rust *(Cronartium ribicola* A. Fisch.).

Crusader *(Ottawa 381)*.--Originated in Ottawa, Ontario, Canada, by the Division of Horticulture, Central Experimental Farm. Introduced commercially in 1948. *Ribes ussuriense* Jancz. x Kerry; selected August 7, 1942. Fruit: black; most nearly resembles standard black currant varieties. Bush: most valuable characteristic is its immunity from rust *(Cronartium ribicola* A. Fisch.).

Holländische Rote.--See **Viking.**

Minnesota 70.--See **Cascade.**

Ottawa 381.--See **Crusader.**

Ottawa 393.--See **Coronet.**

Red Lake.--Originated in Excelsior, Minnesota, by the Minnesota Agricultural Experiment Station (W. H. Alderman). Introduced commercially in 1933. Parentage unknown. Fruit: large berries equal to those of Perfection; clusters long and well-filled. Bush: superior to those of the Perfection variety.

Rφd Hollandsk Druerips.--See **Viking.**

Stephens *(Stephens 9).*--Originated in Orilla, Ontario, Canada, by C. L. Stephens. Introduced commercially in 1933. Parentage unknown. Fruit: very large; attractive red; subacid; excellent quality; medium long clusters; comparable to Red Lake; superior to most common varieties. Bush: vigorous; somewhat spreading; very hardy; productive.

Stephens 9.--See **Stephens.**

Viking *(Hollandische Rote, Rφd Hollandsk Druerips).*--Originated in Europe where it has been known for many years. Introduced commercially in the United States of America from Norway by the United States Department of Agriculture (Glenn Gardner Hahn). *Ribes petraeum* Wulf. x *R. rubrum* L. (direction of cross not known). Fruit: red; matures late. Plant: immune to white pine blister rust *(Cronartium ribicola)*; productive; only red currant grown in white pine territory (according to Dr. W. H. Alderman, University of Minnesota (1945)).

DATE

Desert Dew.--Originated in Yuma, Arizona, by C. D. McGinnis. Introduced commercially in 1946. Discovered in 1909 among some off-shoots taken from Bard Valley, California to the McGinnis date grove in Yuma. Fruit: ripens earlier, slightly larger, better flavor before processing than Deglet Noor which it most closely resembles; does not crack or check.

Medjhool *(Talfilalet).*--Originated in Bou Denib, French Morocco, North Africa. Introduced by the United States Department of Agriculture (Walter T. Swingle) in 1927. Parentage unknown. Fruit: large size; excellent eye appeal; quality good; cures well. Tree: high tolerance to rain and high humidity; prolific offshoot production.

Sphinx.--Origin unknown; imported as Hayany into the United States in 1920 by the Phoenix Date Company, Phoenix, Arizona. Introduced commercially in 1925. Open pollinated seedling, supposedly of Hayany; selected in 1920. Fruit: small seed and very little rag; most nearly resembles Maktoon, except in color. Tree: very heavy producer (four-year record of 350 pounds per palm).

Talfilalet.--See **Medjhool**.

ELDERBERRY

Adams.--Originated in Union Springs, New York, by William W.
Adams. Introduced for trial in 1926. Selections made from wild
forms; present variety constitutes two clonal selections.
Fruit: clusters and berries exceptionally large. Bush: strong;
vigorous; productive.

FIG

Beall.--Originated in Santa Clara Valley, California, by W. A.
Beall. Introduced commercially in 1924. Parentage unknown;
seedling transplanted to Fresno, California, and first fruited
there about 1922. Fruit: purplish black with amber pulp;
excellent in California in Imperial Valley, San Diego County,
and Fresno. Tree: produces two crops for fresh fruit purposes.

Kearney *(USDA Rixford 2830)*.--Originated in Kearney Park,
Fresno, California, by the United States Department of Agriculture (G. P. Rixford). Introduced commercially in 1925.
Parentage unknown; selected in 1925. Fruit: skin green; pulp
violet-purple; size above medium to large. Tree: abundant
cropper; caprifig.

King.--Originated in Madera, California, by the Western Evergreen Company (Sisto Pedrini), San Francisco, California.
Introduced commercially in 1940 by the King Fig Plantation,
San Francisco, California. Trademarked in 1941. Parentage unknown; discovered in June, 1930. Fruit: sweet; skin smooth,
thin, dark green; flesh pink; matures in cool coastal climates
as far north as British Columbia; most nearly resembles Genoa;
one of the White San Pedro group; large; pyriform; of excellent quality.

USDA Rixford 2830.--See **Kearney.**

FILBERT

Bixby *(Jones 200)*.--Originated in Lancaster, Pennsylvania, by
J. F. Jones. Introduced commercially in 1937. Rush *(Corylus
americana)* x Italian Red *(C. avellana)*; tree first bore in
1924. Nut: appearance attractive; kernels clean and sweet.
Tree: very hardy; prolific..

Brag.--Originated in Westbank, British Columbia, Canada, by
J. U. Gellatly. Introduced commercially in 1928. F_2 open poll-

inated seedling of Kentish Cob; selected in 1926. Nut: large; free-husking; clean kernels; 3 to 4 nuts per cluster; cracks easier than Craig, which it most nearly resembles.

Carlola.--Originated in River Falls, Wisconsin, by Carl Weschcke. Introduced commercially in 1941. *Corylus americana* x Brag. Nut: matures early; shell very thin; large. Tree: very prolific; resistant to wild hazel blight.

Comet.--Originated in Westbank, British Columbia, Canada, by J. U. Gellatly. Introduced commercially in 1928. Seedling of unknown parentage. Nut: very attractive; long; shell thin; kernel clean, smooth, plump. Tree: produces good crops if cross-pollinated.

Craig.--Originated in Westbank, British Columbia, Canada, by J. U. Gellatly. Introduced commercially in 1928. F_2 open pollinated seedling of Kentish Cob; selected in 1926. Nut: large; oval; medium shell; large kernel. Tree: produces good crops if cross-pollinated.

Dolores.--Originated in River Falls, Wisconsin, by Carl Weschcke. Introduced commercially in 1941. *Corylus americana* x Brag. Nut: kernel has very thin pellicle; light-colored meats; shell thin; matures early.

Fitzgerald.--Originated in Washougal, Washington, by D. Fitzgerald. Introduced commercially in 1936. Parentage unknown; open pollinated seedling; discovered in 1936. Fruit: round type; good size.

G 2.--See **Holder.**

Holder *(G 2).*--Originated in Westbank, British Columbia, Canada, by J. U. Gellatly. Introduced commercially in 1928. F_2 open pollinated seedling of Kentish Cob; selected in 1926. Nut: high quality; shell thin; kernel 50 to 53% of dried nut, smooth, high oil content. Tree: late-blossoming.

Jones 200.--See **Bixby.**

Magdalene.--Originated in River Falls, Wisconsin, by Carl Weschcke. Introduced commercially in 1941. *Corylus americana* x Brag. Nut: matures early; shell thin; large.

Nonpareil.--Originated in Washougal, Washington, by D. Fitzgerald. Introduced commercially in 1938. Parentage unknown. Nut: kernel white; round type.

Royal.--Originated in Stayton, Oregon, by E. Roy. Introduced commercially in 1934 by H. L. Pearcy Nursery, Salem, Oregon.

Barcelona x Daviana; discovered in 1930. Nut: extremely thin shell; large kernel; color and markings similar to Daviana; larger than either parent. Tree: early production; heavy yield.

Woodford.--Originated in Forest Grove, Oregon, by E. W. Woodford. Introduced commercially in 1936. Parentage unknown. Tree: pollinator for Barcelona.

GOOSEBERRY

Como *(Minnesota 43).*--Originated in Excelsior, Minnesota, by the University of Minnesota Fruit Breeding Farm. Introduced commercially in 1922. Pearl x Columbus; cross made in 1908. Fruit: greenish yellow; quality good. Bush: very productive; resistant to sunscald.

Fredonia.--Originated in Geneva, New York, by the New York State Agricultural Experiment Station (Richard Wellington). Introduced for trial in 1927. Open pollinated seedling of unknown English-type gooseberry; originated in 1910. Fruit: very large; skin dark red; of the English type; ripens late; quality good; appearance attractive; keeps and ships well.

Glendale.--Originated in Little Silver, New Jersey, by the United States Department of Agriculture (Walter Van Fleet). Introduced commercially in 1932. ((*Grossularia missouriense* x Red Warrington) x Triumph) x Keepsake; selected in 1905. Fruit: excellent for jam; seeds small. Plant: vigorous; best for southern limit of gooseberry growing.

Minnesota 43.--See **Como.**

Pixwell.--Originated in Fargo, North Dakota, by the North Dakota Agricultural Experiment Station (A. F. Yeager). Introduced commercially in 1932. Oregon Champion x *Ribes missouriense;* cross of 1920. Fruit: size medium; pink when ripe; in clusters and borne on long pedicels; few thorns. Bush: hardy; very productive.

GRAPE

Almission.--Originated in Fresno, California, by L. O. Bonnet. Introduced commercially in 1941. Mission x Alicante Bouschet; selected about 1936. Fruit: black; cluster loose, large; juice red. Vine: vigorous. A wine grape variety.

Athens.--Originated in Geneva, New York, by the New York State Agricultural Experiment Station (Richard Wellington). Introduced for trial in 1938. Hubbard x Portland; cross made in

1925. Fruit: early; black; large clusters; most nearly resembles Concord. Vine: very productive.

Beaver.--Originated in Mountain Grove, Missouri, by the Missouri State Fruit Experiment Station (Paul H. Shepard). Introduced commercially in 1947. Open pollinated seedling of Triumph; selected in 1945. Fruit: black; high quality; ripens a week before Moore's Early; hangs well without cracking or shattering. Vine: productive; vigorous; blossoms perfect.

Black Beauty.--Originated in Newton, Illinois, by L. A. Richards. Introduced commercially in 1949. Parentage unknown; selected in 1940. Fruit: large; black; good for jelly, wine, and dessert; ripens October and early November. Vine: self-pollinating; heavy producer; regular bearer. Labrusca type.

Bluebell *(Minnesota 158)*.--Originated in Excelsior, Minnesota, by the University of Minnesota Fruit Breeding Farm. Introduced commercially in 1944. Parentage unknown; selected in 1923. Fruit: most nearly resembles Concord in size and color; high quality for dessert, juice or jelly; matures about mid-September. Vine: productive; vigorous; hardy.

Blue Eye.--Originated in Mountain Grove, Missouri, by the Missouri State Fruit Experiment Station (Paul H. Shepard). Introduced commercially in 1947. Ellen Scott x America; selected in 1947. Fruit: sweet; firm; tough skin; handles and keeps well; ripens about 10 days later than Concord; berry and cluster larger than Concord; cluster compact; produces attractive red juice. Vine: vigorous; flowers fertile.

Blue Jay *(Minnesota 69)*.--Originated in Excelsior, Minnesota, by the University of Minnesota Fruit Breeding Farm. Introduced commercially in 1944. Parentage unknown; selected in 1923. Fruit: dark blue; nearly size of Concord; good for juice and jelly; matures mid-September. Vine: hardy; productive; requires cross-pollination.

Bokay.--Originated in Mountain Grove, Missouri, by the Missouri State Fruit Experiment Station (Paul H. Shepard). Introduced commercially in 1947. Captain x Terret Monstre; selected in 1947. Fruit: large; yellow; meaty; pleasing flavor; compact clusters; ripens at Concord time and keeps well on the vine or in storage for two months without breakdown; most nearly resembles Malaga.

Bonnet Seedless.--Originated in Fresno, California, by L. O. Bonnet. Introduced commercially in 1934. Patent no. 88; March 13, 1934. Muscat of Alexandria x Thompson Seedless; selected in 1932. Fruit: only partially seedless; appears to be much inferior to Thompson Seedless in all characteristics under

California conditions. Vine: weak grower, not fruiting uniformly.

Bonnet Seedless Muscat.--Originated in Fresno, California, by L. O. Bonnet. Introduced commercially in 1941. Muscat of Alexandria x Sultana; selected about 1936. Fruit: berry small, variable; cluster medium; seeds partly hardened. Vine: produces irregular crops; weak grower. Now obsolete.

Brocton.--Originated in Geneva, New York, by the New York State Agricultural Experiment Station (S. A. Beach). Introduced for trial in 1919. Brighton x New York 125 (Winchell x Diamond); cross made in 1899. Most nearly resembles Niagara. Fruit: white; quality good; flavor less foxy than Niagara.

Bronx Seedless.--Originated in Geneva, New York, by the New York State Agricultural Experiment Station in cooperation with the New York Botanical Garden (A. B. Stout). Introduced for trial in 1937. New York 8536 (Goff x Iona) x Sultanina; cross made in 1925. Fruit: large; red; seedless; quality good; large clusters; cracks easily during wet weather. Recommended where cracking is not prevalent.

Brownie.--Originated in Experiment, Georgia, by the Georgia Agricultural Experiment Station (J. G. Woodroof). Introduced commercially in 1933. Open pollinated seedling of San Monta; selected in 1930. Fruit: highest sugar content of muscadine varieties, quality excellent. Not recommended for commercial planting by Muscadine Grape Committee, Southern Section, American Society for Horticultural Science.

Bryant.--Originated in Mountain Grove, Missouri, by the Missouri State Fruit Experiment Station (Paul H. Shepard). Introduced commercially in 1947. Muench x Terret Monstre; selected in 1947. Fruit: black; firm, juicy, tender; sweet, pleasing flavor; late ripening, four weeks after Concord; clusters large, loose. Vine: vigorous; productive.

Buffalo.--Originated in Geneva, New York, by the New York State Agricultural Experiment Station (Richard Wellington). Introduced for trial in 1938. Herbert x Watkins; cross made in 1921. Most nearly resembles Herbert. Fruit: black; pleasing flavor; ripens about one week before Concord; most nearly resembles Herbert. Vine: productive.

Burgaw.--Originated in Willard, North Carolina, by the United States Department of Agriculture and the North Carolina Department of Agriculture (Charles Dearing). Introduced commercially in 1946. Thomas x V19 R7 B2 (Scuppernong x male); selected from a cross made about 1912. Vine: muscadine type; can be used as a pollinator; perfect-flowered; self- and cross-fertile; most nearly resembles Thomas.

Cape Fear.--Originated at the Coastal Plains Experiment Station, Willard, North Carolina, by the United States Department of Agriculture and the North Carolina Department of Agriculture (Charles Dearing). Introduced commercially in 1946. Burgaw x V20 R36 B4 (V19 R7 B2 (Scuppernong x male) x Kilgore); cross made about 1915 or 1916. Fruit: muscadine type; color white; matures very late; most nearly resembles Scuppernong. Vine: pistillate variety.

Cardinal.--Originated in Fresno, California, by the United States Department of Agriculture (Elmer Snyder and Frank N. Harmon). Introduced commercially in October, 1946. Flame Tokay x Ribier (Alphonse Lavallee); selected in 1943. Fruit: matures early; quality good; most nearly resembles Ribier except for red color; often sets irregular clusters.

Christmas.--Originated in Santa Rosa, California, by Luther Burbank. First introduced commercially in 1915 by the originator; reintroduced in 1926 by a California nursery. Claimed to be a seedling of Pierce. Fruit: similar to Concord; late; long ripening season. Vine: very vigorous; suitable for arbor planting.

Creek.--Originated in Experiment, Georgia, by the Georgia Agricultural Experiment Station (J. G. Woodroof). Introduced commercially in 1938. Open pollinated seedling of San Monta; selected in 1934. Fruit: thinnest skin and highest percentage of free run juice of muscadine varieties; high in sugar and acidity; ripens late; recommended for commercial planting in southern half of muscadine region by Muscadine Grape Committee, Southern Section, American Society for Horticultural Science.

Creswell.--Originated in eastern North Carolina by the United States Department of Agriculture and the North Carolina Department of Agriculture (Charles Dearing) of Willard, North Carolina. Introduced commercially in 1946. Parentage unknown; discovered about 1915. Fruit: muscadine type; fine flavor; ripens over a long period. For home use.

Dawn.--Originated in Experiment, Georgia, by the Georgia Agricultural Experiment Station (H. P. Stuckey). Introduced commercially in 1938. Scuppernong x black male muscadine; selected in 1937. Fruit: earliest ripening variety; most nearly resembles Scuppernong. Not recommended by Muscadine Grape Committee, Southern Section, American Society for Horticultural Science.

Delight.--Originated in Davis, California, by the California Agricultural Experiment Station (H. P. Olmo). Introduced com-

mercially in the spring of 1947. Scolokertek kiralynoje 26 x
Sultanina marble; cross made in 1936; first fruited in 1940.
Fruit: seedless, oval, yellow-green, firm; cluster large,
shouldered, well-filled; most nearly resembles Thompson Seedless but ripens 10 days earlier, shatters less; in most localities has a slight Muscat flavor.   Vine: fruitful when spur
pruned. A table and raisin variety.

Dulcet.--Originated in Experiment, Georgia, by the Georgia
Agricultural Experiment Station (J. G. Woodroof). Introduced
commercially in 1934. Open pollinated seedling of Irene; selected in 1928. Fruit: excellent quality, persistent; most
nearly resembles Thomas. Vine: foliage very resistant to black
rot. Recommended for the home vineyard by Muscadine Grape Committee, Southern Section, American Society for Horticultural
Science.

Dunkirk.--Originated in Geneva, New York, by the New York
State Agricultural Experiment Station (S. A. Beach). Introduced
for trial in 1920. Brighton x Jefferson; cross made in 1899.
Fruit: larger than Delaware; good shipper; ripens late; clusters uniform, compact, most nearly resembling Delaware. Vine:
vigorous; hardy; healthy; productive; very short internodes;
may have value for wine.

Duplin.--Originated at the Coastal Plains Experiment Station,
Willard, North Carolina, by the United States Department of
Agriculture and the North Carolina Department of Agriculture
(Charles Dearing). Introduced commercially in 1946. Stanford x
V10 R15 B4 (Eden x V23 R4 B2 (Eden x Munsoniana)) ; cross made
about 1912. Fruit: muscadine type; large; black; clusters
fair; most nearly resembles James. Vine: perfect flowered type
for pollination purposes.

Early Giant.--Originated in Altus, Arkansas, by Herman J. B.
Wiederkehr. Introduced commercially in 1932. Patent no. 42;
November 8, 1932; assigned to Stark Brothers Nurseries and
Orchards Company, Louisiana, Missouri. Parentage unknown.
Fruit: Concord type; larger and earlier than Campbell Early,
which it most nearly resembles; similar to Worden in flavor.
Vine: thrifty; dark green foliage.

Eden.--Originated in Geneva, New York, by the New York State
Agricultural Experiment Station (Richard Wellington). Introduced for trial in 1938. Ontario x New York 10085 (Triumph x
Mills); cross made in 1923. Fruit: pleasing flavor; most nearly resembles Concord; clusters are too scraggly for a commercial variety.

Eleven Point.--Originated in Mountain Grove, Missouri, by the
Missouri State Fruit Experiment Station (Paul H. Shepard). In-

troduced commercially in 1947. Captain x Terret Monstre; selected in 1947. Fruit: much better in quality and larger in size than Captain; compact cluster cylindrical all the way to tip, often over a foot long; suitable for table or red wine.

Emerald Riesling.--Originated in Davis, California, by the California Agricultural Experiment Station (H. P. Olmo). Introduced commercially in 1948. Muscadelle (of California) x White Riesling; cross made in 1936; first fruited in 1939. Fruit: clusters large, conical, well-filled; berry round; skin thick, dark bluish green; pulp bright green; for production of white table wine of good acidity, of Chablis type. Vine: vigorous; heavy foliage cover; wood matures late in autumn; very productive.

Empress *(Seedless Emperor)*.--Originated in Visalia, California, by Vahan Mkhalian. Introduced commercially in 1939. Patent no. 311; January 17, 1939. Bud mutation of Emperor; discovered in 1928. Fruit: seedless, but retains characteristics of parent; berry much smaller than parent.

Favorite.--Originated in Brenham, Texas, by John Neiderauer. Introduced commercially about 1938. Probably Black Spanish x Herbemont; selected in the early 1930's. Fruit: clusters medium to large, similar to Black Spanish in appearance but more compact with larger berries and less acid, of more pleasing taste; it makes an attractive dark purple juice. Vine: very productive, six tons per acre or more in favorable seasons.

Fredonia.--Originated in Fredonia, New York, by the New York State Agricultural Experiment Station (F. E. Gladwin). Introduced for trial in 1927. Champion x Lucile; cross made in 1915. Fruit: 2 weeks earlier than Worden; clusters medium, cylindrical, compact; berries large; skin thick and tough; quality good, superior to any other black variety of its season. Vine: susceptible to downy mildew.

Gasconade.--Originated in Mountain Grove, Missouri, by the Missouri State Fruit Experiment Station (Paul H. Shepard). Introduced commercially in 1947. Captain x Terret Monstre; selected in 1947. Fruit: size medium; black; flavor good; ripens two weeks after Concord; suitable for juice, wine, or table use; clusters large, compact. Vine: productive.

Golden Muscat.--Originated in Geneva, New York, by the New York State Agricultural Experiment Station (R. D. Anthony). Introduced for trial in 1927. Muscat Hamburg x Diamond; cross made in 1915. Fruit: berry large, oval, juicy, tender, sweet, aromatic; ripens 2 weeks later than Concord; for home use; clusters large, tapering, compact; most nearly resembles Diamond in golden color; some aroma of European Muscat. Vine: viggorous; productive.

Hanover.--Originated in Geneva, New York, by the New York State Agricultural Experiment Station (S. A. Beach). Introduced commercially in 1924. Brighton x Niagara; selected at Fredonia, New York, by F. E. Gladwin, October 3, 1924. Fruit: quality holds longer than that of either parent; has promise for dessert and white wine; most nearly resembles Brighton. Vine: more vigorous and productive than either parent; more hardy than Niagara; flowers are self-fruitful.

Hector.--Originated in Geneva, New York, by the New York State Agricultural Experiment Station (Richard Wellington). Introduced for trial in 1937. Chasselas Rose x Brocton; cross made in 1923. Fruit: attractive; red; long, slender clusters; quality good; subject to mildew; most nearly resembles Chasselas Rose.

Howard.--Originated in Experiment, Georgia, by the Georgia Agricultural Experiment Station (H. P. Stuckey). Introduced commercially in 1929. Scuppernong x black male muscadine; selected in 1926. Fruit: resembles Scuppernong. Not recommended by Muscadine Grape Committee, Southern Section, American Society for Horticultural Science.

Hunt.--Originated in Experiment, Georgia, by the Georgia Agricultural Experiment Station (H. P. Stuckey). Introduced commercially in 1920. Flowers x white male muscadine; selected in 1918. Fruit: quality excellent; very even in ripening, unusual in muscadine grapes; dull black with little bloom when prime ripe; skin medium to thin with abundant pigment prized by manufacturers of wine and frozen pulp; sugar content higher than Scuppernong variety, containing appreciable amount of sucrose. Vine: very prolific. Considered the best dark fruiting variety, the only one unanimously recommended for commercial plantings in the southeastern States by the Muscadine Grape Committee, Southern Section, American Society for Horticultural Science.

Interlaken Seedless.--Originated in Geneva, New York, by the New York State Agricultural Experiment Station (A. B. Stout, G. D. Oberle, and Richard Wellington). Introduced commercially September 17, 1946. Ontario x Sultanina; selected September 6, 1937. Fruit: seedless; non-slipskin type; flesh crisp and meaty; most nearly resembles Sultanina but has slight Ontario flavor. Vine: seems to be sufficiently hardy for the eastern United States.

Irene.--Originated in Experiment, Georgia, by the Georgia Agricultural Experiment Station (H. P. Stuckey). Introduced commercially in 1920. Thomas x black male muscadine; selected in 1918. Not recommended by Muscadine Grape Committee, Southern Section, American Society for Horticultural Science.

Italia.--Originated in Rome, Italy, by the Institute of Fruit Culture (A. Pirovano). Introduced commercially in California by the California Agricultural Experiment Station in 1946. Bicane x Muscat Hamburg; cross made in 1911. Fruit: berries very large, golden, with Muscat flavor; cluster loose, conical. Vine: very productive.

Jumbo Red.--Originated in Bridgman, Michigan, by Ackerman Nurseries. Introduced commercially in 1946. Believed to be a seedling of Concord; discovered in a vineyard of Concord in 1941. Fruit: dark color when fully ripe; very sweet flavor when ripe; very large seeds; resembles *Vitis vinifera*.

Kendaia.--Originated in Geneva, New York, by the New York State Agricultural Experiment Station (Richard Wellington). Introduced for trial in 1939. Portland x Hubbard; cross made in 1925. Fruit: matures early; pleasing flavor; most nearly resembles Moore Early. Vine: productive; hardy. Recommended as promising in New Hampshire.

Keuka.--Originated in Geneva, New York, by the New York State Agricultural Experiment Station (Richard Wellington). Introduced for trial in 1924. Chasselas rose x Mills; cross made in 1913; seed germinated in 1914; first fruited in 1919. Fruit: dark red with heavy bloom; cluster and berry medium sized; cluster compact; flesh crisp and hardly slipskin; viniferatype flavor; ripens about 1 week before Catawba; most nearly resembles Delaware in appearance.

Kilgore.--Originated at the North Carolina Coastal Plains Experiment Station, Willard, North Carolina, by the United States Department of Agriculture and the North Carolina Department of Agriculture (Charles Dearing). Introduced commercially in 1946. Open pollinated seedling of Labama; cross of 1908. Fruit: muscadine type; flesh melting; seeds separate from pulp; flavor fair. Vine: weak.

La Pryor.--Originated in La Pryor, Texas, by the Texas Agricultural Experiment Station. Introduced commercially in 1934. Parentage unknown, probably *Vitis candicans* x *V. rupestris* hybrid; discovered in 1933. Fruit: size medium; sweet; black; clusters small; light producer. Valuable for rootstock purposes only.

Lucida.--Originated in Experiment, Georgia, by the Georgia Agricultural Experiment Station (J. G. Woodroof). Introduced commercially in 1933. Open pollinated seedling of Irene; selected in 1930. Fruit: largest bronze colored variety. Not recommended by Muscadine Grape Committee, Southern Section, American Society for Horticultural Science.

Melton.--Originated in Geneva, New York, by the New York State Agricultural Experiment Station (Richard Wellington). Introduced commercially in 1923. Triumph x New York 4064 ((Winchell x Diamond) x Jefferson). Fruit: clusters long and attractive; quality good; texture good. This variety was dropped from the list recommended for trial for New York because of the tendency of the berries to crack during ripening.

Minnesota 45.--See **Red Amber**.

Minnesota 66.--See **Moonbeam**.

Minnesota 69.--See **Blue Jay**.

Minnesota 158.--See **Bluebell**.

Moonbeam *(Minnesota 66).*--Originated in Excelsior, Minnesota, by the University of Minnesota Fruit Breeding Farm. Introduced commercially in 1944. Parentage unknown; selected in 1923. Fruit: large; greenish yellow; bland flavor; larger than Concord; ripens in early September. Vine: vigorous; easy to propagate; winter hardy.

Morrison.--Originated at the Coastal Plains Experiment Station, Willard, North Carolina, by the United States Department of Agriculture and the North Carolina Department of Agriculture (Charles Dearing). Introduced commercially in 1946. Scuppernong x a selected white male; cross made in 1909. Fruit: muscadine type; quality good; matures early; most nearly resembles Scuppernong. Vine: pistillate; growth weak.

Myakka.--Originated in southern Florida by Joseph L. Fennell. Introduced commercially in 1947. *(Vitis shuttleworthii* x *V. smalliana)* x *V. vinifera* hort. var. Malaga; selected in 1943. Fruit: clusters large; sweet flavored; purple skin; most nearly resembles Sultana except for purple color. Vine: productivity high; vigorous; moderate disease resistance; for semitropical conditions.

Nevermiss.--Originated in Gay, Meriwether County, Georgia, by M. Aubrey Owen. Introduced commercially in 1945. Patent no. 692; May 28, 1946; assigned to H. G. Hastings Company. Fruit: muscadine type; color white or bronze; sugar content high; cluster size much better than Scuppernong which it most nearly resembles. Vine: production regular; resistant to disease.

New River.--Originated at the Coastal Plains Experiment Station, Willard, North Carolina. by the United States Department

of Agriculture and the North Carolina Department of Agriculture (Charles Dearing). Introduced commercially in 1946. Open
pollinated seedling of San Jacinto; 1908 seedling. Fruit: muscadine type; white; matures early; most nearly resembles Scuppernong. Vine: a pistillate variety.

North Fork.--Originated in Mountain Grove, Missouri, by the
Missouri State Fruit Experiment Station (Paul H. Shepard). Introduced commercially in 1947. Agawam x Early Daisy; selected
in 1947. Fruit: large; black; skin tough and does not crack
from moisture at harvest time; ripens about ten days ahead of
Concord; clusters large, compact. Vine: vigorous; productive;
perfect flowers.

November.--Originated in Experiment, Georgia, by the Georgia
Agricultural Experiment Station (H. P. Stuckey). Introduced
commercially in 1920. Scuppernong x black male muscadine; selected in 1918. Not recommended by Muscadine Grape Committee,
Southern Section, American Society for Horticultural Science.

Onslow.--Originated at the Coastal Plains Experiment Station,
Willard, North Carolina, by the United States Department of
Agriculture and the North Carolina Department of Agriculture
(Charles Dearing). Introduced commercially in 1946. V22 R5 B4
(Scuppernong x male) x Burgaw; cross made about 1916. Fruit:
muscadine type; black; clusters fair to good; most nearly re-
sembles James. Vine: pistillate.

Orton.--Originated at the Coastal Plains Experiment Station,
Willard, North Carolina, by the United States Department of
Agriculture and the North Carolina Department of Agriculture
(Charles Dearing). Introduced commercially in 1946. Latham x
Burgaw; cross made about 1915. Fruit: muscadine type; sweeter
than Scuppernong which it most nearly resembles. Vine: better
foliage than Scuppernong; a pistillate variety.

Ozark Prize.--Originated in Mountain Grove, Missouri, by the
Missouri State Fruit Experiment Station (Paul H. Shepard). Introduced commercially in 1947. Dr. Collier x Sheridan; selected in 1947. Fruit: large; black; firm; flavor good, sweet;
persistent; good keeper; ripens almost with Concord; most
nearly resembles Sheridan; medium to large, compact cluster
similar to Sheridan.

Pender.--Originated at the Coastal Plains Experiment Station,
Willard, North Carolina, by the United States Department of
Agriculture and the North Carolina Department of Agriculture
(Charles Dearing). Introduced commercially in 1946. Latham x
V20 R36 B4 (Kilgore x V19 R7 B2 (Scuppernong x male)); cross
made about 1917. Fruit: muscadine type; white to yellowish;
apple-flavored. Vine: perfect flowered for pollination pur-

poses; most nearly resembles Scuppernong.

Perlette.--Originated in Davis, California, by the California Agricultural Experiment Station (H. P. Olmo). Introduced commercially in 1946. Scolokertek kiralynoje 26 x Sultanina marble; cross made in 1936; vine first fruited in 1940. Fruit: seedless; berry white, larger than Thompson Seedless; spherical, crisp, neutral flavor, low in sugar and acidity; cluster large; very early ripening, one month before Thompson Seedless. Vine: vigorous; fruitful when spur pruned; very productive.

Piney.--Originated in Mountain Grove, Missouri, by the Missouri State Fruit Experiment Station (Paul H. Shepard). Introduced commercially in 1947. Open pollinated seedling of Merrimac; selected in 1945. Fruit: black; skin thin and tough; flavor good; ripens about with Concord; larger clusters than Concord or Merrimac, which it most nearly resembles. Vine vigorous; productive; flowers fertile.

Pontiac.--Originated in Geneva, New York, by the New York State Agricultural Experiment Station (S. A. Beach). Introduced for trial in 1922. Herbert x Worden; cross made in 1903. Fruit: berries large; skin dark purple; rarely cracks; long-keeping; flavor sweet and vinous; small number of seeds; quality high; good for home use; clusters large and well-formed. Vine: self-sterile. No longer recommended for planting.

Qualitas.--Originated in Experiment, Georgia, by the Georgia Agricultural Experiment Station (H. P. Stuckey). Introduced commercially in 1920. Thomas x black male muscadine; selected in 1918. Not recommended by Muscadine Grape Committee, Southern Section, American Society for Horticultural Science.

Red Amber *(Minnesota 45)*.--Originated in Excelsior, Minnesota, by the University of Minnesota Fruit Breeding Farm. Introduced commercially in 1944. Parentage unknown; selected in 1923. Fruit: sweet; reddish amber; aromatic; berry smaller than Concord; cluster medium size, compact; very good quality; ripens in early September. Vine: hardy.

Roubidoux.--Originated in Mountain Grove, Missouri, by the Missouri State Fruit Experiment Station (Paul H. Shepard). Introduced commercially in 1947. Open pollinated seedling of Prune de Cazouls; selected in 1945. Fruit: large; blue; commonly oval, resembling *Vitis vinifera;* firm; ripens late, with Catawba; cluster medium sized and loose. Vine: hardy; extremely vigorous; productive; has perfect flowers.

Ruby.--Originated in Geneva, New York, by the New York State Agricultural Experiment Station (Richard Wellington). Intro-

duced for trial in 1938. Keuka x Ontario; cross made in 1923.
Fruit: attractive; red; quality good; ripens after Concord;
most nearly resembles Chasselas rose. Vine: productive.

Ruby Cabernet.--Originated in Davis, California, by the California Agricultural Experiment Station (H. P. Olmo). Introduced commercially in 1948. Carignane x Cabernet Sauvignon;
cross made in 1936; first fruited in 1940. Fruit: clusters
medium, loose; berry black, juicy, resistant to spoilage; produces table wine of high quality, similar to that of Cabernet
Sauvignon but of more intense color and earlier maturation.
Vine: vigorous; more productive than Cabernet Sauvignon.

Sanderson Special.--Originated in Glendale, Arizona, by Ches-
ter A. Sanderson. Introduced commercially in 1948. Patent no.
782; January 20, 1948; unassigned. Parentage unknown; discovered in 1942. Fruit: slipskin type; skin maroon-colored;
similar to Concord but milder; table grape. Vine: vigorous.

Sanger Sweet.--Originated in Sanger, California, by E. L.
Magnone. Introduced commercially in 1942. Patent no. 509;
April 14, 1942. Open pollinated seedling of Muscat of Alexandria; selected about 1924. Fruit: sweet, with a Muscat flavor; firm; good shipper; seedless.

Scarlet.--Originated in Davis, California, by the California
Agricultural Experiment Station (H. P. Olmo). Introduced commercially in 1946. Golden Muscat x Teinturier; cross made in
1935; first fruited in 1939. Fruit: black; cluster compact;
berry medium size; juice abundant, dark red, high sugar and
acid, mild Concord-type flavor; resembles Teinturier in color
of berry and juice. Vine: resistant to *Oidium;* dormant buds
fruitful; foliage blood red in autumn. For home and commercial production of grape juice.

Schuyler.--Originated in Geneva, New York, by the New York
State Agricultural Experiment Station (Richard Wellington and
G. D. Oberle). Introduced commercially September 17, 1946.
Zinfandel x Ontario; selected in 1932. Fruit: a hybrid which
has much of the flavor and flesh characteristics of a vinifera
grape; resembles Zinfandel more than it does Ontario. Vine:
appears to be sufficiently hardy and disease resistant to be
adapted to the climate of the eastern United States.

Seedless Emperor.--See **Empress.**

Seminole.--Originated in southern Florida by Joseph L. Fennell.
Introduced commercially in 1947. *(Vitis shuttleworthii* x *V.
rufotomentosa)* x *(V. candicans* x Rommel); selected in 1945.
Vine: flowers perfect; vigorous, productive, and disease resistant in semi-tropical climate; most nearly resembles Catawba

or Extra.

Seneca.--Originated in Geneva, New York, by the New York State Agricultural Experiment Station (R. D. Anthony). Introduced for trial in 1930. Lignan blanc x Ontario; seed borne in 1917. Fruit: berry oval, yellow; clusters medium, compact; skin tender. Vine: vigorous, hardy, productive; of vinifera type.

Sheridan.--Originated in Geneva, New York, by the New York State Agricultural Experiment Station (S. A. Beach). Introduced for trial in 1921. Herbert x Worden; cross made in 1903. Fruit: black; clusters compact, large; skin tough; stores exceptionally well; matures about 1 week after Concord. Vine: hardy; productive.

Spalding.--Originated at Experiment, Georgia, by the Georgia Agricultural Experiment Station (H. P. Stuckey). Introduced commercially in 1920. Flowers x white male muscadine; selected in 1918. Not recommended by Muscadine Grape Committee. Southern Section, American Society for Horticultural Science.

St. Francis.--Originated in Mountain Grove, Missouri, by the Missouri State Fruit Experiment Station (Paul H. Shepard). Introduced commercially in 1947. Muench x Gros Guillaume; selected in 1947. Fruit: large; black; flesh firm, tender, separates from seed easily; flavor sweet, sprightly; ripens two weeks after Concord; large compact cluster. Vine: perfect flowers.

Stanford.--Originated at the Coastal Plains Experiment Station, Willard, North Carolina, by the United States Department of Agriculture and the North Carolina Department of Agriculture (Charles Dearing). Introduced commercially in 1946. Open pollinated seedling of San Jacinto; selected about 1910. Fruit: muscadine type; white; large. Vine: pistillate; most nearly resembles Scuppernong.

Steuben.--Originated in Geneva, New York, by the New York State Agricultural Experiment Station (Richard Wellington and G. D. Oberle). Introduced commercially September 17, 1946. Wayne x Sheridan; selected October 5, 1937. Fruit: sugar content high; quality high; skin tough; keeping quality good; berry resembles Wayne; cluster resembles Sheridan; flavor resembles Eumelan. Vine: production heavy; resistant to black rot and downy mildew; winter hardiness.

Stout Seedless.--Originated in Geneva, New York, by the New York State Agricultural Experiment Station (A. B. Stout). Introduced for trial in 1930. (Triumph x Dutchess) x Sultanina rose; cross made in 1921; first fruited in 1926. Fruit: small; oval; skin greenish yellow; flesh juicy, sweet, vinous; clusters large, medium compact. Vine: fairly hardy but cannot be grown in severe climates. No longer recommended for planting.

Stuckey.--Originated in Experiment, Georgia, by the Georgia Agricultural Experiment Station (H. P. Stuckey). Introduced commercially in 1920. Scuppernong x black male muscadine; selected in 1918. Fruit: excellent quality. Not recommended by Muscadine Grape Committee, Southern Section, American Society for Horticultural Science due to low yields, weak growth, and susceptibility of foliage to black rot.

Tarheel.--Originated at the Coastal Plains Experiment Station, Willard, North Carolina, by the United States Department of Agriculture and the North Carolina Department of Agriculture (Charles Dearing). Introduced commercially in 1946. Luola x V36 R15 B4 (Eden x V23 R4 B2 (Eden x Munsoniana)) ; selected from a cross made about 1912. Vine: muscadine type; variety for use as a pollinator; perfect flowered; self- and cross-fertile; most nearly resembles Eden.

Tetra.--Originated in Mountain Grove, Missouri, by the Missouri State Fruit Experiment Station (Paul H. Shepard). Introduced commercially in 1947. Herbert x Worden. Fruit: large, equal to Columbian and Golden Giant; flavor good; ripens with Concord. Vine: growth fair; production good; flowers with recurved stamens.

Topsail.--Originated at the Coastal Plains Experiment Station, Willard, North Carolina, by the United States Department of Agriculture and the North Carolina Department of Agriculture (Charles Dearing). Introduced commercially in 1946. Latham x Burgaw; selected from a cross made about 1915. Fruit: muscadine type; large; sweeter than Scuppernong which it most nearly resembles. Vine: more vigorous than Scuppernong.

Urbana.--Originated in Geneva, New York, by the New York State Agricultural Experiment Station (S. A. Beach). Introduced for trial in 1912. Ross x Mills; cross made in 1899. Fruit: red; keeps well; flesh crisp; quality good; matures late; most nearly resembles Catawba. Vine: subject to mildew.

Van Buren.--Originated in Fredonia, New York, by the Vineyard Laboratory of the New York State Agricultural Experiment Station (F. E. Gladwin). Introduced commercially in 1935. Fredonia x Worden. Fruit: quality of unfermented juice excellent; table quality good; skin tender like that of Worden which it most nearly resembles in all fruit characters except berry size; very early ripening season; susceptible to downy mildew. Vine: vigorous; winter hardy; productive.

Wallace.--Originated at the Coastal Plains Experiment Station,

Willard, North Carolina, by the United States Department of Agriculture and the North Carolina Department of Agriculture (Charles Dearing). Introduced commercially in 1946. Selection V26 R5 B4 (Scuppernong x male) x Willard; cross made about 1915. Vine: muscadine type; a pollinator variety; perfect flowered; self- and cross-fertile; most nearly resembles Scuppernong.

Watkins.--Originated in Geneva, New York, by the New York State Agricultural Experiment Station (Richard Wellington). Introduced commercially in 1930. Mills x Ontario; first fruited in 1915. Fruit: quality outstanding; most nearly resembles Mills in flavor, texture, and quality. Variety no longer recommended for planting in New York because of its unreliable productivity and lack of hardiness.

Wayne.--Originated in Geneva, New York, by the New York State Agricultural Experiment Station (Richard Wellington). Introduced commercially in 1927. Mills x Ontario; first fruited in 1916. Fruit: most nearly resembles Mills in flavor, color, texture, and quality; its quality, texture, and flavor are more nearly viniferous than most varieties of its period of introduction. Variety has been dropped for plantings in New York because of its late season, its tendency to shell, and its unreliable productivity.

Westfield.--Originated in Fredonia, New York, at the Vineyard Laboratory of the New York State Agricultural Experiment Station (F. E. Gladwin). Introduced commercially in 1935. Herbert x Concord Seedless. Fruit: labrusca type, slipskin; skin blue; pigment content high which was considered valuable from the standpoint of use in blending in the making of wines and unfermented juices.

Willard.--Originated at the North Carolina Coastal Plains Experiment Station, Willard, North Carolina, by the United States Department of Agriculture and the North Carolina Department of Agriculture (Charles Dearing). Introduced commercially in 1946. Stanford x V19 R7 B2 (Scuppernong x male); selected from a cross made about 1910. Vine: muscadine type; for use as a pollinator; perfect-flowered; self- and cross-fertile; most nearly resembles Scuppernong.

Yates.--Originated in Geneva, New York, by the New York State Agricultural Experiment Station (Richard Wellington). Introduced for trial in 1937. Mills x Ontario; cross made in 1923. Fruit: red; skin tough; quality good; ships well; season before Catawba; most nearly resembles Catawba.

Yuga.--Originated in Experiment, Georgia, by the Georgia Agricultural Experiment Station (J. G. Woodroof). Introduced commercially in 1934. Open pollinated seedling of San Monta; selected in 1932. Fruit: quality excellent; sweet; thin reddish-bronze skin. For the home vineyard. Not recommended for commercial plantings by Muscadine Grape Committee due to late and uneven ripening.

Not named.--Originated in Athenia, New Jersey, by T. C. Kevitt. Introduced commercially in 1936. Patent no. 195; September 15, 1936; assigned to Meyer Aronowitz, Barclay Nursery, New York, New York. Seedling of Niagara; selected about 1929. Fruit: amber color when ripe; slightly larger and sweeter than Niagara; ripens four or five days earlier than Niagara. Vine: more thrifty, hardier, and more productive than Niagara.

GRAPEFRUIT

Henninger's Ruby.--See Ruby.

John Garner.--Originated in Texas by George W. Baylor. Introduced commercially in 1934. Open pollinated seedling of Duncan. Fruit: size similar to Duncan; nearly seedless; ripens about 2 weeks later than Duncan; quality good.

Red Blush.--See Ruby.

Ruby *(Ruby Red, Red Blush, Henninger's Ruby).*--Originated in McAllen, Texas, by Albert Henninger. Introduced commercially in 1934 or 1935. Patent no. 53; January 24, 1933. Bud mutation of Thompson; discovered in 1929. Fruit: red blush on rind; flesh pink; deeper red than Thompson *(Marsh Pink).*

Ruby Red.--See Ruby.

GUAVA

Hart.--Originated in New Smyrna, Florida, by J. Y. Detwiler. Introduced commercially in 1945. Seedling of Detwiler; parent variety was grown by Mr. Detwiler from seed reported to have come from India; named after W. S. Hart of New Smyrna, Florida. Fruit: flesh white to yellow; large; sugar content about 8%. Tree: vigorous; hardy in southern California.

Red Indian.--Originated in Dade County, Florida, by Fred Lenz. Introduced commercially in 1946. Open pollinated seedling of P. I. 57828; discovered in 1940. Fruit: large; sweet; flesh red; quality good; ascorbic acid content averages 195 mg. per 100 grams fresh fruit; total sugars average 7 to 10%. Tree: productive.

Redland.--Originated in Homestead, Florida, by the Florida Subtropical Experiment Station (S. J. Lynch and H. S. Wolfe). Introduced commercially in 1941. Parentage unknown; seed obtained from Atkins Institute, Arnold Arboretum, Cuba; selected in 1938. Fruit: large; pyriform; no musky guava odor; flavor mild; matures in winter. Tree: heavy cropper; susceptible to algal leaf spot.

Ruby.--Originated in Homestead, Florida, by the Florida Subtropical Experiment Station (George D. Ruehle). Introduced commercially in 1946. Open pollinated seedling of P. I. 81849; selected in 1944. Fruit: large; flesh red, sweet, thick, mild; quality good; seeds few; ascorbic acid averages 180 mg. per 100 grams fresh fruit; total sugars average 9 or 10%.

Supreme.--Originated in Homestead, Florida, by the Florida Subtropical Experiment Station (George D. Ruehle). Introduced commercially in 1946. Parentage unknown; seed planted in 1936; selected in 1940. Fruit: large, averaging 6-10 ounces; flesh thick; flavor mild; small seed cavity, few seeds; ascorbic acid 247 mg. per 100 grams of fresh fruit; total sugars 7 or 8%. Tree: productive; thrifty; vigorous; resistant to algal leaf spot.

HICKORY

Murdock.--Originated in Crown Point, New York, by John Murdock. Introduced commercially about 1940. Parentage unknown; shagbark, probably discovered as a chance seedling about 1936. Nut: quality high. Tree: hardy; bears early.

Weschcke.--Originated in Fayette, Iowa, by Carl Weschcke. Introduced commercially in 1936. Unknown seedling of shagbark; selected about 1928. Nut: matures September 1 to 15; papershell; kernel full and rich, cracking out in entire halves. Grafts well on wild bitternut hickory *(Carya cordiformis)*.

LEMON

Armstrong Seedless.--Originated in Riverside, California, by Sanford Johnson. Introduced commercially in 1939. Patent no. 342; October 10, 1939. Bud mutation of Eureka. Tree: appears to be more vigorous but less fruitful than parent.

Frost Eureka.--Originated in Riverside, California, by the California Citrus Experiment Station (Howard B. Frost). Introduced commercially in 1948. A nucellar seedling of Eureka; selected in 1918. Fruit: most nearly resembles Eureka. Tree: added vigor and disease resistance in comparison with other strains of Eureka.

Perrine.--Originated in Eustis, Florida, by the United States Department of Agriculture (Walter T. Swingle). Introduced commercially in 1931. Genoa lemon x Mexican lime; selected in 1909. Fruit: size, shape, and quality of commercial lemon. Tree: resistant to scab and withertip, but highly susceptible to gummosis caused by *Diplodia natalensis*. Variety going out of commercial production.

Pink-Fleshed *(Variegated)*.--Originated in San Fernando, California, by a Mr. Field of Erocton, Massachusetts, and first propagated by A. D. Shamel. Introduced commercially in December, 1937. Bud mutation of Eureka; discovered in 1935. Fruit: flesh and juice pink; rind variegated white, yellow, and green. Tree: foliage variegated; flowers pink. A plant novelty.

Variegated.--See **Pink-Fleshed.**

LIME

Eustis.--Originated in Eustis, Florida, by the United States Department of Agriculture (Walter T. Swingle). Introduced commercially in 1923. Mexican lime *(Citrus aurantifolia)* x round kumquat *(Fortunella japonica)*; selected in 1910. Fruit: fine quality; juicy; smooth, thin rind; hardy. Tree: resistant to withertip; hardy.

Idemor.--Originated in Homestead, Florida, by George L. Polk. Introduced commercially in 1941. Patent no. 444; January 28, 1941. Bud mutation of Tahiti (Persian) lime *(Citrus aurantifolia)*; selected prior to 1934. Tree: resistant to disease; heavy bearing. Most nearly resembles parental type.

Lakeland.--Originated in Eustis, Florida, by the United States Department of Agriculture (Walter T. Swingle). Introduced commercially in 1923. Mexican lime *(Citrus aurantifolia)* x round kumquat *(Fortunella japonica)*; selected in 1910. Fruit: fine quality; juicy; rind smooth, thin. Tree: resistant to withertip; hardy.

Newell *(Newell's Thornless Key)*.--Originated in Orlando, Florida, on the John Buchanan place. Introduced commercially in 1945. Parentage unknown; discovered about 1940. Fruit: seedless; smooth-skinned; flavor like Mexican lime. Tree: stands more frost than Mexican lime; thornless; everbearing; pollen sterile. Most nearly resembles Mexican or 'Key' lime.

Newell's Thornless Key.--See **Newell.**

MANGO

Brooks *(Brooks Late)*.--Originated in Miami, Florida, by the Charles Deering Estate. Introduced commercially in 1924. Open pollinated seedling of Sandersha; selected in 1916. Fruit: quality fair; not particularly attractive, but late in season (August to October). Tree: weak growing; heavy bearer.

Brooks Late.--See **Brooks**.

Fascell.--Originated in Miami, Florida, by Michael Fascell. Introduced commercially in 1942. Patent no. 451; February 18, 1941. Brooks x Haden (?); selected in 1936. Fruit: ovate, compressed laterally; 250 to 500 grams; pale yellow to dark carmine blush; ships well; quality good. Tree: bears heavily and regularly. Seems resistant to anthracnose.

Fragrance.--Originated in Naples, Florida, by·E. G. Wilkinson. Introduced commercially in 1938. Patent no. 119; January 15, 1935. Open pollinated seedling of Mulgoba. Fruit: excellent flavor; long season.

Kent.--Originated in Miami, Florida, by Leith D. Kent. Introduced commercially in 1944. Open pollinated seedling of Brooks; selected in 1938. Fruit: quality excellent; very little fiber; seed small; skin blushed crimson; season later than Haden. Tree: bears well.

Macpherson.--Originated in Encinitas, California, by L. L. Bucklew. Introduced commercially in 1945. Parentage unknown; grown from seeds shipped in from Florida; seedling selected in 1944. Fruit: oblong-ovate; small conspicuous protuberance near stem; skin with a deep pink blush; flesh yellow, fiber not excessive, sweet; season October to January.

Schobank.--Originated in Schofield Barracks, Hawaii, by the Board of Commissioners of Agriculture and Forestry. Introduced commercially in 1941. Open pollinated seedling of Pirie (Paheri); selected in 1940. Plant: bears at high elevation where rain does not affect blossoms; heavy bearer.

Simmonds.--Originated in Coconut Grove, Florida, by Edward Simmonds. Introduced commercially in 1942. Haden x Carabao; selected in 1934. Fruit: ovate to oblong-ovate; 375 to 525 grams; season July and August, slightly later than Haden; quality fair; fibers few. Tree: bears heavily.

Springfels.--Originated in West Palm Beach, Florida, by Chas. Springfels. Introduced commercially in 1930. Open pollinated seedling of Haden; selected in 1925. Fruit: oblong; large, 600 to 900 grams; quality fair to good; small amount

of fiber; orange yellow with maroon to crimson cheek; season
July and August; ships well. Tree: bears heavily.

Zill.--Originated in Lake Worth, Florida, by Carl King. Introduced commercially in 1940. Probably open pollinated seedling
of Haden; seedling first fruited in 1930. Fruit: quality very
good; very little fiber; seed small; skin highly colored,
shades of crimson with yellow ground color; ships well. Tree:
heavy bearer.

NATAL PLUM See CARISSA

NECTARINE

Bim.--Originated in Le Grand, California, by F. W. Anderson.
Introduced commercially in 1944. Patent no. 575; April 13,
1943. F_2 seedling of J. H. Hale peach x Lippiatt; selected in
1934. Fruit: quality good; skin bright red; most nearly resembles Kim.

Burbank's Fuzzless.--See **Flaming Gold.**

California 27-12.--See **Philp.**

California 27-12a.--See **Mabel.**

California 27-13.--See **Mabel.**

Early Le Grand.--Originated in Merced, California, by F. W.
Anderson. Introduced commercially in 1950. Patent no. 980;
September 19, 1950; assigned to Reedley Nursery, Reedley,Cal-
ifornia. Open pollinated seedling of Le Grand; selected in
1947. Fruit: resembles Le Grand but ripens from two to three
weeks earlier.

Ferganensis 0932.--See **Krasvynos.**

Flaming Gold *(Fuzzless, Burbank's Fuzzless).*--Originated in
Sebastopol, California, by Luther Burbank. Introduced commercially in 1928. Trademarked by Stark Brothers Nurseries and
Orchards Company, Louisiana, Missouri. Parentage unknown; selected about 1916. Fruit: flesh yellow; freestone; skin smooth
and red blushed; ripens before Elberta.

Fuzzless.--See **Flaming Gold.**

Fuzzless-Berta.--Originated in Blacksburg, Virginia, by Frederick W. HofMann. Introduced commercially in 1942. Patent no.
479; July 22, 1941. Parentage unknown, but probably an F_2

segregate of a cross between peach and nectarine. Fruit: flesh yellow; freestone; similar to Elberta except for glabrous skin; quality fair. Tree: only moderate vigor; blossoms large, showy, light pink.

Garden State.--Originated in New Brunswick, New Jersey, by the New Jersey Agricultural Experiment Station (M. A. Blake). Introduced commercially in 1934. Patent no. 92; April 3, 1934; assigned to the New Jersey Agricultural Experiment Station by M. A. Blake. Elberta, open pollinated; selected in 1922. Fruit: flesh yellow; freestone.

Hayes Late.--Originated in Fresno, California, by Mrs. Signa Larsen Hayes. Introduced commercially in 1944. Patent no. 587; June 8, 1943. Stanwick x a late peach; selected in 1939. Fruit: flesh white; clingstone; large; aromatic; ripens late; good keeping and shipping quality; cans well because of firmness. Most nearly resembles Quetta.

Hunter *(Hunter 1)*.--Originated in White Plains, New York, by Harry Hunter. Introduced for trial in 1930. Open pollinated seedling, supposedly of Elberta; seed planted in 1910; first fruited in 1913; bud sticks received by the New York State Agricultural Experiment Station (U. P. Hedrick) for testing in 1914. Fruit: handsome; flesh yellow; freestone; good size, flavor, and quality; early midseason.

Hunter *(New York 50)*.--Originated in Geneva, New York, by the New York State Agricultural Experiment Station (U. P. Hedrick). Introduced for trial in 1924. Open pollinated seedling of Hunter (Hunter 1); seed planted in 1915; first fruited in 19-20. Fruit: midseason, a week or 10 days later than Hunter (Hunter 1); flesh yellow; freestone; good size and quality. Tree: mildews badly; foliage eglandular. Variety is now supplanted by parent Hunter (Hunter 1).

Hunter 1.--See **Hunter.**

Kim.--Originated in Merced, California, by F. W. Anderson. Introduced commercially in 1938. Patent no. 173; April 7, 1936. J. H. Hale x Lippiatt, from F_2; selected in 1935. Fruit: flesh yellow, firm; freestone; high color; ripens with Gower.

Krasvynos *(Ferganensis 0932* and *P. I. 119844)*.--Originated in the Fergana Valley, Western Asiatic Russia. Introduced commercially in 1944 by the New Jersey Agricultural Experiment Station (M. A. Blake and J. S. Joffe), New Brunswick, New Jersey. Parentage unknown. Fruit: semifreestone; two inches in diameter; flesh white, slightly stringy; quality fair to good; ripens 7 to 10 days before Elberta; subject to cracking, brown rot, and internal breakdown when fully ripe in some seasons.

Tree: productive; hardier than Elberta. Flower: showy. Used as a parent for hardiness.

Le Grand.--Originated in Le Grand, California, by F. W. Anderson. Introduced commercially in 1942. Patent no. 549; October 13, 1942. J. H. Hale x Quetta, from F_2; selected in 1936. Fruit: flesh yellow, firm; clingstone; large.

Mabel *(California 27-12a* and *California 27-13).*--Originated in Winters, California, by the California Agricultural Experiment Station (Guy L. Philp). Introduced commercially in the fall of 1948. Humboldt x Burbank; selected in 1942. Fruit: flesh yellow; freestone; skin highly colored; matures in early midseason. Named in honor of Mrs. Guy L. Philp.

Nectacrest.--Originated in New Brunswick, New Jersey, by the New Jersey Agricultural Experiment Station (M. A. Blake). Introduced commercially in 1947. Garden State x ((Gold Mine x Belle selfed), open pollinated). Fruit: freestone; flesh white; ripens about 10 days before Elberta. Tree: hardier than Elberta. Flower: showy.

Nectaheart.--Originated in New Brunswick, New Jersey, by the New Jersey Agricultural Experiment Station (M. A. Blake). Introduced commercially in 1947. Garden State x ((Gold Mine x Belle selfed), open pollinated). Fruit: freestone; flesh white; ripens about 2 weeks before Elberta. Tree: hardier than Elberta. Flower: showy.

Nectalate.--Originated in New Brunswick, New Jersey, by the New Jersey Agricultural Experiment Station (M. A. Blake). Introduced commercially in 1947. Garden State x selected seedling. Fruit: freestone; flesh white; ripens 1 week after Elberta. Tree: not as hardy as Elberta. Flower: showy.

Nectarose.--Originated in New Brunswick, New Jersey, by the New Jersey Agricultural Experiment Station (M. A. Blake). Introduced commercially in 1947. Garden State x ((Gold Mine x Belle selfed), open pollinated). Fruit: freestone; flesh white; ripens 2½ weeks before Elberta. Tree: hardier than Elberta. Flower: showy.

New York 50.--See **Hunter.**

Philp *(California 27-12).*--Originated in Winters, California, by the California Agricultural Experiment Station (Guy L. Philp). Introduced commercially in the fall of 1948. Humboldt x Burbank; selected in 1942. Fruit: flesh yellow, firm; freestone; matures in early midseason; skin highly colored; size medium to large. Named in memory of Professor Guy L. Philp (1890-1947).

P. I. 119844.--See **Krasvynos.**

Pioneer.--Originated in Ontario, California, by Herbert C. Swim. Introduced commercially in 1949. Patent no. 787; March 9, 1948; assigned to Armstrong Nurseries, Inc., Ontario, California. (Gold Mine nectarine x Rio Oso Gem peach) x self; selected August, 1943. Fruit: freestone; flesh yellow with red coloring, especially around pit; skin red, thin, sufficiently crisp to be eaten with ease; flavor rich, distinctive; ripens in same season as Gold Mine (last week in July); most nearly resembles Lippiatt nectarine; suitable primarily for home planting or local markets. Tree: resistant to delayed foliation, being similar to Redwing peach; flowers large, pink, very showy, making it desirable for ornamental purposes.

Sequoia.--Originated in Porterville, California, by F. D. Williams. Introduced commercially in 1942. Patent no. 496; December 23, 1941. Bud mutation of Hutchison peach; discovered in 1937. Fruit: flesh white, but red at the pit; freestone; large; skin smooth with deep red color; ripens late. Tree: bears well.

Stark Early Flame.--Originated in Sheffield, Alabama, by R. H. King. Introduced commercially in 1946. Patent no. 759; September 2, 1947; assigned to Stark Brothers Nurseries and Orchards Company, Louisiana, Missouri. Open pollinated seedling of Flaming Gold; discovered in 1942. Fruit: flesh yellow; semifreestone; skin attractive red and deep yellow; ripens 14 days before Flaming Gold, around August 1; quality high; most nearly resembles known parent.

Sunbrite.--Originated in Merced, California, by F. W. Anderson. Introduced commercially in 1950. Patent no. 974; August 22, 1950; assigned to Reedley Nursery, Reedley, California. F_2 of (Kim x July Elberta); selected in 1947. Fruit: flesh yellow, firm; freestone; large, about 2½ inches in diameter; ripens between John Rivers and Gower, about July 5.

Tioga.--Originated in Palo Alto, California, by the United States Department of Agriculture (W. F. Wight). Introduced commercially in 1941. (Salwey x Quetta) x Lippiatt. Fruit: flesh yellow; firm until fully mature; freestone; late; quality good; good for frozen pack.

Violet.--Supposedly originated in Hughson, California, by George Edward Alexander. Introduced commercially in 1937. Patent no. 328; April 25, 1939; assigned to Karl K. Snyder, Hughson, California, and A. D. Di Grazia, San Francisco, California. Parentage unknown; discovered in 1929. Fruit: flesh white; freestone; skin color mottled purple, thick, tough, sour, tenacious to flesh, slight tendency to crack; moderately

large. Probably identical with P. I. 65979 which was introduced from Italy by the United States Department of Agriculture.

ORANGE

Armstrong Seedless Valencia.--Originated in Anaheim, California, by Pearl C. Mohn. Introduced commercially in December,
1939. Patent no. 124; March 5, 1935. Bud mutation of Valencia;
discovered about 1928. Fruit: seedless; quality equal to or
slightly better than Valencia.

Cornell (name subject to change).--Originated in Winter Haven,
Florida, by Harold E. Cornell. Not introduced commercially.
Patent no. 657; April 17, 1945; assigned to Mrs. Thelma H.
Cornell. Bud mutation of Parson Brown; discovered in 1938.
Fruit: matures earlier than any other orange in Florida; tree:
new growth has a tendency to be thorny.

Diller.--Originated in Phoenix, Arizona, by Daniel Diller. Introduced commercially in 1920. Claimed to have originated as a
seedling from a shipment of trees purchased in Florida and
fruited in Arizona; selected in 1910. Fruit: claimed to have
only a few seeds. Tree: fairly frost resistant. The variety
resembles Parson Brown.

Dream Navel.--Originated in Seminole County, Florida, by Donald J. Nicholson. Introduced commercially in 1944. Patent no.
625; April 25, 1944. Parentage unknown; selected in 1939.
Fruit: seedless; fine flavor; matures in early October at Orlando, Florida; fine appearance; juice content high. Tree:
heavy bearer.

Lemor.--Originated in Chula Vista, California, by James M.
Ater. Introduced commercially about 1935. Patent no. 142;
October 1, 1935; assigned to originator. Probably an open
pollinated seedling of Valencia; discovered in 1930. Fruit:
shape similar to Lisbon lemon; rind and flesh orange in color,
similar to Valencia; flavor tart, somewhat intermediate between orange and lemon.

Paradise Navel.--Originated in Lake County, Florida, by Donald
J. Nicholson. Introduced commercially in 1944. Patent no. 548;
October 13, 1942. Parentage unknown; discovered in 1934 or
1935. Fruit: seedless; skin very smooth; color attractive.
Tree: heavy bearer; vigorous.

Robertson Navel.--Originated in Redlands, California, by Roy
Robertson. Introduced commercially in 1936. Patent no. 126;
May 28, 1935; assigned to Armstrong Nurseries, Ontario, Cali-

fornia. Bud mutation of Washington Navel; discovered in 1925. Fruit: in some areas ripens from 2 to 4 weeks earlier than Washington. Tree: precocious in bearing habit, but somewhat lacking in vigor on sweet and sour orange rootstocks.

Seedless Pineapple.--Originated in Shiloh, Florida, by Robert S. Ragin. Introduced commercially in 1941. Patent no. 477; June 24, 1941; assigned to Clapp and Clapp, Orlando, Florida. Bud mutation of Pineapple. Fruit: has fewer seeds; in other respects it is identical with its parent.

Summernavel *(Workman Navel)*.--Originated in Riverside, California, by J. A. Workman. Introduced commercially in 1942. Patent no. 347; November 21, 1939. Bud mutation of Washington; discovered about 1934. Fruit: ripens later than parent variety.

Trovita.--Originated in Riverside, California, by the California Citrus Experiment Station (H. B. Frost). Introduced commercially in 1935. Perhaps open pollinated seedling of Washington; selected in 1928. Fruit: matures very early; more juicy than Washington. Tree: very productive. Most nearly resembles Washington.

Workman Navel.--See **Summernavel**.

Zellwood Satin.--Originated in Zellwood, Orange County, Florida, by K. C. Moore. Introduced commercially in 1945. Parentage unknown. Fruit: skin smooth, satiny, glossy; size small; semi-seedless; very juicy; rich flavor. Tree: vigorous, dense, prolific; most nearly resembles Hamlin.

ORANGEQUAT

Nippon.--Originated in Washington, D. C., by the United States Department of Agriculture (Eugene May). Introduced commercially in 1932. Unshiu Satsuma orange *(Citrus reticulata)* x Meiwa kumquat *(Fortunella japonica x F. margarita)*. Fruit: excellent for marmalade; ripens October to February; rind sweet, edible, very attractive. Tree: vigorous, hardy, productive.

PAPAYA

Betty.--Originated in Miami, Florida, by Bronson Bayliss. Introduced commercially about 1934. Parentage unknown; selected about 1933. Fruit: excellent dessert quality; weight 2 to 3 pounds. Tree: semi-dwarf.

PEACH

Afterglow.--Originated in New Brunswick, New Jersey, by the New Jersey Agricultural Experiment Station (M. A. Blake). Introduced commercially in 1938. J. H. Hale x New Jersey 27116; cross made in 1923. Fruit: flesh yellow; freestone; follows Elberta in ripening time.

Alamar.--Originated in Winters, California, by A. L. Martin. Introduced commercially in 1949. Patent no. 930; April 4, 1950; assigned to originator. Parentage unknown; discovered in 1940. Fruit: flesh yellow; freestone; skin yellow with a very high blush; pit small; ships well; ripens 5 to 6 days after J. H. Hale. Tree: pollen sterile.

Albru.--Originated in Port Clinton, Ohio, by Lawrence Satterfield. Introduced commercially in 1948. Patent no. 813; December 7, 1948; assigned to French Nursery Co., Clyde, Ohio. Bud mutation of J. H. Hale; discovered in 1932. Fruit: large; flesh yellow; freestone; skin highly colored; equal halves that hold their shape well when canned; free from undeveloped fruit or "buttons" characteristic of J. H. Hale. Tree: stronger growth habit than J. H. Hale.

All-Red-Free.--See **Erly-Red-Fre.**

Amador.--Originated in Palo Alto, California, by the United States Department of Agriculture (W. F. Wight). Introduced commercially in 1942. Elberta x Ontario. Fruit: flesh yellow; freestone; ripens early midseason; appearance attractive; quality excellent. Tree: somewhat resistant to delayed foliation.

Ambergem.--Originated in New Brunswick, New Jersey, by the New Jersey Agricultural Experiment Station (M. A. Blake). Introduced commercially in 1934. Belle x self; seed gathered in 1914. Fruit: best yellow-fleshed, non-melting clingstone for canning in the East.

Andora.--Originated in Palo Alto, California, by the United States Department of Agriculture (W. F. Wight). Introduced commercially in 1941. Libbee x Lovell. Fruit: flesh yellow; quality good; ripens in early midseason with Peak; commercial canning clingstone.

Anza.--Originated in Riverside, California, by the California Citrus Experiment Station (J. W. Lesley). Introduced commercially in 1948. Rosy x Golden State; selected in 1941. Fruit: flesh yellow; freestone; firm; quality good; midseason. Tree: chilling requirement less than J. H. Hale; may be adapted to regions of mild winters such as the higher mesas of southern California.

Autumn *(New Jersey 145)*.--Originated in New Brunswick, New
Jersey, by the New Jersey Agricultural Experiment Station (M.
A. Blake). Introduced commercially in 1947. (J. H. Hale x
Eclipse) x Late Crawford. Fruit: freestone; flesh yellow,
firm; skin half red with greenish undercolor until soft; ripens 10 to 14 days after Elberta; quality very good. Tree:
hardier than Elberta. Flower: non-showy.

Babcock.--Originated in Berkeley, California, by E. B. Babcock
and C. O. Smith. Selected in 1923 at the California Citrus
Experiment Station (H. B. Frost and J. W. Lesley), and introduced commercially by George P. Weldon, Ontario, California in
1933. F_2 of (Strawberry x Peento); selected in 1923. Fruit:
freestone; flesh white; high blush; rather small. Tree: requires little winter chilling.

Babdon.--Originated in Ontario, California, by Chaffey College
(George P. Weldon). Introduced commercially October 1, 1948.
Babcock x Weldon; selected in 1945. Fruit: freestone; flesh
white, red at pit; skin color similar to Babcock; fairly firm;
quality fair; adheres well to tree.

Bates.--Originated in Delhi, California, by W. H. Bates. Introduced commercially in 1939. Patent no. 604; October 5, 1943.
Parentage unknown; selected in 1935. Fruit: flesh yellow; ripens in Phillips Cling season; commercial canning clingstone.

Bonita.--Originated in Riverside, California, by the California Citrus Experiment Station (J. W. Lesley). Introduced commercially in 1943. Rosy x Golden State; selected in 1940.
Fruit: flesh yellow; freestone. Tree: requires very little
winter chilling.

Brandywine.--Originated in Tulsa, Oklahoma, by Carl Burton
Fox. Introduced commercially in 1943. Patent no. 580; May 4,
1943. Seedling of J. H. Hale; pollen parent unknown; selected
in 1930. Fruit: large; seed small; flesh yellow with shaded
red coloring, firm, develops characteristic flavor when canned.

Brentwood Beauty.--See **July Elberta.**

Burbank's Elberta.--See **July Elberta.**

Burbank's Orchid.--Originated in Santa Rosa, California, by
Luther Burbank. Introduced commercially in 1939. Patent no.
290; September 6, 1938; assigned to Stark Brothers Nurseries
and Orchards Company, Louisiana, Missouri. Parentage unknown.
Most valuable characteristic is the large, double, pink flowers. Fruit: edible; small; flesh white; freestone; resembles
Stark Summer Heath.

Burbank's Santa Rosa.--Originated in Santa Rosa, California, by Luther Burbank. Introduced commercially in 1939. Patent no. 291; September 6, 1937; assigned to Stark Brothers Nurseries and Orchards Company, Louisiana, Missouri. Parentage unknown. Most valuable characteristic is the large, double, crimson flowers. Fruit: edible; small; flesh white; freestone.

Burton.--Originated in Chowchilla, California, by Burton P. Jackson. Introduced commercially in 1950. Assigned to R. C. Randolph, Chico, California. Parentage unknown; discovered in 1943. Fruit: flesh yellow; freestone; ripens very late, October 20 to November 15; flavor good. Tree: bears well.

Buttercup.--Originated in New Brunswick, New Jersey, by the New Jersey Agricultural Experiment Station (M. A. Blake). Introduced commercially in 1925. Lola x Arp; cross made in 1916. Fruit: flesh yellow; semiclingstone; small; very early; some value for local markets in the more northern districts.

C. O. Smith.--Originated in Whittier, California, by the California Agricultural Experiment Station (E. B. Babcock and C. O. Smith). Introduced commercially in 1933. F_2 of (Strawberry x Peento); selected in 1930. Fruit: similar to Lukens Honey, but much larger; too soft for a commercial variety; recommended highly for home use in southern California. Tree: resistant to delayed foliation; vigorous; heavy producer.

Candoka.--Originated in Okanogan, Washington, by William J. Ramsey. Introduced commercially in 1932. Patent no. 51; December 20, 1932; assigned to Columbia & Okanogan Nursery Company, Wenatchee, Washington; trademarked. Parentage unknown. Fruit: large size; beautiful deep red color on yellow undercolor; very firm; excellent quality; almost completely fuzzless; most nearly resembles J. H. Hale. Tree: self-unfruitful.

Carolyn.--Originated in Palo Alto, California, by the United States Department of Agriculture (W. F. Wight). Introduced commercially in 1942. Libbee x Lovell. Fruit: flesh yellow; quality good; commercial canning clingstone; ripens between seasons of Gaume and Sims. Tree: produces heavily.

Chadon.--Originated in Ontario, California, by Chaffey College (George P. Weldon). Introduced commercially October 1, 1948. Chaffey x Weldon; selected in 1945. Fruit: freestone; flesh white; large; skin greenish yellow with a blush; firm; quality good, similar to Chaffey; ripens mid-August to September in southern California. Tree: resistant to delayed foliation.

Chaffey.--Originated in Ontario, California, by Chaffey College (George P. Weldon). Introduced commercially in 1939. Lukens Honey x Elberta. Fruit: flesh white, firm, semisweet;

freestone; quality excellent. Tree: fairly resistant to delayed foliation; dependable producer; vigorous.

Cherryred *(New Jersey 129).*--Originated in New Brunswick, New
Jersey, by the New Jersey Agricultural Experiment Station (M.
A. Blake). Introduced commercially in 1947. Open pollinated
seedling of (J. H. Hale x Goldfinch). Fruit: clingstone; flesh
yellow, non-melting, deeply stained with red; skin deeply
blushed; cooks well and makes an attractive red pie. Ripens 5
days or more before Red Bird. Tree: hardy. Flower: non-showy.

Christensen Early Elberta.--Originated in Brigham City, Utah,
by C. W. Christensen. Introduced commercially in 1929. Open
pollinated seedling of Elberta; selected about 1920. Fruit:
ripens 2 to 3 weeks earlier than known parent; high skin color;
flesh red at center; ships well. Tree: buds only moderately
hardy.

Colora.--Originated in Colora, Maryland, by Lloyd Balderson,
III. Introduced commercially in 1936. Bud mutation of Brackett;
selected in 1933. Fruit: flesh yellow; skin yellow with blush;
high quality; freestone; extreme bud hardiness, producing
crop after 17° F below zero. Most nearly resembles Vedette.

Constitution *(New Jersey 161).*--Originated in New Brunswick,
New Jersey, by the New Jersey Agricultural Experiment Station
(M. A. Blake). Introduced commercially in 1947. (J. H. Hale x
Eclipse) x Late Crawford. Fruit: freestone; flesh yellow; ripens 7 to 10 days after Elberta; good outside color; good quality late in season. Tree: hardier than Elberta. Flower: non-
showy.

Corona.--Originated in Palo Alto, California, by the United
States Department of Agriculture (W. F. Wight). Introduced
commercially in 1942. Libbee x Lovell. Fruit: flesh yellow;
large; commercial canning clingstone; late (after Phillips
Cling by 3 to 4 days); quality good. Tree: heavy producer.

Coronado *(USDA W38-39B).*--Originated in Palo Alto, California,
by the United States Department of Agriculture (W. F. Wight)
and the California Agricultural Experiment Station. Commercially introduced in May, 1950. (Pratt-Low x Tuscan) x Leader
Seedling Cling; selected about 1936. Fruit: good size, almost
round; yellow ground color; clingstone; flesh yellow, firm,
fine textured, some red at pit; flavor good; matures about 10
days before Fortuna, the earliest commercial canning variety.
Tree: vigorous and productive.

Cortez.--Originated in Palo Alto, California, by the United
States Department of Agriculture (W. F. Wight). Introduced
commercially in 1944. Paloro x Halford 1. Fruit: flesh yellow;

clingstone; ripens in the early part of the canning clingstone season.

Cumberland.--Originated in New Brunswick, New Jersey, by the New Jersey Agricultural Experiment Station (M. A. Blake). Introduced commercially in 1925. Belle x Greensboro; cross made in 1914. Fruit: flesh white; almost a freestone; ripens at the same season as Golden Jubilee; most dependable white-fleshed peach for the cooler districts.

Curlew.--Originated in Long Beach, California, by John D. Davis. Introduced commercially in 1945. Patent no. 651; February 27, 1945; assigned to Armstrong Nurseries, Inc., Ontario, California. Open pollinated seedling, probably of Salwey; selected in 1935. Fruit: ripens late, September 20 to October 10 at Ontario, California. Tree: requires less chilling than other late-ripening varieties.

Davidson *(Redleaf, Tennessee Redleaf).*--Found growing on a roadside in southwest Davidson County, Tennessee, by Joseph C. McDaniel. Introduced commercially in 1946 by Peach Ridge Farm, Clemson, South Carolina. Parentage unknown; discovered and first propagated in 1938. Fruit: flesh yellow; freestone; poor edible quality; pits give high germination without special treatment, many double kernels; for use as a rootstock variety. Most of the seedlings are red-leafed, vigorous, and well adapted to June or dormant budding.

Deberard.--Originated in Ontario, California, by the A. M. Deberard Orchard. Introduced commercially October 1, 1948. Bud mutation of Sims; discovered about 1940. Fruit: clingstone; flesh yellow. Tree: as early leafing as Babcock; otherwise it is strikingly similar in every respect to Sims; well adapted to southern California conditions.

Delicious.--Originated in New Brunswick, New Jersey, by the New Jersey Agricultural Experiment Station (M. A. Blake). Introduced commercially in 1925. Belle x Greensboro; cross made in 1914. Fruit: flesh white; freestone; ripens just after Cumberland.

Dillon.--Originated in Norco, California, by Glen O. Dillon. Introduced commercially in 1943. Patent no. 572; March 9, 1943. A seedling tree of unknown parentage. Fruit: freestone; flesh yellow, red at pit, firm; skin greenish-yellow; ripens in late November at place of origin.

Dixigem.--Originated in Fort Valley, Georgia, by the United States Department of Agriculture (J. H. Weinberger). Introduced commercially in 1944. (Admiral Dewey x St. John) x South Haven; seedling planted in 1937. Fruit: early; nearly freestone; good texture and quality.

Dixigold.--Originated in Fort Valley, Georgia, by the United States Department of Agriculture (L. M. Hutchins). Introduced commercially in 1939. Open pollinated seedling of Hiley; probably selected in 1931. Fruit: flesh yellow; freestone; resistant to bacterial spot; most nearly resembles Hiley.

Dixired.--Originated in Fort Valley, Georgia, by the United States Department of Agriculture (J. H. Weinberger). Introduced commercially in May, 1945. Halehaven x self; selected in 1939. Fruit: flesh yellow, firm; clingstone; matures early; appearance attractive.

Donwel.--Originated in Ontario, California, by Chaffey College (George P. Weldon). Introduced commercially October 1, 1948. Babcock x (Elberta x (Elberta x Peento)); selected in 1945. Fruit: freestone; flesh yellow; skin yellow with a blush; quality excellent; ripens with Weldon. Tree: early foliation; bloom showy; recommended for home and semicommercial plantings.

Early Babcock.--Originated in Ontario, California, by Chaffey College (George P. Weldon). Introduced commercially October 1, 1948. Babcock x Nectar; selected in 1945. Fruit: semifreestone; flesh white; larger than Babcock which it most nearly resembles; skin color deep red; quality good; ripens 10 days before Babcock. Tree: subject to some delayed foliation.

Early East *(New Jersey 134)*.--Originated in New Brunswick, New Jersey, by the New Jersey Agricultural Experiment Station (M. A. Blake). Introduced commercially in 1946. Open pollinated seedling of J. H. Hale x (Slappey x Admiral Dewey). Fruit: freestone when tree-ripe; flesh yellow, firm; skin attractive red; ripens 10 days before Golden Jubilee. Tree: hardier than Elberta. Flower: non-showy.

Early Elberta.--See **July Elberta.**

Early Halehaven.-- Originated in Benton Harbor, Michigan, by John Nametz. Introduced commercially in 1939. Patent no. 325; April 4, 1939; assigned to Greening Nursery Company, Monroe, Michigan. Bud mutation of Halehaven; discovered in 1935. Fruit: ripens 7 to 10 days before Halehaven; in other characteristics similar to parent.

Early Hiley.--Originated in Fort Valley, Georgia, by A. J. Evans. Introduced commercially in 1931. Probably an open pollinated seedling of Hiley; selected about 1921. Fruit: matures early. Most nearly resembles Hiley.

Early Rochester.--Originated in Yakima, Washington, by V. C.

Campbell. Introduced commercially in 1940. Patent no. 351; December 26, 1939; assigned to Walter Dibble Plough, Wenatchee, Washington. Open pollinated seedling of Rochester; selected about 1932. Fruit: clingstone; ripens 18 to 21 days earlier than Rochester; in other characteristics similar to Rochester.

Early White Giant.--Originated in Arkadelphia, Arkansas, by Frank Geheb. Introduced commercially in April, 1949. Patent no. 878; November 11, 1949; assigned to Stark Brothers Nurseries and Orchards Company, Louisiana, Missouri. Parentage unknown; discovered in 1937. Fruit: flesh white; semifreestone; large; good quality; ripening very early, a week before Early Red Bird. Tree: responds to early and heavy thinning, being similar to Redhaven in thinning requirements.

Eclipse.--Originated in New Brunswick, New Jersey, by the New Jersey Agricultural Experiment Station (M. A. Blake). Introduced commercially in 1925. Belle x self; seed gathered in 1914. Fruit: flesh yellow; freestone. Tree: hardier than Elberta. Formerly planted to replace Hiley in New Jersey.

Elberta Queen.--Originated in Louisiana, Missouri, by Gus Jordan. Introduced commercially in 1925. Bud mutation of Elberta; discovered in 1902. Fruit: flesh yellow; freestone; an Elberta selection that has fruit of a rounder shape and is somewhat larger than the parent.

Elliott Special.--Originated in Modesto, California, by William C. Elliott. Introduced commercially about 1940. Patent no. 166; February 18, 1936; unassigned. Open pollinated seedling of Lovell. Fruit: flesh yellow; freestone; matures late.

Ellis.--Originated in Palo Alto, California, by the United States Department of Agriculture (W. F. Wight). Introduced commercially in 1935. Phillips Cling x Linden. Fruit: flesh yellow; clingstone; ripens in late midseason; commercial canning clingstone.

Envoy *(New Jersey 102)*.--Originated in New Brunswick, New Jersey, by the New Jersey Agricultural Experiment Station (M. A. Blake). Introduced commercially in 1949 jointly by the New Jersey Agricultural Experiment Station, New Brunswick, and the Horticultural Experiment Station, Vineland, Ontario, Canada. J. H. Hale x Sunbeam. Fruit: freestone; flesh yellow, tender; quality very good; attractive; ripens 4 weeks before Elberta or right after Golden Jubilee. Tree: hardier than Elberta. Flower: showy.

Erly-Red-Fre *(All-Red-Free)*.--Originated in Chase City, Virginia, by W. M. Perry. Introduced commercially in 1938. Patent no. 320; March 28, 1939; assigned to Bountiful Ridge Nurseries, Princess Anne, Maryland. Parentage unknown; discovered in 1936. Fruit: color all red; freestone; larger than Red Bird; ripens in Red Bird season; skin thick; seed small.

Erlyvee *(Ontario 350113)*.--Originated in Vineland, Ontario, Canada, by the Ontario Horticultural Experiment Station. Introduced commercially in 1949. Open pollinated seedling of Golden Jubilee; selected in 1941. Fruit: yellow; semifreestone; high color; size medium; quality fair; matures early, 4 to 5 days after Mayflower.

Evalyn Gem.--Originated in Yuba City, California, by Perry M. Reedy. Introduced commercially in 1951. Patent no. 971; August 8, 1950. Bud mutation of Rio Oso Gem; selected in March, 1945. Fruit: more symmetrical shape than Rio Oso Gem, with a smoother suture; holds color and flavor in freezing process; ripens ahead of Rio Oso Gem, which it most nearly resembles. Tree: larger, more erect and more symmetrical than Rio Oso Gem.

Fairberta.--Originated in Tyler, Texas, by Robert W. Fair. Not introduced commercially. Patent no. 283; August 23, 1938; unassigned. Chance seedling. Fruit: size medium; somewhat pointed at the stylar end; yellow; freestone; skin highly blushed; ripens 7 to 10 days before Elberta; quality excellent.

Fairhaven.--Originated in South Haven, Michigan, by the Michigan Agricultural Experiment Station (Stanley Johnston). Introduced commercially in 1946. J. H. Hale x South Haven; selected in 1935. Fruit: flesh yellow, resists browning; freestone; medium-large; bright yellow ground color with bright red cheek; matures 3 weeks before Elberta; ships well; good for freezing and canning. Tree: productive.

Fallate *(New Jersey 183)*.--Originated in New Brunswick, New Jersey, by the New Jersey Agricultural Experiment Station (M. A. Blake). Introduced commercially in 1947. (J. H. Hale x Eclipse) x Berks. Fruit: freestone; flesh white, firm; ripens week to 10 days after Elberta. Tree: hardier than Elberta. Flower: non-showy.

Farida.--Originated in Palo Alto, California, by the United States Department of Agriculture (W. F. Wight). Introduced commercially in 1938. Leader seedling 26-13 (clingstone) x (Paloro x Tuscan). Fruit: ripens early (Tuscan season); clingstone; recommended especially as an early shipping clingstone, but may be canned.

Fertile Hale.--Originated in Lawrence, Michigan, by L. B. Le Duke. Introduced commercially in 1935. Patent no. 175; April 28, 1936; assigned to Greening Nursery Company, Monroe, Michigan. Bud mutation of J. H. Hale; discovered in 1927. Fruit:

size of J. H. Hale. Flowers: self-fertile. Tree: vigorous; more hardy than parent or Elberta.

Fireglow.--Originated in New Brunswick, New Jersey, by the New Jersey Agricultural Experiment Station (M. A. Blake). Introduced commercially in 1939. J. H. Hale x Marigold; cross made in 1923. Fruit: flesh yellow; freestone; outstanding size, attractiveness, and quality. Tree: very sensitive to environment, hence not widely adapted.

Flamingo.--Originated in Ontario, California, by Walter E. Lammerts. Introduced commercially in January, 1948. Patent no. 661; November 20, 1945; assigned to Armstrong Nurseries, Inc., Ontario, California. Open pollinated seedling of Rio Oso Gem; selected in 1940. Fruit: more uniform and more smoothly shaped than Rio Oso Gem which it most nearly resembles; ripens five to ten days earlier than Rio Oso Gem and in same season as J. H. Hale. Tree: lower chilling requirement than Rio Oso Gem, being similar to that of Socala, making this new variety better suited to southern California and other mild winter areas; begins to leaf and flower earlier than Rio Oso Gem.

Floretta.--Originated in Le Grand, California, by F. W. Anderson. Introduced commercially in 1926. Quetta nectarine x Florence peach; selected in 1925. Fruit: flesh white; clingstone; quality good; ripens following Florence which it most nearly resembles.

Fontana.--Originated in Ontario, California, by Chaffey College (George P. Weldon). Introduced commercially in 1939. Sims x (Feicheng x Bolivian Cling). Fruit: clingstone; pit small; excellent canner; hangs well on tree; deep yellow flesh even when skin still appears green. Tree: more resistant to delayed foliation than Sims; good producer. Most nearly resembles Sims.

Fortuna.--Originated in Palo Alto, California, by the United States Department of Agriculture (W. F. Wight). Introduced commercially in 1941. Leader seedling (clingstone) x (Tuscan x Paloro). Fruit: flesh yellow; clingstone; quality good; ripens early (Tuscan season or earlier); commercial canning clingstone. Tree: heavy producer.

Fowler.--Originated in Marlboro, New York, by George R. Fowler. Introduced commercially in 1943. Patent no. 567; February 23, 1943. Parentage unknown. Fruit: large; skin yellow, tough, fuzzless; freestone; firm; of the Elberta type. Tree: hardy and vigorous.

Frankie.--Originated in Marble Falls, Texas, by Kirk Schroeter. Introduced commercially in 1938. Thought to be a mutation of Frank; discovered in 1936. Fruit: flesh yellow; freestone; slightly red around the pit. Tree: prolific bearer; adapted to mild winter climate. Closely resembles Frank.

Freeland.--Originated in Clarinda, Iowa, by E. W. Freeland. Still under test (1950) but some acreage has been planted. Patent no. 623; April 11, 1944; assigned to Stark Brothers Nurseries and Orchards Company, Louisiana, Missouri. Parentage unknown; discovered in 1932. Fruit: flesh yellow; freestone; ripens in Elberta season; an Elberta type. Tree: hardy in some areas.

Frostqueen *(New Jersey 159 and New Jersey 185)*.--Originated in New Brunswick, New Jersey, by the New Jersey Agricultural Experiment Station (M. A. Blake). Introduced commercially in 1947. (J. H. Hale x Eclipse) x Berks. Fruit: freestone; flesh white, firm; ripens up to 3 weeks after Elberta. Tree: hardier than Elberta. Flower: non-showy.

Giant Elberta.--Originated in Paonia, Colorado, by Gilbert Hice. Introduced commercially in 1947; assigned to Carlton Nurseries, Forest Grove, Oregon. Parentage unknown; discovered in 1946. Fruit: ripens 7 days before Early Elberta; most nearly resembles July Elberta.

Giant Snowball.--Originated in Star City, Indiana, by F. A. Ogle. Introduced commercially in 1930. Parentage unknown. Fruit: flesh white; freestone; pit small; size of J. H. Hale; matures in mid-season.

Glamar.--Originated in Osoyoos, British Columbia, Canada, by J. S. Leekie. Introduced commercially in 1942. Patent no. 592; June 15, 1943. Bud mutation of Rochester; selected in 1939. Fruit: ripens 3 weeks earlier than parent; in most other characteristics same as Rochester.

Gloribloom.--Originated in Ontario, California, by Chaffey College (George P. Weldon). Introduced commercially October 1, 1948. Babcock x (Elberta x (Elberta x Peento)); selected in 1945. Fruit: freestone; flesh light yellow; skin light yellow, blushed; ripens with Weldon; quality fair. Flower: showy. Recommended for home planting because of striking large pink flowers.

Gold Dust *(Stribling S-47-4)*.--Originated in Merced, California, by T. B. Stribling, Jr. Introduced commercially in 1950. Patent applied for by T. B. Stribling, Jr., Stribling's Nurseries, Merced, California. Open pollinated seedling of Kim Elberta; selected in 1947. Fruit: skin red-blushed; freestone; flesh firm, yellow; ripens 40 days ahead of Elberta; good for shipping.

Golden Blush.--Originated in Lakeside, California, by B. H. Haley. Introduced commercially in 1938. Patent no. 473; June 3, 1941; assigned to Armstrong Nurseries, Inc., Ontario, California. Parentage unknown; selected in 1925. Fruit: flesh yellow; freestone; high flavor; ripens in same season as Elberta, which it resembles. Tree: more resistant to delayed foliation in southern California than Elberta.

Golden Early Bird.--Originated in Downers Grove, Illinois, by R. H. Christofferson. Introduced commercially in April, 1949. Patent no. 970; August 1, 1950; assigned to Stark Brothers Nurseries and Orchards Company, Louisiana, Missouri. Open pollinated seedling of Crawford; discovered in 1937. Fruit: flesh yellow; semifreestone; good quality; ripening very early, 6 days before Mikado.

Goldeneast *(New Jersey 87)*.--Originated in New Brunswick, New Jersey, by the New Jersey Agricultural Experiment Station (M. A. Blake). Introduced commercially in 1937. Elberta x New Jersey 38 E. G.; cross made in 1923. Fruit: flesh yellow; freestone; ripens in midsummer; the most popular yellow-fleshed peach in southern New Jersey; has largely replaced Eclipse.

Golden Elberta Cling.--Originated in Fort Smith, Arkansas, by Will R. Gaunaway. Introduced commercially in 1925. Trademarked in 1925 by Stark Brothers Nurseries and Orchards Company, Louisiana, Missouri. Parentage unknown; discovered in 1911. Fruit: flesh yellow; clingstone; ripens 5 days before Elberta; most nearly resembles July Elberta.

Golden Globe.--Originated in New Brunswick, New Jersey, by the New Jersey Agricultural Experiment Station (M. A. Blake). Introduced commercially in 1937. J. H. Hale x Marigold; cross made in 1923. Fruit: flesh yellow; freestone; firm; very large. Tree: only medium in hardiness.

Golden Jubilee.--Originated in New Brunswick, New Jersey, by the New Jersey Agricultural Experiment Station (M. A. Blake). Introduced commercially in 1926. Elberta x Greensboro; cross made in 1914. Fruit: flesh yellow; freestone; best of this class in many localities.

Golden State.--Originated in Riverside, California, by the California Citrus Experiment Station (J. W. Lesley). Introduced commercially in 1942. Paragon x F_2 seedling (Elberta x Peento); selected in 1933. Fruit: freestone; yellow; firm. Tree: requires little winter chilling.

Goldfinch.--Originated in New Brunswick, New Jersey, by the New Jersey Agricultural Experiment Station (M. A. Blake). Introduced commercially in 1925. Slappey x Admiral Dewey; cross made in 1916. Fruit: flesh yellow; freestone, sometimes adhering a little; quality high; ripens with Golden Jubilee. Useful in breeding.

Goldray.--Originated in Lexington, South Carolina, by J. Roy Cunningham. Introduced commercially in fall of 1950. Bud mutation of Golden Jubilee; selected in 1939. Fruit: identical in color, size, and quality with Golden Jubilee; only semifreestone; ripens 10 to 14 days earlier than Golden Jubilee. Tree: thrifty.

Gomes.--Originated in Modesto, California, by Felix Gomes. Introduced commercially in 1936. Parentage unknown; selected in 1935. Fruit: flesh yellow; ripens in late Phillips Cling season; commercial canning clingstone. Most nearly resembles Stuart.

Goodcheer *(New Jersey 152)*.--Originated in New Brunswick, New Jersey, by the New Jersey Agricultural Experiment Station (M. A. Blake). Introduced commercially in 1947. (J. H. Hale x Eclipse) x Laterose. Fruit: freestone; flesh yellow; quality good; ripens about 1 week after Elberta, prolonging the Elberta season; good for canning and freezing. Tree: hardier than Elberta. Flower: non-showy.

Halate.--Originated in the test orchard of Stark Brothers Nurseries and Orchards Company, Louisiana, Missouri. Introduced commercially in 1937. Parentage unknown; discovered in 1924. Fruit: flesh yellow; freestone; ripens 2 weeks after Elberta; most nearly resembles J. H. Hale.

Hal-Berta Giant.--Originated near Xenia, Clay County, Illinois, by J. E. Markham. Introduced commercially in 1932. Patent no. 7; February 16, 1932; assigned to Stark Brothers Nurseries and Orchards Company, Louisiana, Missouri. Parentage unknown; discovered in 1928. Fruit: flesh yellow; freestone; very large; skin smooth; matures in J. H. Hale season. Tree: hardy; bears well.

Hale Harrison Brilliant.--Originated in Crozet, Albermarle County, Virginia, by Oscar F. Jones. Introduced commercially in November, 1949. Patent no. 814; December 14, 1948; assigned to Harrison Brothers Nurseries, Berlin, Maryland. Parentage unknown; discovered in 1936. Fruit: flesh yellow; freestone; large, 3 inches in diameter; skin yellow with blush; flavor pleasing and better than Elberta; ripens during Elberta season; thought to be firm and to ship well.

Halehaven.--Originated in South Haven, Michigan, by the Michigan (South Haven) Agricultural Experiment Station. Introduced commercially in 1932. J. H. Hale x South Haven; cross made in

1924. Fruit: color high; flesh firm enough for commercial handling; freestone; quality excellent; use fresh or canned; most nearly resembles South Haven, but firmer and with better color.

Halford 1 *(McKnight)*.--Originated in Modesto, California, by John Halford. Introduced commercially in 1921. Parentage unknown. Fruit: ripens 3 or 4 days before Halford 2; a commercial canning clingstone; flesh yellow. Tree: foliage with reniform glands.

Halford 2.--Originated in Modesto, California, by John Halford. Introduced commercially in 1921. Parentage unknown; discovered in 1919. Fruit: commercial canning clingstone; flesh yellow; heavy crops with excellent canning quality.

Halo.--Originated in Clarkston, Washington, by H. Lynn Tuttle. Introduced commercially in 1942. Open pollinated seedling of Tuscan (Tuskena); selected about 1936. Fruit: freestone; very high color 1 or 2 weeks before ripening; size good; flavor excellent. Tree: resistant to spring frosts; bears early and heavily.

Hardee.--Originated in Sandusky, Ohio, by D. S. Byers. Introduced commercially in 1936. Patent no. 120; January 15, 1935. Parentage unknown; selected in 1925. Fruit: flesh yellow; freestone; pronounced flavor; most nearly resembles an elongated Elberta. Tree: growth intermediate between J. H. Hale and Elberta; more resistant to cold than Elberta.

Hardy-Berta.--Originated near Mount Vernon, Jefferson County, Illinois, by Marsh Harpole. Introduced commercially in 1934. Patent no. 271; February 15, 1938; assigned to Stark Brothers Nurseries and Orchards Company, Louisiana, Missouri. Parentage unknown; discovered in 1932. Fruit: flesh yellow; freestone; ripens 2 weeks after Elberta, which it most nearly resembles.

Herb Hale.--Originated in Yakima, Washington, by Herbert Donahey. Introduced commercially in 1944. Patent no. 588; June 8, 1943; assigned to Columbia & Okanogan Nursery Co., Wenatchee, Washington. Parentage unknown. Fruit: freestone; flesh yellow; tart flavor; high quality. Tree: rapid and hardy grower; 3 or 4 weeks earlier than J. H. Hale.

Hermosa.--Originated in Riverside, California, by the California Citrus Experiment Station (J. W. Lesley). Introduced commercially in 1942. J. H. Hale x Babcock; selected in 1937. Fruit: appearance attractive; flesh white; freestone. Tree: requires little winter chilling.

Hiraoka Flame.--Originated in Fowler, California, by Ross and

Harry Hiraoka. Introduced commercially in February, 1950. Fay Elberta x J. H. Hale; selected in 1939. Fruit: large as J. H. Hale, which it most nearly resembles; freestone; flesh yellow; firm; good flavor; keeps well in storage; good quality for shipping, freezing or drying. Tree: low growing; self-fertile.

Hoffman. --Originated in Live Oak, California, by Phillip B. Hoffman. Introduced commercially in 1937. Patent no. 593; June 23, 1943. Parentage unknown; selected in 1935. Fruit: commercial canning clingstone; ripens in Phillips Cling season. Leaves: glandless.

Honeyberta. --Originated in Ontario, California, by Chaffey College (George P. Weldon). Introduced commercially October 1, 1948. Lukens Honey x Elberta; selected in 1945. Fruit: freestone; flesh yellow; skin yellow with an attractive blush; fairly firm; ripens in Elberta time; quality good. Tree: early foliation; production good.

Honey Dew Hale. --Originated in New Cumberland, Pennsylvania, by Charles O. Grissinger. Introduced commercially in April, 1949. Patent no. 888; November 1, 1949; assigned to Stark Brothers Nurseries and Orchards Company, Louisiana, Missouri. Bud mutation of J. H. Hale; discovered in 1936. Fruit: skin white with pink blush; flesh white, marbled with yellow, with thin yellow segment from pit through skin, along suture; large size; good shipping qualities; most nearly resembles J. H. Hale.

Honeygem *(New Jersey Low Acid 8).* --Originated in New Brunswick, New Jersey, by the New Jersey Agricultural Experiment Station (M. A. Blake). Introduced commercially in 1947. (J. H. Hale x P. I. 55564) x Estella. Fruit: freestone; flesh yellow, firm, attractive; low in titratable acidity; suitable for the diet of persons troubled with hyperacidity or peptic ulcers; ripens about a week after Elberta. Tree: not as hardy as Elberta. Flower: showy.

Howard Fisher. --Originated in Queenston, Ontario, Canada, by C. Howard Fisher. Introduced commercially in 1936. Patent no. 233; February 9, 1937. Bud mutation of Valiant; discovered in 1934. Fruit: ripens early; large; flavor very fine; butter-yellow with bright red blush; good shipper; will not drop from tree even when fully ripe; semifreestone. Most nearly resembles Valiant.

Hutchison. --Originated in Woodville, California, by Perry Hutchison. Introduced commercially in 1938. Parentage unknown; selected in 1934. Fruit: flesh white; freestone; large; texture smooth; ripens well when picked hard; good for frozen pack. Tree: vigorous.

Illinois K40.--See **Prairie Schooner.**

Illinois K43.--See **Prairie Rambler.**

Illinois K47.--See **Prairie Clipper.**

Illinois K69.--See **Prairie Daybreak.**

Illinois K73.--See **Prairie Dawn.**

Illinois K74.--See **Prairie Sunrise.**

Illinois K80.--See **Prairie Rose.**

Impon.--Originated in Ontario, California, by Chaffey College (George P. Weldon). Introduced commercially October 1, 1948. Imperial x Paragon; selected in 1945. Fruit: freestone; flesh yellow; large as Elberta; skin yellow; quality good, subacid; ripens end of Babcock season; quality superior to Imperial which it most nearly resembles.

Improved Pallas.--See **Melba.**

J. L. Ames.--Originated in Live Oak, California, by John L. Ames. Introduced commercially in 1948; being sold by Fowler Nurseries, Newcastle, California. Bud mutation of July Elberta; discovered in 1943. Fruit: flesh yellow, firm; freestone; ripens 10 days earlier than its parent; large; skin highly colored.

Jerseyland *(New Jersey 135)*.--Originated in New Brunswick, New Jersey, by the New Jersey Agricultural Experiment Station (M. A. Blake). Introduced commercially in 1946. Open pollinated seedling of J. H. Hale x (Slappey x Admiral Dewey). Fruit: freestone; flesh yellow; ripens a few days before Golden Jubilee; ships well; superior to Golden Jubilee. Tree: hardier than Elberta. Flower: non-showy.

Jewell.--See **July Elberta.**

Johnson Early Elberta.--Originated in Brigham City, Utah. Introduced commercially in 1935. Parentage unknown (but probably an open pollinated seedling of Elberta or Early Elberta); selected in 1922. Fruit: ripens with Early Elberta; firmer and better color than Early Elberta. Tree: very hardy; buds only moderately hardy.

Jubilant.--Originated in Danville, Morgan County, Alabama, by Penn-Orr-McDaniel Orchards (William Arthur Penn, Lovic Orr, and Joseph C. McDaniel). Introduced commercially in 1947. Trademark and patent pending. Bud mutation of Golden Jubilee;

discovered and first propagated in 1945. Fruit: flesh yellow; freestone; as firm as Golden Jubilee, which it most nearly resembles; shape slightly rounder, higher color, ripens seven to ten days earlier than Golden Jubilee. Tree: growth vigorous; productive. Useful as a similar variety to precede Golden Jubilee.

July Elberta *(Burbank Elberta, Kim Early Elberta, Brentwood Beauty, Early Elberta, Jewell)*.--Originated in Sebastopol, California, by Luther Burbank. Introduced commercially in 1930. Patent no. 15; April 15, 1932; assigned to Stark Brothers Nurseries and Orchards Company, Louisiana, Missouri. Parentage unknown. Fruit: flesh yellow; freestone; highly colored; pit small; ripens before Elberta.

July Gold.--Originated in Sebastopol, California, by Luther Burbank. Introduced commercially in 1930. Parentage unknown; selected in 1928. Fruit: flesh orange; freestone; no red at pit. Tree: very hardy.

Jun-Berta.--Originated in Dover, Arkansas, by Henry Frank Smith. Introduced commercially in April, 1949. Patent applied for by Stark Brothers Nurseries and Orchards Company, Louisiana, Missouri. Bud mutation of Fair's Beauty; discovered in 1942. Fruit: attractive yellow; semiclingstone; early, ripening two weeks before its parent.

Kalhaven.--Originated in South Haven, Michigan, by the Michigan (South Haven) Agricultural Experiment Station. Introduced commercially in 1936. J. H. Hale x Kalamazoo; cross made in 1924. Fruit: matures 4 to 7 days before Elberta, helping to fill in the season between Halehaven and Elberta; firm; ships well; quality excellent; most nearly resembles J. H. Hale, but smaller in size.

Kim Early Elberta.--See **July Elberta**.

Kirkman Gem *(Late Rio Oso Gem)*.--Originated in Madera, California, by William T. Kirkman. Introduced commercially in 1946. Patent no. 506; March 17, 1942; assigned to Kirkman Corporation, Tracy, California. Bud mutation of Rio Oso Gem; discovered in 1939. Fruit: flesh yellow, with a reddish early ripening suture line; freestone; flesh firmer than Rio Oso Gem; flavor spicy; high color; 4 or 5 weeks later in maturity than Rio Oso Gem.

Klondyke Early Elberta.--Originated in Tremonton, Utah. Introduced commercially in 1930. Parentage unknown; discovered in 1925. Fruit: ripens in Early Elberta season; high color; flesh firm; good shipping quality; dessert quality good. Tree: vigorous; productive; moderately hardy.

Late Kirkman.--Originated in Madera County, California, by William T. Kirkman. Introduced commercially in 1951. Patent no. 920; February 7, 1950; assigned to Kirkman Corporation, Tracy, California. Open pollinated seedling of Kirkman Gem. Fruit: flesh yellow; freestone; yellow suture line ripens evenly with the fruit as distinguished from the reddish early ripening suture line of the Kirkman Gem; most nearly resembles Kirkman Gem, but has a later ripening period, mid-September to mid-October; hangs well on tree. Tree: vigorous grower.

Late Rio Oso Gem.--See **Kirkman Gem.**

Laterose *(New Jersey 109).*--Originated in New Brunswick, New Jersey, by the New Jersey Agricultural Experiment Station (M. A. Blake). Introduced commercially in 1945. J. H. Hale x Delicious. Fruit: freestone; flesh white, firm; large; ripens immediately after Elberta and White Hale; excellent for home canning and freezing. Tree: hardier than Elberta. Flower: nonshowy.

Lawrence.--Originated in Puyallup, Washington, by Alex Lawrence. Introduced commercially in 1941. Parentage unknown. Fruit: semifreestone; resembles Rochester in fruit characteristics and quality, but ripens 2 weeks earlier. Tree: bears early and regularly; hardy to spring frosts.

Leeton.--Originated in Palo Alto, California, by the United States Department of Agriculture (W. F. Wight). Introduced commercially in 1935. Open pollinated seedling of Leader. Fruit: early (Triumph season); flesh yellow; semiclingstone; dessert type.

Loring.--Originated in Mountain Grove, Missouri, by the Missouri State Fruit Experiment Station (Paul H. Shepard). Introduced commercially in 1946. Frank x Halehaven; selected in 1943. Fruit: freestone; flesh yellow; large, firm; ripens 10 days before Elberta; most nearly resembles Golden Jubilee.

Lovell Cling.--See **Wiser.**

Lucas.--Originated in Cucamonga, California, by Vincent G. Lucas. Introduced in 1933. Patent no. 81; November 14, 1933; assigned to the Lucas Ranching Co., Cucamonga, California. Parentage unknown; discovered about 1927 as a sucker outgrowth of the rootstock. Fruit: flesh yellow; freestone; quality good; ripens in October at Ontario, California. Tree: resistant to delayed foliation. Not distributed commercially.

Lyman Late.--Originated in St. Helena, California, by W. W. Lyman. Introduced commercially about 1925. Parentage unknown; discovered in 1920. Fruit: flesh yellow; freestone; large;

ripens 10 to 14 days later than Krummel at St. Helena.

Marigold.--Originated in New Brunswick, New Jersey, by the New Jersey Agricultural Experiment Station (M. A. Blake). Introduced commercially in 1925. Lola x Arp; cross made in 1916. Fruit: flesh yellow; semiclingstone; quality high; ripens about 1 week before Howard Fisher. Tree: hardy.

Massasoit.--Originated in New Brunswick, New Jersey, by the New Jersey Agricultural Experiment Station (M. A. Blake). Introduced commercially in 1925. Slappey x Admiral Dewey; cross made in 1916. Fruit: flesh yellow; freestone; ripens with Triogem, but only medium firm. Tree: hardy; late blooming.

Maxine.--Originated in Palo Alto, California, by the United States Department of Agriculture (W. F. Wight). Introduced commercially in 1935. Michigan Late 1 x Lemon Free. Cross made at Michigan Agricultural Experiment Station; seedling fruited in California. Fruit: flesh lemon-yellow; freestone; early midseason. Tree: very heavy producer.

Maybelle *(New Jersey 164).*--Originated in New Brunswick, New Jersey, by the New Jersey Agricultural Experiment Station (M. A. Blake). Introduced commercially in 1948. Raritan Rose x ((J. H. Hale x Goldfinch), open pollinated). Fruit: medium size; semifreestone; flesh white; attractive; ripens one week before Red Bird. Tree: hardier than Elberta. Flower: non-showy.

Maydon.--Originated in Ontario, California, by Chaffey College (George P. Weldon). Introduced commercially October 1, 1948. Mayflower x Weldon; selected in 1945. Fruit: freestone; flesh white, juicy; very large; skin light green or yellow with a blush; quality good; ripens with Babcock. Tree: bears well; recommended for planting in southern California.

Maywel.--Originated in Ontario, California, by Chaffey College (George P. Weldon). Introduced commercially October 1, 1948. Mayflower x Weldon; selected in 1945. Fruit: freestone; flesh white; skin yellow or greenish with attractive blush; large; shape excellent; ripens about 5 days ahead of Babcock. Tree: very fruitful; early foliation; well adapted to southern California conditions.

McGuigan.--Originated in Cedar Springs, Ontario, Canada, by J. C. McGuigan. Introduced commercially in 1920. Patent no. 624; April 18, 1944; assigned to E. D. Smith & Sons, Limited, Winona, Ontario, Canada. Possibly a hybrid between Elberta and Chili; selected in 1920. Fruit: ripens earlier than Elberta; freestone; flesh yellow; resembles Elberta in size and shape.

McKnight.--See **Halford 1.**

Meadow Lark.--Originated in Ontario, California, by Walter E. Lammerts. Introduced commercially in 1947. Patent no. 528; June 30, 1942: assigned to Armstrong Nurseries, Inc., Ontario, California. (Early Imperial x Coolidge Double Red) x Socala; selected in 1941. Fruit: superficially most nearly resembles Elberta. Tree: sufficiently low chilling requirement to be well suited to growing in southern California, being about one grade better than Babcock in this respect.

Melba *(Improved Pallas).*--Originated in San Antonio, Texas, by a Mr. Yost. Introduced commercially in 1936. Parentage unknown; originated as a chance seedling in the yard of Mr. Yost; later propagated by local nurseries as Improved Pallas; Wolfe Nursery, Stephenville, Texas, obtained buds from F. P. Wittmann, Horticulturist, Missouri Pacific Lines, Dilley, Texas, and renamed it Melba since Improved Pallas was misleading. Fruit: size of Belle of Georgia; pit small; honey flavor; ripens 25 days ahead of Elberta. Tree: adapted to mild winters.

Merrill 49'er.--Originated in Red Bluff, California, by Grant Merrill. Introduced commercially in January, 1950. Open pollinated seedling of J. H. Hale; selected in July, 1943. Fruit: flesh yellow; freestone; 1 week earlier than J. H. Hale, which it most nearly resembles. Tree: vigorous; self-fertile.

Merrill Beauty.--Originated in Red Bluff, California, by Grant Merrill. Introduced commercially in June, 1947. Patent no. 905; December 6, 1949. Open pollinated seedling of J. H. Hale; selected in June, 1943. Fruit: freestone; flesh yellow; very large; highly colored; ripens 5 weeks before Elberta and one week before Redhaven.

Merrill Brilliant.--Originated in Red Bluff, California, by Grant Merrill. Introduced commercially in January, 1950. July Elberta x Florence; selected in June, 1945. Fruit: flesh white, clingstone; very brillinat color; tough skin; very early; most nearly resembles Alexander.

Merrill Dandy.--Originated in Red Bluff, California, by Grant Merrill. Introduced commercially in January, 1950. Open pollinated seedling of Candoka; selected in June, 1943. Fruit: flesh yellow; freestone; 3 weeks earlier than Candoka, which it most nearly resembles. Tree: vigorous; heavy bearer; self-fertile.

Merrill Delicious.--Originated in Red Bluff, California, by Grant Merrill. Introduced commercially in June, 1947. Open pollinated seedling of J. H. Hale; selected in June, 1943. Fruit: freestone; flesh yellow; ripens 5 weeks before Elberta;

flavor very good.

Merrill Gem.--Originated in Red Bluff, California, by Grant Merrill. Introduced commercially in June, 1947. Patent no. 868; August 30, 1949. J. H. Hale x Red Bird; selected June, 1943. Fruit: clingstone; flesh yellow; texture firm to hard; skin dark red; large; matures 7 weeks before Elberta.

Merrill Gold Rush.--Originated in Red Bluff, California, by Grant Merrill. Introduced commercially in January, 1950. Open pollinated seedling of J. H. Hale; selected in July, 1942. Fruit: flesh yellow; freestone; 3 weeks earlier than J. H. Hale, which it most nearly resembles. Tree: very vigorous; self-fertile.

Merrill Home Canner.--Originated in Red Bluff, California, by Grant Merrill. Introduced commercially in January, 1950. Open pollinated seedling of J. H. Hale of F_2 generation; selected in June, 1944. Fruit: flesh yellow; clingstone; 4 weeks later than J. H. Hale which it most nearly resembles. Tree: vigorous.

Merrill June.--Originated in Red Bluff, California, by Grant Merrill. Introduced commercially in June, 1947. Patent no. 869; August 30, 1949. Open pollinated seedling of J. H. Hale; selected in June, 1943. Fruit: semifreestone; flesh yellow; matures 6 weeks before Elberta.

Merrill Late Canner.--Originated in Red Bluff, California, by Grant Merrill. Introduced commercially in January, 1950. Open pollinated seedling of J. H. Hale of F_2 generation; selected in September, 1947. Fruit: flesh yellow; clingstone; 8 weeks later than J. H. Hale, which it most nearly resembles.

Merrill Late Gold.--Originated in Red Bluff, California, by Grant Merrill. Introduced commercially in January, 1950. Open pollinated seedling of Kirkman Gem; selected in September, 1946. Fruit: flesh yellow; freestone; no soft stripe on suture; most nearly resembles Kirkman Gem. Tree: self-sterile.

Merrill Necta-Heath.--Originated in Red Bluff, California, by Grant Merrill. Introduced commercially in January, 1950. J. H. Hale x Quetta; selected in July, 1940. Fruit: flesh white; clingstone; larger, more persistant, more red color on skin and around pit, and 4 weeks earlier than White Heath, which it most nearly resembles.

Merrill Schooldays.--Originated in Red Bluff, California, by Grant Merrill. Introduced commercially in January, 1950. Open pollinated seedling of J. H. Hale; selected in August, 1942. Fruit: flesh yellow; freestone; ripens 3 weeks later than J. H. Hale, which it most nearly resembles. Tree: very vigorous;

self-fertile.

Merrill Surprise.--Originated in Red Bluff, California, by Grant Merrill. Introduced commercially in January, 1950. Open pollinated seedling of July Elberta; selected in June, 1944. Fruit: flesh yellow; freestone; ripens 3 weeks earlier than July Elberta, which it most nearly resembles.

Merrill Yellow King.--Originated in Red Bluff, California, by Grant Merrill. Introduced commercially January, 1950. Open pollinated seedling of J. H. Hale; selected in 1945. Fruit: flesh yellow; freestone; ripens 1 week later than J. H. Hale, which it most nearly resembles. Tree: self-fertile.

Meteor.--Originated in New Brunswick, New Jersey, by the New Jersey Agricultural Experiment Station (M. A. Blake). Introduced commercially in 1925. Belle x self; seed gathered in 1914. Fruit: flesh yellow; freestone; ripens just before Elberta.

Midway.--Originated in New Brunswick, New Jersey, by the New Jersey Agricultural Experiment Station (M. A. Blake). Introduced commercially in 1939. J. H. Hale x New Jersey 27116; cross made in 1923. Fruit: flesh yellow; freestone; dark red blush; ripens just after Goldeneast.

Missouri.--Originated in Mountain Grove, Missouri, by the Missouri State Fruit Experiment Station (Paul H. Shepard). Introduced commercially in 1946. Open pollinated seedling of Sunbeam; selected in 1942. Fruit: round, larger than Sunbeam; flesh yellow, firm; good flavor; red blushed skin, fuzz short; clingstone; small pit; ripens 4 or 5 weeks before Elberta. Resembles Tuscan (Tuskena) in outward appearance.

Nectar.--Originated in Bakersfield, California, by Oliver P. Blackburn. Introduced commercially in 1935. Patent no. 86; February 6, 1934; propagation rights assigned to California Nursery Company, Niles, California. Parentage unknown (probably Early Wheeler x Stanwick). Fruit: freestone; very large; ripens early; sweet with nectarine flavor. Tree: bears regularly; growth vigorous; foliage heavy. Most nearly resembles Red Bird.

Nectar-Florence.--Originated in Di Giorgio, California, by the Earl Fruit Company (Edward Champness), now Di Giorgio Fruit Corp. Not introduced commercially. Patent no. 161; December 17, 1935; assigned to the Earl Fruit Company. Florence x Quetta nectarine; selected about 1929. Fruit: flesh reddish yellow, firm; semiclingstone; skin with deep red blush, smooth; matures with Florence which it most closely resembles. Tree: shy bearer and as a result no longer propagated.

Nestor.--Originated in Palo Alto, California, by the United States Department of Agriculture (W. F. Wight). Introduced commercially in 1938. Muir x Paloro. Fruit: flesh yellow; freestone; drying use.

Newcheer *(New Jersey Low Acid 5).*--Originated in New Brunswick, New Jersey, by the New Jersey Agricultural Experiment Station (M. A. Blake). Introduced commercially in 1947. (J. H. Hale x Mexican Honey) x (J. H. Hale x Iron Mountain). Fruit: freestone; flesh white; low in titratable acidity; suitable for the diet of persons troubled with hyperacidity or peptic ulcers; ripens just after Elberta. Tree: hardier than Elberta. Flower: non-showy.

Newday *(New Jersey 79).*--Originated in New Brunswick, New Jersey, by the New Jersey Agricultural Experiment Station (M. A. Blake). Introduced commercially in 1938. J. H. Hale x New Jersey 40 C. S.; cross made in 1923. Fruit: flesh yellow; semiclingstone; regarded by some New Jersey growers as the best yellow peach to follow Golden Jubilee.

New Jersey 41SD.--Originated in New Brunswick, New Jersey, by the New Jersey Agricultural Experiment Station (M. A. Blake). Never introduced commercially but has value as a parent in breeding for hardiness. Slappey x Admiral Dewey. Fruit: large; freestone; flesh yellow. Tree: very hardy. Recommended for very hardy parent. Flower: non-showy.

New Jersey 66.--See **Sixty-six**

New Jersey 79.--See **Newday.**

New Jersey 87.--See **Goldeneast.**

New Jersey 99.--See **Pacemaker.**

New Jersey 101.--See **Summerrose.**

New Jersey 102.--See **Envoy.**

New Jersey 109.--See **Laterose.**

New Jersey 118.--See **Wildrose.**

New Jersey 126.--See **Redcrest.**

New Jersey 129.--See **Cherryred.**

New Jersey 134.--See **Early East.**

New Jersey 135.--See **Jerseyland.**

New Jersey 145.--See **Autumn**.

New Jersey 152.--See **Goodcheer**.

New Jersey 159.--See **Frostqueen**.

New Jersey 161.--See **Constitution**.

New Jersey 164.--See **Maybelle**.

New Jersey 183.--See **Fallate**.

New Jersey 185.--See **Frostqueen**.

New Jersey E.--See **Rutgers Green Leaf**.

New Jersey Low Acid 5.--See **Newcheer**.

New Jersey Low Acid 8.--See **Honeygem**.

Ontario 290159.--See **Vesper**.

Ontario 350113.--See **Erlyvee**.

Oriole.--Originated in New Brunswick, New Jersey, by the New Jersey Agricultural Experiment Station (M. A. Blake). Introduced commercially in 1925. Slappey x Admiral Dewey; cross made in 1916 at Vineland, Ontario, Canada. Fruit: flesh yellow; freestone; medium to large; quality high; ripens just before Golden Jubilee. Tree: vigorous and productive.

Osage.--Originated in Mountain Grove, Missouri, by the Missouri State Fruit Experiment Station (Paul H. Shepard). Introduced commercially in 1946. Open pollinated seedling of Alton; selected in 1945. Fruit: clingstone; flesh resembles the Indian peach in color and flavor; high quality canner; ripens two weeks before Elberta. Tree: vigorous; resistant to low temperatures.

Ozark.--Originated in Mountain Grove, Missouri, by the Missouri State Fruit Experiment Station (Paul H. Shepard). Introduced commercially in 1946. Frank x Halehaven; selected in 1943. Fruit: flesh yellow, firm; freestone; large; full red skin color; ripens 2 weeks before Elberta; most nearly resembles J. H. Hale. Tree: hardy.

Pacemaker *(New Jersey 99)*.--Originated in New Brunswick, New Jersey, by the New Jersey Agricultural Experiment Station (M. A. Blake). Introduced commercially in 1939. J. H. Hale x Marigold; cross made in 1923. Fruit: flesh yellow, firm; semi-clingstone; large; attractive; extends the Goldeneast season.

Pacific Gold.--Originated in Buckley, Washington, by W. M. Schwab, Buckley Nursery Co. Introduced commercially in 1933. Trademarked in 1930. Open pollinated seedling of Rochester; discovered in 1929. Fruit: large; firm; most nearly resembles Rochester. Tree: long life producer. Apparently similar to or identical with Rochester.

Pearson Hiley.--Originated in Lee Pope, Georgia, by John W. Pearson. Introduced under restriction in 1946. Patent no. 760; July 1, 1946. Bud mutation of Early Hiley; discovered in 1941. Fruit: early maturing. Most nearly resembles Hiley.

Pedersen.--Originated in Modesto, California, by L. E. Pedersen. Introduced commercially in 1937. Parentage unknown; selected in 1935. Fruit: ripens in Phillips Cling season; commercial canning clingstone.

Penryn.--Originated in Palo Alto, California, by the United States Department of Agriculture (W. F. Wight). Introduced commercially in 1938. Maxine x Leader. Fruit: ripens early; quality good; appearance attractive; a dessert variety; freestone; flesh yellow.

Pioneer.--Originated in New Brunswick, New Jersey, by the New Jersey Agricultural Experiment Station (M. A. Blake). Introduced commercially in 1925. Belle x Greensboro; cross made in 1915. Fruit: flesh white; almost a freestone; resembles Cumberland, which is now generally preferred.

Plantz.--Originated in Marysville, California, by William Plantz. Introduced commercially in 1936. Patent no. 262; September 14, 1937. Parentage unknown; selected in 1935. Fruit: ripens in Phillips Cling season; commercial canning clingstone.

Polly.--Originated in Glenwood, Iowa, by the Iowa State Agricultural Experiment Station (S. A. Beach). Introduced commercially in 1934. Open pollinated seedling of an F_2 seedling of Hill's Chili; selected in 1916; fruited first in 1920. Fruit: flesh white; high quality; most nearly resembles Champion. Tree: very hardy. Not entirely desirable for commercial planting; well adapted for home orchards in Iowa.

Pomeroy.--Originated in Merced, California, by the California Packing Corporation. Introduced commercially in 1934. Parentage unknown. Selected in 1932. Fruit: ripens in Peak season; commercial canning clingstone.

Poppy.--Originated in Mountain Grove, Missouri, by the Miss-

ouri State Fruit Experiment Station (Paul H. Shepard). Introduced commercially in 1947. Frank x Halehaven; selected in
1947. Fruit: flesh yellow; freestone; fine texture and flavor;
ripens 8 days before Elberta, which it most nearly resembles;
appears to be ripe a week or ten days before it actually
reaches the hard ripe stage; good shipper.

Prairie Clipper *(Illinois K47)*.--Originated in the Horticultural Farm, Olney, Illinois, by the Illinois Agricultural
Experiment Station (M. J. Dorsey). Introduced commercially in
1946. J. H. Hale x Gage; cross made in 1933. Fruit: very large;
medium yellow with dark red blush, dull appearance; flesh
yellow, deeper color at stone, firm J. H. Hale type of flesh;
quality good, flavor sharp; freestone; ripens 3 days before
Elberta.

Prairie Dawn *(Illinois K73)*.--Originated in the Horticultural
Farm, Olney, Illinois, by the Illinois Agricultural Experiment
Station (M. J. Dorsey). Introduced commercially in 1946. Valiant x Halehaven; cross made in 1937. Fruit: medium to large;
medium yellow, light red blush, attractive; flesh medium
yellow, tender, juicy; freestone when fully mature; ripens 40
days before Elberta. Fruit buds hardier than Elberta.

Prairie Daybreak *(Illinois K69)*.--Originated in the Horticultural Farm, Olney, Illinois, by the Illinois Agricultural
Experiment Station (M. J. Dorsey). Introduced commercially in
1946. Halehaven x Sun Glo; cross made in 1937. Fruit: large;
oval; medium yellow, dark red blush, dull appearance; flesh
light yellow, tender, firm, moderately juicy; freestone;
ripens 37 days before Elberta.

Prairie Rambler *(Illinois K43)*.--Originated in the Horticultural Farm, Olney, Illinois, by the Illinois Agricultural Experiment Station (M. J. Dorsey). Introduced commercially in
1946. Elberta x Gage; cross made in 1933. Fruit: very large;
greenish yellow, light to dark red blush, attractive; flesh
yellow with some red at stone, firm, juicy, subacid, spicy
flavor; freestone; ripens 3 days after Elberta.

Prairie Rose *(Illinois K80)*.--Originated in the Horticultural
Farm, Olney, Illinois, by the Illinois Agricultural Experiment Station (M. J. Dorsey). Introduced commercially in 1946.
Gage x Halehaven; cross made in 1937. Fruit: medium to large;
round; medium yellow, blushed and splashed with dark red, very
attractive; flesh medium yellow with occasional trace of red
through flesh and at stone, medium firm, juicy; freestone; ripens 25 days before Elberta.

Prairie Schooner *(Illinois K40)*.--Originated in the Horticultural Farm, Olney, Illinois, by the Illinois Agricultural Ex-

periment Station (M. J. Dorsey). Introduced commercially in 1946. Elberta x South Haven; cross made in 1933. Fruit: large; oval; light yellow, light red blush; flesh light yellow, lighter color at stone, tender, juicy; semicling until fully mature; ripens 21 days before Elberta. Tree: inclined to overset.

Prairie Sunrise *(Illinois K74)*.--Originated in the Horticultural Farm, Olney, Illinois, by the Illinois Agricultural Experiment Station (M. J. Dorsey). Introduced commercially in 1946. Valiant x Halehaven; cross made in 1937. Fruit: large; round; medium yellow, dark red blush, attractive; flesh medium yellow, tender, juicy; semicling until fully mature; ripens 37 days before Elberta.

Primrose.--Originated in New Brunswick, New Jersey, by the New Jersey Agricultural Experiment Station (M. A. Blake). Introduced commercially in 1925. Belle x Elberta; cross made in 1915. Fruit: flesh yellow; freestone; large; ripens at same season as Summercrest.

R. L. Stoner.--Originated near Dayton, Ohio. by R. L. Stoner. Introduced commercially in 1948. Patent no. 798; May 11, 1948; assigned to originator. Bud sport of Early Elberta; discovered in 1929. Fruit: red blush, finely pubescent; freestone; flesh cream, firm, fine textured; shipping and canning quality good; most nearly resembles Belle of Georgia. Tree: vigorous, consistent bearer; very hardy.

Radiance.--Originated in New Brunswick, New Jersey, by the New Jersey Agricultural Experiment Station (M. A. Blake). Introduced commercially in 1925. Belle x Greensboro; cross made in 1914. Fruit: flesh white; almost a freestone; not equal to Delicious.

Ramona.--Originated in Riverside, California, by the California Citrus Experiment Station (J. W. Lesley). Introduced commercially in 1943. F_2 seedling of Peak x P. I. 32374; selected in 1933. Fruit: flesh yellow, non-melting; clingstone. Tree: requires little winter chilling.

Raritan Rose.--Originated in New Brunswick, New Jersey, by the New Jersey Agricultural Experiment Station (M. A. Blake). Introduced commercially in 1936. J. H. Hale x Cumberland; cross made in 1926. Fruit: flesh white; the best white freestone to ripen with Golden Jubilee where extreme winter hardiness is not necessary.

Redcrest *(New Jersey 126)*.--Originated in New Brunswick, New Jersey, by the New Jersey Agricultural Experiment Station (M. A. Blake). Introduced commercially in 1946 Parentage unknown.

Fruit: very attractive; flesh yellow, firm; large; excellent for freezing and canning; ripens a week before Elberta. No longer recommended by the New Jersey Agr. Exp. Sta. for commercial planting because of the frequent occurrence of the breakdown of the flesh adjacent to the pit cavity as the fruit becomes mature. Tree: not as hardy as Elberta. Flower: nonshowy.

Redelberta.--Originated in Kennewick, Washington, by Jay Perry. Introduced commercially in 1936. Patent no. 232; February 2, 1937; assigned to Columbia & Okanogan Nursery Company, Wenatchee, Washington. Bud mutation of Elberta; discovered in 1928. Fruit: ripens 10 days earlier than Elberta; more highly colored than parent; smaller than Elberta.

Redhaven.--Originated in South Haven, Michigan, at the Michigan (South Haven) Agricultural Experiment Station. Introduced commercially in 1940. Halehaven x Kalhaven; cross made in 1930. Fruit: season very early, 30 days before Elberta; flesh very firm, permitting commercial handling and shipping; color brilliant red; freestone.

Redleaf.--See **Davidson.**

Redrose.--Originated in New Brunswick, New Jersey, by the New Jersey Agricultural Experiment Station (M. A. Blake). Introduced commercially in 1940. J. H. Hale x Delicious; cross made in 1925. Fruit: flesh white; freestone.

Redskin.--Originated in College Park, Maryland, by the University of Maryland Department of Horticulture (A. L. Schrader and I. C. Haut). Introduced commercially in 1944. J. H. Hale x Elberta; selected in 1931. Fruit: freestone; flesh yellow, firm; skin high color; good size even with heavy production; shipping and keeping quality good; ripens slightly ahead of Elberta; canning and freezing quality good. Tree: spreading; very vigorous; shorter chilling requirement than Elberta. Flower: large and showy.

Redwing.--Originated in Ontario, California, by Walter E. Lammerts. Introduced commercially in 1944. Patent no. 621; March 28, 1944; assigned to Armstrong Nurseries, Inc., Ontario, California. Babcock x Stensgaard July Elberta; selected in 1939. Fruit: matures early; large; good blend of sugar and acid; skin color excellent. Tree: resistant to delayed foliation, having a short chilling requirement. Most nearly resembles Babcock.

Rio Oso Gem.--Originated in Rio Oso, California, by W. F. Yerkes. Introduced commercially in 1933. Patent no. 84; November 28, 1933. Parentage unknown; selected in 1926. Fruit: ripens later than J. H. Hale, extending that season; more highly colored than J. H. Hale, which it most nearly resembles. Self-fruitful.

Robin.--Originated in Ontario, California, by Walter E. Lammerts. Introduced commercially in 1944. Patent no. 529; June 30, 1942; assigned to Armstrong Nurseries, Inc., Ontario, California. Babcock x Mayflower; selected in 1941. Fruit: ripens very early, June 1 to 10; skin color excellent; flavor good, sweet with acid blend; larger than Mayflower; semi-clingstone.

Romance.--Originated in Mountain Grove, Missouri, by the Missouri State Fruit Experiment Station (Paul H. Shepard). Introduced commercially in 1947. Wilma x Halehaven; selected in 1947. Fruit: takes on full color while still firm; flesh yellow, fine grained; flavor good; good shipper; ripens 16 days before Elberta. Tree: buds and bloom more resistant to cold than Elberta. Most nearly resembles Wilma.

Rosebud.--Originated in New Brunswick, New Jersey, by the New Jersey Agricultural Experiment Station (M. A. Blake). Introduced commercially in 1925. Carman x Slappey; cross made in 1916. Fruit: flesh white; semiclingstone; small; ripens 5 to 7 days before Cumberland or Raritan Rose. Tree: very hardy; prolific.

Rosy.--Originated in Riverside, California, by the California Citrus Experiment Station (J. W. Lesley). Introduced commercially in 1942. J. H. Hale x Columbiana-Peento-Elberta hybrid; selected in 1935. Fruit: large; flesh white; freestone. Tree: little winter chilling required.

Royal Fay.--Originated in Porterville, California, by Fred D. Williams. Introduced commercially in 1945. Patent no. 795; March 21, 1948; assigned to Fred D. Williams, Route 2, Box 470, Porterville, California. Bud mutation of Fay Elberta; discovered in 1941. Fruit: freestone; flesh yellow, firm; pubescence sparse and short; similar to parent but with higher color.

Rubidoux.--Originated in Riverside, California, by the California Citrus Experiment Station (J. W. Lesley). Introduced commercially in 1949. Ancestry includes Elberta, Late Champion, Lukens Honey, Peento; selected in 1940. Fruit: large; freestone; flesh yellow; dull red blush; firm; ripens about 10 days after J. H. Hale; keeps well. Tree: vigorous; prolific; short winter chilling requirement.

Rutgers Green Leaf *(New Jersey E.)*.--Originated in New Brunswick, New Jersey, by the New Jersey Agricultural Experiment

Station (M. A. Blake). Introduced commercially in 1947. Parentage unknown. Fruit: freestone; flesh white; very small; of no value. Flower. showy. Tree: suggested as a source of vigorous hardy seedling rootstocks.

Rutgers Red Leaf.--Originated in New Brunswick, New Jersey, by the New Jersey Agricultural Experiment Station (M. A. Blake). Introduced commercially in 1947. Parentage unknown. Fruit: very small; freestone; flesh white; of no value. Flower: showy. Tree: suggested as a source of hardy seedling rootstocks; may have slight dwarfing effect; readily identified in nursery because of dark color of young leaves.

S-37 *(Stribling S-37-18).*--Originated in Stribling's Nurseries Experiment Station, Atwater, California, by Thomas B. Stribling, Jr. Introduced commercially in 1947. Patent no. 904; December 6, 1949; assigned to Thomas B. Stribling, Jr., Stribling's Nurseries, Merced, California. Seedling of the ornamental flowering peach from seeds planted in 1935; selected about 1937. A rootstock resistant to garden nematode and crown gall.

Shannon.--Originated in Modesto, California, by the Hume Cannery. Introduced commercially in 1939. Parentage unknown; selected in 1935. Fruit: ripens in Phillips Cling season; commercial canning clingstone.

Sharon.--Originated in McFarland, California, by R. E. Armantrout and E. W. Root. Introduced commercially in 1943. Patent no. 540; August 18, 1942. Parentage unknown; selected in 1930. Fruit: flesh white, firm; freestone; flavor distinctive; ripens August 15 to 30 at McFarland, California.

Shasta.--Originated in Palo Alto, California, by the United States Department of Agriculture (W. F. Wight). Introduced commercially in 1941. Leader seedling (clingstone) x (Tuscan x Paloro). Fruit: quality good; ripens early (Tuscan season or earlier); commercial canning clingstone. Tree: heavy producer.

Sixty-six *(New Jersey 66).*--Originated in New Brunswick, New Jersey, by the New Jersey Agricultural Experiment Station (M. A. Blake). Introduced commercially in 1945. J. H. Hale x (Carman x Slappey). Fruit: large; fairly firm; red all over; flesh white; ripens about with Carman. Tree: hardy as Elberta. Flower: non-showy.

Socala.--Originated in Ontario, California, by Mrs. C. C. Barnes. Introduced commercially about 1942. Parentage unknown; discovered about 1935. Fruit: matures earlier than July Elberta in southern California; most nearly resembles July Elberta. Tree: requires less winter chilling than other varieties of the July Elberta type and season

Solo *(Summerland S-11-3)*.--Originated in Summerland, British Columbia, Canada, by the Dominion Experiment Station (J. E. Britton). Introduced commercially in November, 1949. J. H. Hale x Veteran; cross made in 1933; selected in 1941 by A. J. Mann. Fruit: large; flesh yellow, juicy, firm; freestone; easily handled with minimum amount of bruising; promising canning variety; ripens with Valiant and Veteran; most nearly resembles J. H. Hale. Tree: heavy annual bearer; medium size; moderately hardy; requires heavy thinning.

South Haven *(Sun Glo)*.--Originated in South Haven, Michigan, by A. G. Spencer. Introduced commercially in 1920. Bud mutation of St. John; discovered in 1911. Fruit: large; very firm; much more productive than other yellow freestones. Became a commercial variety quickly, but is now being replaced by Halehaven. Most nearly resembles Crawford type.

Southland.--Originated in Fort Valley, Georgia, by the United States Department of Agriculture (J. H. Weinberger). Introduced commercially July 15, 1946. Halehaven x self; selected in June, 1939. Fruit: flesh yellow; freestone; large; ripens with Hiley; firmer, slower softening flesh and more attractive color than Halehaven which it most nearly resembles.

Spotlight.--Originated in Summerland, British Columbia, Canada, by the Dominion Experimental Station (J. E. Britton). Introduced commercially in 1946. Veteran x Rochester; cross made in 1934; original tree planted in April, 1937; selected in 1942 (A. J. Mann). Fruit: flesh yellow, firm, good to above fair in quality; semiclingstone; attractive high color; excellent canning variety; matures 1 week earlier than Rochester.

Stanford.--Originated in Palo Alto, California, by the United States Department of Agriculture (W. F. Wight). Introduced commercially in 1935. Hauss x Phillips Cling. Fruit: ripens in late midseason (Halford 2 season or slightly later); commercial canning clingstone; quality good; hangs well on tree. Tree: heavy producer.

Starking Delicious.--Originated in Dover, Arkansas, by Henry Frank Smith. Introduced commercially in April, 1949. Patent no. 803; July 27, 1948; assigned to Stark Brothers Nurseries and Orchards Company, Louisiana, Missouri. Bud mutation of July Elberta; discovered in 1944. Fruit: flesh yellow; freestone when full ripe; high quality; early, ripens 18 days before July Elberta and about 6 days before Redhaven. Most nearly resembles July Elberta.

Stark Sure Crop.--Originated in Ash Grove, Missouri, by John

W. Nicholson. Introduced commercially in 1946. Patent no. 670; January 15, 1946; assigned to Stark Brothers Nurseries and Orchards Company, Louisiana, Missouri. Open pollinated seedling of Greensboro. Fruit: flesh white; clingstone; matures very early. Tree: hardy; regular cropper under adverse conditions.

Stribling S-37-18.--See S-37.

Stribling S-47-4.--See **Gold Dust**.

Stuart.--Originated in French Camp, California, by J. F. Stuart. Introduced commercially in 1927. Open pollinated seedling of Lovell; selected in 1925. Fruit: flesh yellow; commercial canning clingstone; ripens in Phillips Cling season; most nearly resembles Gomes.

Sullivan 1.--Originated in Tudor, California, by C. E. Sullivan. Introduced commercially in 1936. Patent no. 186; June 23, 1936. Parentage unknown; selected in 1928. Fruit: flesh yellow; ripens in late midsummer season; commercial canning clingstone. Resembles Johnson.

Sullivan 4.--Originated in Tudor, California, by C. E. Sullivan. Introduced commercially in 1940. Parentage unknown; selected in 1929. Fruit: flesh yellow; ripens in Phillips Cling season; commercial canning clingstone.

Sullivans Early Elberta.--Originated in Zebulon, Georgia, by P. M. Sullivan. Introduced commercially in 1938. Bud mutation of Elberta; discovered in 1933. Fruit: flesh yellow; freestone; ripens a week earlier than Elberta, which it closely resembles.

Summercrest.--Originated in New Brunswick, New Jersey, by the New Jersey Agricultural Experiment Station (M. A. Blake). Introduced commercially in 1938. J. H. Hale x Cumberland; cross made in 1926. Fruit: flesh yellow; freestone; ripens just before Elberta; popular for local market in New Jersey.

Summerland S-11-3.--See Solo.

Summerrose *(New Jersey 101).*--Originated in New Brunswick, New Jersey, by the New Jersey Agricultural Experiment Station (M. A. Blake). Introduced commercially in 1947. J. H. Hale x Delicious. Fruit: freestone; flesh white, large; oval; quality good; ripens 10 days to two weeks before Elberta; most nearly resembles Belle of Georgia in shape and appearance. Tree: hardier than Elberta. Flower: non-showy.

Sunbeam.--Originated in New Brunswick, New Jersey, by the New Jersey Agricultural Experiment Station (M. A. Blake). Introduced commercially in 1925. Slappey x Admiral Dewey; cross made in 1916. Fruit: flesh yellow; semiclingstone; rather small but attractive; early; free from catechol tannin; used in breeding.

Sunday *(Sunday Elberta)*.--Originated in Baroda, Michigan, by George P. Sunday. Introduced commercially in 1940. Patent no. 418; August 27, 1940; assigned to Greening Nursery Company, Monroe, Michigan. Parentage unknown; selected in 1927. Fruit: shape similar to Elberta; color, firmness, and quality similar to J. H. Hale; pubescence little; ripens 1 week or more after Elberta. Tree: very hardy.

Sunday Elberta.--See **Sunday.**

Sun Glo.--See **South Haven.**

Sunglow.--Originated in Riverside, California, by the California Citrus Experiment Station (J. W. Lesley). Introduced commercially in 1942. F_2 of J. H. Hale x seedling of Bolivian Cling; selected in 1936. Fruit: freestone; flesh yellow; quality good. Tree: little winter chilling required.

Sungold.--Originated in Des Moines, Iowa; Professor T. J. Maney of Iowa State College was the first to recognize its possible value and first called it to public attention about 1924. Rights to propagation assigned to Interstate Nurseries, Hamburg, Iowa. Introduced commercially in 1936. Parentage unknown; selected about 1928. Fruit: freestone; flesh yellow; flavor fine; large; ripens 1 week earlier than Elberta; most nearly resembles J. H. Hale. Tree: productive.

Sunhigh.--Originated in New Brunswick, New Jersey, by the New Jersey Agricultural Experiment Station (M. A. Blake). Introduced commercially in 1938. J. H. Hale x New Jersey 40 C. S.; cross made in 1923. Fruit: flesh yellow; semiclingstone; large; firm; high-colored; very popular in the New York market.

Superior.--Originated in Summerland, British Columbia, Canada, by the Dominion Experimental Station (J. E. Britton). Introduced commercially in 1946. J. H. Hale x Veteran; cross made in 1933; original tree planted in 1936; selected in 1941 (A. J. Mann). Fruit: size above medium; flesh yellow; practically freestone (being similar to Vedette and Valiant); flesh moderately firm; quality above fair; fair as a canning variety; similar season to that of Valiant and Veteran.

Taylor.--Originated in Placer County, California, by E. G. Taylor. Introduced commercially in 1936. Parentage unknown; selected in 1930. Fruit: flesh yellow; ripens in Phillips Cling season; commercial canning clingstone; Leaves: glandless.

Tennessee Redleaf.--See **Davidson.**

Texaberta.--Originated in Belton, Texas, by E. E. Griffith. Introduced commercially in 1938. Parentage unknown; discovered in 1936. Fruit: flesh yellow; freestone; slightly red around the pit; most nearly resembles Elberta. Tree: requires less chilling than Elberta.

Tom Thumb.--Originated in Argentonsur-Creuse (Indre), France, by Leon Maillochon and Ernest Marlaud. Introduced commercially in about 1938 by Stark Brothers Nurseries and Orchards Company, Louisiana, Missouri. Patent no. 306; November 29, 1938; assigned to Stark Brothers Nurseries and Orchards Company, Louisiana, Missouri on July 13, 1937. Parentage unknown; discovered during the late 1920's. Fruit: edible, of poor quality; resembles Mayflower. Tree: once considered valuable as a low-growing oranamental with rather attractive flowers.

Triogem.--Originated in New Brunswick, New Jersey, by the New Jersey Agricultural Experiment Station (M. A. Blake). Introduced commercially in 1938. J. H. Hale x Marigold; cross made in 1923. Fruit: flesh yellow; an early, firm, high-colored freestone; ripens soon after Golden Jubilee.

Tropico.--Originated in Fullerton, California, by Lawrence W. Sherwood. Introduced commercially in 1951. Patent no. 924; February 14, 1950; assigned to Lawrence W. Sherwood, Sherwood Specialty Nursery, Fullerton, California. Parentage unknown; discovered about 1930. Fruit: skin cream with blush; flesh white, juicy, firm; freestone; seed small; quality good, non-splitting; ripens about October 1. Tree: heavy bearer; vigorous.

Tudor.--Originated in Palo Alto, California, by the United States Department of Agriculture (W. F. Wight). Introduced commercially in 1941. Libbee x Newkom. Fruit: ripens in mid-season (Gaume to Sims season); canning clingstone of best quality. Tree: heavy producer.

Tulip.--Originated in Mountain Grove, Missouri, by the Missouri State Fruit Experiment Station (Paul H. Shepard). Introduced commercially in 1947. Open pollinated seedling of Sunbeam; selected in 1947. Fruit: good color before picking time; fuzz short; flesh yellow, firm, texture fine; flavor good; freestone; good shipper; ripens 6 to 7 weeks before Elberta.

USDA W21-19C.--See **Vivian.**

USDA W38-39B.--See **Coronado.**

Valiant.--Originated in Vineland, Ontario, Canada, by the Ontario Horticultural Experiment Station. Introduced commercially in 1925. Open pollinated seedling of Elberta; selected in 1922 from 1917 pollination. Fruit: flesh yellow, freestone; Elberta type but rounder, better quality, and matures 2½ weeks earlier than known parent.

Vanguard.--Originated in Vineland, Ontario, Canada, by the Ontario Horticultural Experiment Station. Introduced commercially in 1941. Vaughan x Valiant; selected in 1930 from 1925 pollination. Fruit: ripens 6 weeks before Elberta and 5 days after June Elberta; flesh yellow; freestone; quality and appearance good. Most nearly resembles Valiant.

Vaughan.--Originated in Vineland, Ontario, Canada, by the Ontario Horticultural Experiment Station. Introduced commercially in 1925. Leamington x self; selected in 1919 from 1913 pollination. Fruit: flesh yellow; freestone; appearance dullish; ripens early. Tree: unusually hardy in fruit bud. Most nearly resembles Rochester.

Vedette.--Originated in Vineland, Ontario, Canada, by the Ontario Horticultural Experiment Station. Introduced commercially in 1925. Open pollinated seedling of Elberta; selected in 1921 from 1915 pollinations. Fruit: flesh yellow; normally freestone, in some seasons semifree only; Elberta type, but fuller, better quality, and matures 3 weeks earlier than Elberta.

Veefreeze.-- Originated in Vineland, Ontario, Canada, by the Ontario Horticultural Experiment Station. Introduced commercially in 1940. Ontario 11041 (Elberta x open) x Arp Beauty; selected in 1926 from 1920 pollinations. Fruit: flesh yellow; freestone; retains full peach flavor in frozen pack; exposed flesh (fresh) does not oxidize or brown for hours after being cut. Most nearly resembles Elberta.

Vesper *(Ontario 290159)*.--Originated in Vineland, Ontario, Canada, by the Ontario Horticultural Experiment Station. Introduced commercially in 1949. J. H. Hale x Vedette; selected in 1934. Fruit: medium large; flesh yellow; freestone; good quality; subject to bacterial leaf spot; ripens five days later than Elberta.

Veteran.--Originated in Vineland, Ontario, Canada, at the Ontario Horticultural Experiment Station. Introduced commercially in 1928. Vaughan x Stark Early Elberta; selected in 1925 from 1919 breeding. Fruit: flesh yellow; semifreestone to full freestone; Elberta type, but matures 8 to 10 days before Elberta.

Vetter Elberta.--Originated neaɪ Reedley, California, by Joseph J. Vetter. Introduced commercially in January, 1948. Patent no. 966; July 18, 1950; assigned to Roy R. Huth, Huth's Nursery, Visalia, California; trademarked Vetter Elberta. Bud mutation of July Elberta; discovered in June, 1940. Fruit: flesh yellow; freestone; ripens about June 10, some three weeks earlier than its parent; keeps well. Tree: strong grower; blooms four weeks later than July Elberta; yields well.

Viceroy.--Originated in Vineland, Ontario, Canada, by the Ontario Horticultural Experiment Station. Introduced commercially in 1929. Vaughan x Stark Early Elberta; selected in 1925 from 1919 breeding. Fruit: flesh yellow; freestone; Elberta type, but fuller, better quality, and matures 3 weeks earlier than Elberta. Tree: hardy.

Vivian *(USDA W21-19C)*.--Originated in Palo Alto, California, by the United States Department of Agriculture (W. F. Wight) and the California Agricultural Experiment Station. Commercially introduced in May, 1950. (Maxine x Leader) x ((Tuscan x Paloro) x (Paloro x Pratt-Low)) ; selected about 1936. Fruit: good size; round, symmetrical; yellow ground color; clingstone; flesh firm, fine textured, yellow, very little red at pit; flavor good canned; matures about 5 days after Fortuna and 9 days before Cortez.

Wahlbert.--Originated in Clarkston, Washington, by Albert W. Wahl. Introduced commercially in 1942. Patent no. 520; May 26, 1942; assigned to H. Lynn Tuttle, Clarkston, Washington. Parentage unknown; first observed in 1918 and propagated in 1935. Fruit: flesh yellow; freestone; firm; handles and ships well; matures two weeks earlier than J. H. Hale which it most nearly resembles.

Welberta.--Originated in Ontario, California, by Chaffey College (George P. Weldon). Introduced commercially October 1, 1948. Weldon x Elberta; selected in 1945. Fruit: freestone; flesh yellow; skin yellow with red streaks; firm; quality good; ripens 10 to 14 days ahead of Elberta which it most nearly resembles. Tree: resistant to delayed foliation; adapted to southern California conditions.

Weldon.--Originated in Ontario, California, by Chaffey College (George P. Weldon). Introduced commercially in 1939. Babcock x (Elberta x (Elberta x Peento) . Fruit: quality good; precedes Elberta in ripening; freestone. Tree: highly resistant to delayed foliation; dependable producer.

White Hale.--Originated in New Brunswick, New Jersey, by the New Jersey Agricultural Experiment Station (M. A. Blake). Introduced commercially in 1932. Patent no. 31: October 11,

1932. J. H. Hale x Belle; cross made in 1922. Fruit: flesh white; large; very firm; midseason freestone for districts south of New Brunswick, New Jersey.

Wickersham.--Originated in Yakima, Washington, by J. A. Wickersham. Introduced commercially in 1949. Patent no. 821; February 1, 1949; assigned to May Nursery Company, Yakima, Washington. Parentage unknown; discovered in 1948. Fruit: flesh yellow, streaked with red next to stone; highly colored; flavor mild; freestone; sugar content high; good keeping quality; ripens one week later than Elberta; most nearly resembles J. H. Hale.

Wildrose *(New Jersey 118)*.--Originated in New Brunswick, New Jersey, by the New Jersey Agricultural Experiment Station (M. A. Blake). Introduced commercially in 1947. J. H. Hale x Delicious. Fruit: freestone; flesh white, firm; skin with high red blush; large; quality good; ripens after Raritan Rose. Tree: hardier than Elberta. Flower: non-showy.

Williams.--Originated in Merced, California, by the California Packing Corporation. Introduced commercially about 1936. Parentage unknown; selected about 1932. Fruit: flesh yellow; ripens in Halford 2 time; commercial canning clingstone.

Wiser *(Lovell Cling)*.--Originated in Gridley, California, by Ray B. Wiser. Introduced commercially in 1943. Patent no. 507; March 17, 1942. Sims x Lovell; selected in 1933. Fruit: commercial canning clingstone; ripens in Phillips Cling season; flesh yellow; free from red at pit. Tree: growth willowy and vigorous; bears heavily. Most nearly resembles Lovell.

World's Earliest.--Originated in Moscow, Tennessee, by E. L. Morris. Introduced commercially in 1936. Trademarked by Stark Brothers Nurseries and Orchards Company, Louisiana, Missouri. Parentage unknown; discovered in 1933. Fruit: flesh white; clingstone; ripens early; most nearly resembles Red Bird.

Yelo.--Originated in Ontario, California, by Chaffey College (George P. Weldon). Introduced commercially October 1, 1948. (Lukens Honey x Elberta) x Weldon; selected in 1945. Fruit: freestone; flesh light yellow; skin yellow with a blush; ripens in mid-August, about the same time as Elberta; quality high.

PEAR

Bantam *(Minnesota 3)*.--Originated in Excelsior, Minnesota, by the University of Minnesota Fruit Breeding Farm. Introduced commercially in 1940. Parentage unknown; seed planted in 1914 or 1915. Fruit: small; flesh tender, melting, juicy; early; quality good. Tree: very hardy; resistant to fire blight.

Cashman.-- Originated in Ortonville, Minnesota, by Francis Black. Introduced commercially in 1942 by Cashman Nurseries, Owatonna, Minnesota. Parentage unknown; discovered about 1940. Fruit: identical in shape and color but a trifle larger than Parker, which it most nearly resembles. Tree: more hardy in northern climates than Parker.

Cayuga.--Originated in Geneva, New York, by the New York State Agricultural Experiment Station (U. P. Hedrick). Introduced for trial in 1920. Open pollinated seedling of Seckel; seed borne in 1906. Fruit: Bartlett size; similar in shape to Seckel; color of Clairgeau. Tree: some blight resistance.

Caywood.--Originated in Geneva, New York, by the New York State Agricultural Experiment Station (U. P. Hedrick). Introduced for trial in 1938. Open pollinated seedling of Seckel; seed collected in 1908; first full crop in 1922. Fruit: larger, rounder, and more russeted than Seckel; sweet, highly aromatic, Seckel flavor; season a little after Early Seckel.

Chapin.--Originated in Geneva, New York, by the New York State Agricultural Experiment Station (U. P. Hedrick). Introduced commercially in 1945. Open pollinated seedling of Seckel; from seed borne in 1908; first full crop in 1920. Fruit: about size of Seckel, little longer in shape; greenish yellow with considerable russet; richly aromatic; very sweet; season after Beurré Giffard and ahead of Early Seckel; desirable for home use; most nearly resembles Seckel.

Christmas Holiday.--Originated in Sebastopol, California, by Luther Burbank. Introduced commercially in 1940 by Stark Brothers Nurseries and Orchards Company, Louisiana, Missouri. Parentage unknown. Fruit: large; skin russet; appearance attractive; quality good; matures late; most nearly resembles Bosc in shape and flavor. Tree: produces well.

Clyde.--Originated in Geneva, New York, by the New York State Agricultural Experiment Station (U. P. Hedrick). Introduced for trial in 1932. Open pollinated seedling of Seckel; seed collected in 1908; first full crop in 1921. Fruit: larger, less obovate, longer necked than Seckel; skin light greenish-russet over entire surface; flavor not as rich as Seckel; season 2 to 3 weeks later than Seckel; keeps longer than Seckel.

Covert.--Originated in Geneva, New York, by the New York State Agricultural Experiment Station (Richard Wellington). Introduced for trial in 1935. Bartlett x Dorset; cross made in 1912; first full crop in 1921. Fruit: one of largest of all pears;

similar to Bartlett but not as pale yellow; flesh tender, granular; fair for eating, better as canning and shipping sort; season November through December.

Devoe.--Originated in Marlboro, New York, by Charles A. Greiner. Introduced commercially in 1947. Patent no. 728; March 25, 1947. Parentage unknown, but thought to be an open pollinated seedling of Clapp Favorite. Fruit: shape similar to Bosc. Tree: said to be resistant to fire blight and pear psylla.

Early Seckel.--Originated in Geneva, New York, by the New York State Agricultural Experiment Station (U. P. Hedrick). Introduced for trial in 1935. Open pollinated seedling of Seckel; seed collected in 1906; first full crop in 1915. Fruit: resembles Seckel but ripens 2 to 3 weeks earlier; keeps in storage longer than Seckel; recommended for local and roadside markets.

Ewart.--Originated in East Akron, Ohio, by Mortimer Ewart. Introduced commercially in 1928. Parentage unknown. Fruit: size medium; quality good; skin greenish yellow, netted with russet; flesh fine, melting, tender, juicy; season 2 to 3 weeks later than Bartlett which it most nearly resembles. Tree: blight resistance unknown.

Golden Spice *(Minnesota 4)*.--Originated in Excelsior, Minnesota, by the University of Minnesota Fruit Breeding Farm. Introduced commercially in March, 1949. Parentage unknown; selected about 1924 from seed planted in 1914. Fruit: small; clear yellow with blush; flesh light yellow, juicy; flavor pleasant, tart, spicy; ripening in midseason; most nearly resembles Seckel in size, but not as sweet. Tree: very hardy; productive; a good parent for further breeding.

Gorham.--Originated in Geneva, New York, by the New York State Agricultural Experiment Station (Richard Wellington). Introduced for trial in 1923. Bartlett x Josephine de Malines; cross made in 1910. Fruit: ripens 1 month later than Bartlett; keeps 6 to 8 weeks longer than Bartlett; quality excellent; most nearly resembles Bartlett.

Grand Champion.--Originated in Hood River, Oregon, by W. F. Shannon. Introduced commercially in 1943. Patent no. 585; May 18, 1943; assigned to Stark Brothers Nurseries and Orchards Company, Louisiana, Missouri. Bud mutation of Gorham; discovered in 1936. Fruit: all-over golden russet skin color, which does not show bruises; flesh white, juicy; flavor spicy; good keeping quality.

Guraly Jr.--Originated in Fairport Harbor, Ohio, by Joseph T.

Guraly, Jr. Introduced commercially in 1940. Patent no. 435; December 17, 1940. Parentage unknown. Fruit: ripens early (early August); flesh white with red streaks radially from core.

Max-Red Bartlett.--Originated in Zillah, Washington, by A. D. MacKelvie. Introduced commercially in August, 1945. Patent no. 741; July 1, 1947. Trademarked Max-Red. Bud mutation of Bartlett; discovered in 1938. Fruit: skin cranberry-red; ripens 12 to 15 days later than Bartlett.

Mendel.--Originated in New Ulm, Minnesota, by William Pfaender, Jr. Introduced commercially in 1920. Parentage unknown. Fruit: large to medium; pyriform; yellow; flesh juicy, firm yet medium tender; quality good; season to mid-September. Tree: upright, vigorous, moderately hardy.

Minnesota 1.--See Parker.

Minnesota 3.--See Bantam.

Minnesota 4.--See Golden Spice.

Orient *(P. I. 64224)*.--Originated in Chico, California, by the United States Department of Agriculture (Walter Van Fleet). Introduced commercially in 1945 through the Tennessee Agricultural Experiment Station. *Pyrus communis* x *Pyrus* sp. from China; direction of cross unknown. Fruit: firm; juicy; slightly sweet; lacking in flavor; nearly round; ripens August 15 to 18 at Knoxville, Tennessee; good for canning. Tree: free from blight; produces medium annual crops; mostly of interest in Tennessee and southward.

Ovid.--Originated in Geneva, New York, by the New York State Agricultural Experiment Station (Richard Wellington). Introduced for trial in 1931. Bartlett x Dorset; cross made in 1912. Fruit: large; color resembles Bartlett but has russet patches; flesh fine-grained, tender, nearly white, sweet, agreeably flavored; quality good; ripens in December at Geneva; most nearly resembles Dorset.

Parker *(Minnesota 1)*.--Originated in Excelsior, Minnesota, by the University of Minnesota Fruit Breeding Farm. Introduced commercially in February, 1934. Open pollinated seedling of a Manchurian cultivated pear (probably *Pyrus communis*); selected in 1920. Fruit: medium to large; quality good. Tree: fairly hardy.

Phelps.--Originated in Geneva, New York, by the New York State Agricultural Experiment Station (Richard Wellington). Introduced for trial in 1925. Winter Nelis x Russet Bartlett; cross made in 1912. Fruit: ripens much later than Bartlett, around Thanksgiving, and keeping until Christmas; color duller than Bartlett; pleasant vinous flavor; flesh juicy, tender.

P. I. 64224.--See **Orient**.

Pioneer 3.--Originated in Brooks, Alberta, Canada, by A. L. Young. Introduced commercially in 1934. Parentage unknown; fruited first in 1931. Fruit: small; oval to pyriform; skin greenish yellow blushed dull red; flesh whitish, medium firm, granular, juicy; sweet, spicy as dessert fruit; fair as sauce; season mid-September. Tree: upright; vigorous; hardy; productive.

Pulteney.--Originated in Geneva, New York, by the New York State Agricultural Experiment Station (Richard Wellington). Introduced for trial in 1925. Winter Nelis x Russet Bartlett; cross made in 1912. Fruit: ripens 4 weeks later than Bartlett with fruits a little more regular in outline, skin smoother, but not as attractive in color as Bartlett.

Richard Peters.--Originated in State College, Pennsylvania, by the Pennsylvania State College (E. L. Nixon). Introduced commercially in 1927. Probably an open pollinated seedling of Kieffer; selected in 1924. Fruit: most nearly resembles Bartlett. Tree: practically immune to fire blight; vigorous grower.

Royal Red.--Originated in Milpitas, California, by Victor A. Silvera. Introduced commercially in 1940. Patent no. 380; April 23, 1940. Bud mutation of Hardy; discovered in 1934. Identical with parental type except for the red skin color of the mature fruit.

Tait-Dropmore.--Originated in Carterton, Ontario, Canada, by David Tait. Introduced commercially in 1928 by F. L. Skinner, Skinners Nursery, Dropmore, Manitoba, Canada. Open pollinated seedling of Patten; discovered about 1935. Fruit: small; pyriform; skin greenish yellow blushed dull carmine; flesh dull yellow, coarse, gritty; flavor sweet, pleasant as dessert fruit; fair as sauce; season early to mid-September. Tree: upright spreading; very hardy; resistant to fire blight.

USDA 66131.--See **Waite**.

Waite *(USDA 66131)*.--Originated in Arlington, Virginia, by the United States Department of Agriculture (M. B. Waite). Introduced commercially in 1938. Parentage unknown; selected about 1920. Fruit: almost as large as Bartlett, which it resembles in shape; ripens about Kieffer time; flesh smooth, almost free of grit cells; more acid than Bartlett; excellent for cooking and canning, fairly good for dessert. Tree: good blight resistance; rather weak type of growth; cross pollination essential.

Willard.--Originated in Geneva, New York, by the New York State Agricultural Experiment Station (Richard Wellington). Introduced for trial in 1931. Bartlett x Dorset; cross made in 1912. Fruit: ripens 2 weeks later than Ovid; resembles Bartlett in shape and color; surface uneven; flesh yellowish, fine-grained, tender, juicy, with a piquant flavor; quality good.

Not named.--Originated in northern Wisconsin by R. N. Ruedlinger. To be introduced commercially in the fall of 1951. Patent no. 309; January 17, 1939; assigned to Ruedlinger Nursery, St. Louis Park, Minnesota. Parentage unknown. Fruit: quality fine; keeps and ships well; most nearly resembles Anjou. Tree: very hardy.

Not named.--Originated in Youngstown, Ohio, by R. C. Bowman. Introduced commercially in 1947. Patent no. 757; September 2, 1947. Probably Kieffer x Anjou. Fruit: shape similar but smaller than Anjou; good keeping quality; faint core and few seeds; stem thick. Tree: somewhat blight resistant; blossoming is in two cycles about two weeks apart.

PECAN

Brake.--Originated in Rocky Mount, North Carolina, by H. L. Brake. Introduced commercially in 1937. Parentage unknown; seed planted in 1910. Patent no. 47; November 29, 1932. Nut: shell extremely thin; high kernel percentage; easily shelled; shorter and smaller than Schley. Tree: hardy; resistant to disease, especially scab.

Desirable *(USDA 7191)*.--Originated in Ocean Springs, Mississippi, by C. Forkert. Introduced for trial in 1930, and commercially in 1945. Probably Success x Russell; discovered about 1903. Nut: large, about the size of Success; excellent kernel. Tree: prolific; regular bearer.

Fisher.--Originated in New Memphis, Illinois, by Jacob Fisher. Introduced commercially in 1938. Parentage unknown; a seedling tree selected by Joseph Gerardi of O'Fallon, Illinois. Nut: flavor good; size medium; good cracker. Tree: heavy bearer.

Humble.--Originated in Zavalla County, Texas, by J. A. Simpson. Introduced commercially in 1933. Patent no. 73; July 25, 1933; assigned to Humble Oil & Refining Company, Houston, Texas. Parentage unknown. Tree: bears heavily and regularly; pronounced precocity; growth vigorous; wide range of adaptability; immune to disease and insects; relatively little chilling requirement.

John Garner.--Originated in San Saba, Texas, by E. E. Risen. Introduced commercially in 1934. San Saba Improved x Onliwon; selected in 1933. Nut: shell thin; large; attractive appearance; most nearly resembles Burkett. Tree: vigorous, prolific bearer.

Royal.--Originated in Riverside, California, by Robert A. Harris. Introduced commercially in 1949. Patent no. 833; April 26, 1949; assigned to Lawrence Sherwood, Sherwood Specialty Nursery, Fullerton, California. Open pollinated seedling of Schley. Nut: smooth; highly flavored kernel; matures early; fills well; thin shell but dense; keeps well without becoming rancid. Tree: prolific; comes into bearing very early.

Select.--Originated in Riverside, California, by Robert A. Harris. Introduced commercially in 1943. Patent no. 510; March 28, 1942; assigned to Lawrence Sherwood, Sherwood Specialty Nursery, Fullerton, California. Open pollinated seedling of Altman. Nut: shell thin; fills well; large; matures in early fall. Tree: exceptionally heavy bearer; starts bearing at an early age; vigorous grower; wide climatic adaptability.

Stark Hardy Paper Shell.--Originated in Chariton, Missouri, by Frank Munson. Introduced commercially in 1949 by Stark Brothers Nurseries and Orchards Company, Louisiana, Missouri. Parentage unknown; discovered in 1932. Nut: large size; shell thin. Tree: hardy; short growing season.

Texhan.--Originated in Belton, Texas, by N. H. Harder. Introduced commercially about 1946. Open pollinated seedling of Mahan; discovered in 1941. Nut: large, 45 per pound; 56.3% kernel; 76.87% oil content; most nearly resembles Moore in color, and Schley in size and shape; ripens early. Tree: vigorous growth; heavy foliage; profuse producer of staminate and pistillate flowers; large nut clusters; heavy producer.

USDA 7191.--See **Desirable.**

PERSIMMON

Creggs.--Originated in Harrisburg, Illinois, by Mr. Creggs. Introduced commercially in 1949. Parentage unknown; selected in 1945 from the native American species. Fruit: American type; few seeds; early maturing, about 15th of August in Caseyville, Illinois.

Jumbu.--Originated in Fullerton, California, by J. M. Alcorn. Introduced commercially in 1938. Parentage unknown; selected about 1930. Fruit: non-astringent; very large; resembles Hyakume in shape, Fuyu in type. Probably identical with the

Japanese variety Hana Fuyu.

Penland *(Pennland's Seedless)*.--Originated near Penland, North Carolina. Introduced commercially about 1937. Seedling clone of *Diospyros virginiana* growing in a cut-over forest; called to the attention of the Tennessee Valley Authority Division of Forestry Relations (Spencer B. Chase) in 1935; named in 1935 by J. C. McDaniel; first grafted at Norris, Tennessee in 1937. Fruit: almost seedless, varying with the abundance of pollination from native male persimmon trees.

Pennland's Seedless.--See **Penland**.

Spencer.--Originated near Harrisburg, Illinois, by E. R. Spencer. Introduced commercially in 1949. Seedling of the native American species. Fruit: good quality; two or three seeds per fruit; early maturing, about the first of September in Caseyville, Illinois.

PLUM

Albion.--Originated in Geneva, New York, by the New York State Agricultural Experiment Station (Richard Wellington). Introduced for trial in 1929. Golden Drop x Grand Duke; cross made in 1908; seed germinated in 1909. Fruit: purplish black; stone clings tenaciously; flesh a little coarse and stringy; ripens late; quality better than Grand Duke which it most nearly resembles.

Algoma *(Ottawa 302)*.--Originated in Ottawa, Ontario, Canada, by the Division of Horticulture, Central Experimental Farm. Introduced for trial in 1937. Sand cherry *(Prunus besseyi)* x Burbank; selected in 1935. Fruit: good size and quality for a plum of this type; intermediate between the sand cherry and the plum. Tree: extremely hardy; bushy habit; early bearing.

American Mirabelle.--Originated in Geneva, New York, by the New York State Agricultural Experiment Station (Richard Wellington). Introduced for trial in 1925. Imperial Epineuse x Mirabelle; cross made in 1911; seed germinated in 1912. Fruit: golden yellow color of Mirabelle, but of larger size, flavor good; for dessert or culinary use; most nearly resembles Mirabelle.

Anoka *(Minnesota 118)*.--Originated in Excelsior, Minnesota, by the University of Minnesota Fruit Breeding Farm. Introduced commercially in 1922. Burbank x De Soto; cross made in 1915; selected in 1918. Fruit: medium to large; skin red; firm; flesh yellow; quality only fair; clingstone. Variety has been abandoned because of low quality.

Bluebell.--Originated in Mountain Grove, Missouri, by the Missouri State Fruit Experiment Station (Paul H. Shepard). Introduced commercially in 1947. Stanley x President; selected in 1947. Fruit: larger than Stanley, which it most nearly resembles; skin blue; freestone; flesh firm, yellow; flavor good, sweet. Tree: vigorous; upright; holds its fruit through a long harvesting period.

Bluefre.--Originated in Mountain Grove, Missouri, by the Missouri State Fruit Experiment Station (Paul H. Shepard). Introduced commercially in 1947. Stanley x President; selected in 1947. Fruit: large; skin blue; freestone; flesh firm, thick, greenish-yellow; flavor good; ripens just before Stanley; most nearly resembles President; will hang on tree in good condition for about thirty days after normal harvest time.

Bonnie.--Originated in Mountain Grove, Missouri, by the Missouri State Fruit Experiment Station (Paul H. Shepard). Introduced commercially in 1947. Open pollinated seedling of America; selected in 1947. Fruit: larger, redder, ripens earlier than America, which it most nearly resembles; firm; good shipper. Tree: vigorous; bud and bloom very hardy.

Bounty *(Morden 105).*--Originated in Morden, Manitoba, Canada, by the Dominion Experimental Station. Introduced commercially in 1939. Open pollinated seedling of Assiniboine; selected in 1933; seed originally sent from Minnesota State Fruit Breeding Farm in 1922. Fruit: medium to large; skin dark red; flesh orange yellow, tender, juicy, sweet; quality fair for dessert, good for canning; season third week of August. Tree: upright spreading; very hardy; productive; suitable for northern conditions.

Brilliant.--Originated in Mountain Grove, Missouri, by the Missouri State Fruit Experiment Station (Paul H. Shepard). Introduced commercially in 1947. Burbank x Methley; selected in 1947. Fruit: skin red with light blue bloom; large; round; smooth; flesh firm, yellow, sweet; clingstone; ripens about middle of July. Tree: productive; resembles Methley in growth habit.

Burbank's Flaming Delicious.--See **Flaming Delicious.**

Burbank's Great Yellow.--See **Great Yellow.**

Burbank's June Redskin.--See **June Redskin.**

Burbank's Mammoth Cardinal.--See **Mammoth Cardinal.**

Crystal Red.--Originated in North Grimsby, Ontario, Canada, by A. W. Eickmeier. Introduced commercially in 1943. Patent no.

560; December 22, 1942. Parentage unknown, but of Japanese type; selected in 1940. Fruit: matures 2 to 3 weeks earlier than Burbank, which it resembles; highly colored; excellent shipper. Tree: regular and early bearer; strong grower; upright spreading; hardy.

Early Santa Rosa.--See **Star Rosa**.

Elephant Heart.--Originated in Sebastopol, California, by Luther Burbank. Introduced commercially in 1929 by Stark Brothers Nurseries and Orchards Company, Louisiana, Missouri. Parentage unknown; selected about 1920. Fruit: flesh blood red; freestone; very large; quality good. Tree: strong; hardy.

Elliot *(Minnesota 8).*--Originated in Excelsior, Minnesota, by the University of Minnesota Fruit Breeding Farm. Introduced commercially in 1920. *Prunus salicina* (probably Apple variety) x *P. americana* (unnamed seedling); selected in 1911. Fruit: large; quality good; red; matures late. Tree: medium height; very hardy; production heavy and reliable.

Ember *(Minnesota 83).*--Originated in Excelsior, Minnesota, by the University of Minnesota Fruit Breeding Farm. Introduced commercially in February, 1936. Shiro x South Dakota 33; cross made in 1913, selected in 1918. Fruit: matures late; high dessert and culinary quality; will keep for 2 to 3 weeks after ripening.

Eugene.--Originated in Elk Grove, California, by Claud Tribble. Introduced commercially in 1944. Apparently an open pollinated seedling of a Japanese-type plum; selected in 1940. Fruit: of large size and good quality. Tree: very productive.

Fiebing.--Originated in Deephaven, Minnesota, by Charles Haralson. Introduced commercially about 1929. Wickson (probably) x Kaga; selected about 1929. Fruit: large size. Tree: very hardy.

Flaming Delicious *(Burbank's Flaming Delicious).*--Originated in Sebastopol, California, by Luther Burbank. Introduced commercially in 1934. Patent no. 14; April 15, 1932; assigned to Stark Brothers Nurseries and Orchards Company, Louisiana, Missouri. Parentage unknown. Fruit: flesh red; freestone; early maturing. Tree: heavy bearer; hardy.

Florida.--See **Red Ace**.

Giant.--Originated in Milford, Connecticut, by DeRoss and Duane Kellogg. Introduced commercially in 1946. Patent no. 793; March 23, 1948; assigned to Stark Brothers Nurseries and Orchards Company, Louisiana, Missouri. Open pollinated seedling of Abundance; discovered August 27, 1940. Fruit: size 1½ inches in diameter; flesh yellow but red next to skin; subacid; clingstone; most nearly resembles Compass.

Golden Rod *(Minnesota 120).*--Originated in Excelsior, Minnesota, by the University of Minnesota Fruit Breeding Farm. Introduced commercially in 1923. Shiro x Howard's Yellow *(Prunus americana);* cross made in 1913; selected in 1920. Fruit: large; yellow; firm. No longer recommended because it is a very shy bearer.

Great Yellow *(Burbank's Great Yellow).*--Originated in Sebastopol, California, by Luther Burbank. Introduced commercially in 1931 by Stark Brothers Nurseries and Orchards Company, Louisiana, Missouri. Patent no. 13; April 5, 1932. Parentage unknown; selected about 1920. Fruit: flesh yellow; freestone; flavor mild; quality good; large; matures early. Tree: hardy.

Grenville.--Originated in Ottawa, Ontario, Canada, by the Division of Horticulture, Central Experimental Farm. Introduced commercially in 1941. Burbank x *Prunus nigra;* selected in 1932. Fruit: quality excellent; Japanese type; large; red; most nearly resembles Burbank. Tree: very hardy.

Hall.--Originated in Geneva, New York, by the New York State Agricultural Experiment Station (Richard Wellington). Introduced for trial in 1923. Golden Drop x Grand Duke; cross made in 1908; seed germinated in 1909. Fruit: large; attractive; quality good; most nearly resembles Grand Duke.

Hennepin *(Minnesota 132).*--Originated in Excelsior, Minnesota, by the University of Minnesota Fruit Breeding Farm. Introduced commercially in 1923. Satsuma x *Prunus americana;* cross made in 1911, selected about 1918. Fruit: flesh red; good preserving quality. Tree: hardy; very productive.

Hollywood.--Originated in Modesto, California, by L. L. Brooks. Introduced commercially in 1936. *Prunus pissardi* x *P. salicina* (direction of cross unknown); discovered about 1932; first commercially propagated by Ralph S. Moore, Visalia, California. Fruit: flesh red, like a giant cherry; ripens early, in Beauty season; used for jelly and canning; most nearly resembles Satsuma. Tree: most nearly resembles *Prunus pissardi.*

Honeymoon.--Originated in Sebastopol, California, by Luther Burbank. Introduced commercially in 1931 by Stark Brothers Nurseries and Orchards Company, Louisiana, Missouri. Green Gage x an unknown variety; selected in 1920. Fruit: golden yellow; large; quality high; midseason; most nearly resembles known parent.

Howard Miracle.--Originated in Montebello, California, by Frederick H. Howard. Introduced commercially in 1947. Patent no. 721; December 31, 1946; assigned to Howard and Smith, Montebello, California. Parentage unknown; discovered about 1941. Fruit: Japanese type; large; flesh firm; matures late in August in the vicinity of Montebello; flavor very good and distinctive; ships well. Tree: needs cross-pollination.

Improved Satsuma.--See **Mariposa.**

June Redskin *(Burbank's June Redskin)*.--Originated in Sebastopol, California, by Luther Burbank. Introduced commercially in 1934. Patent no. 12; April 5, 1932; assigned to Stark Brothers Nurseries and Orchards Company, Louisiana, Missouri. Parentage unknown; selected about 1922. Fruit: flesh yellow, acid to sweet; skin red; round; season early, June 25 at Sebastopol.

La Crescent *(Minnesota 109)*.--Originated in Excelsior, Minnesota, by the University of Minnesota Fruit Breeding Farm. Introduced commercially in 1923. Shiro x Howard's Yellow *(Prunus americana)*; cross made in 1913; selected in 1919. Fruit: small; yellow; good dessert quality.

Late President.--Originated in Le Grand, California, by F. W. Anderson. Introduced commercially in 1944. Patent no. 573; March 16, 1943. Bud mutation of President; discovered in 1935. Fruit: ripens about 2 weeks later than President, otherwise identical with parental type.

Lewis.--See **Prinlew.**

Maglio.--Originated in Nelson, British Columbia, Canada, by Carmine Maglio. Introduced commercially in 1936. Patent no. 413; July 23, 1940. Parentage unknown; first fruited in 1925. Fruit: medium size; skin red, tough, bitter; clingstone; juicy; flavor at pit unpleasant; of Japanese type; hangs well on tree so picking season is long; matures about same season as Italian, but cannot compete with Italian for quality. Tree: upright, spreading; vigorous; not too winter hardy.

Mammoth Cardinal *(Burbank's Mammoth Cardinal)*.--Originated in Sebastopol, California, by Luther Burbank. Introduced commercially in 1934. Patent no. 16; May 10, 1932; assigned to Stark Brothers Nurseries and Orchards Company, Louisiana, Missouri. Parentage unknown; selected about 1919. Fruit: skin red; flesh yellow; clingstone; large; quality high; ships well; ripens July 14 at Sebastopol; similar if not identical with Formosa.

Mandarin.--Originated in Dropmore, Manitoba, Canada, by F. L. Skinner. Introduced commercially in 1941 by the Manitoba Hardy Plant Nursery, Dropmore, Manitoba. Open pollinated seedling of *Prunus salicina*; selected in 1940. Fruit: skin purple;

flesh meaty, sweet, cooks up well; 1 to 1¼ inches in diameter; ripens in August. Tree: hardy throughout western Canada.

Mariposa *(Improved Satsuma)*.--Originated in Pasadena, California, by Mrs. J. B. Thompson. Introduced commercially in 1935. Patent no. 111; November 13, 1934; assigned to Armstrong Nurseries, Inc., Ontario, California. Parentage unknown; selected as a seedling in 1923. Fruit: sweeter than Satsuma, which it resembles. Tree: resistant to delayed foliation in southern California.

Marvel.--Originated in Mountain Grove, Missouri, by the Missouri State Fruit Experiment Station (Paul H. Shepard). Introduced commercially in 1947. Burbank x Methley; selected in 1947. Fruit: large; better skin color than either parent; solid red flesh; clingstone; uniform in size and color; does not drop readily. Tree: highly productive.

Mendota *(Minnesota 5)*.--Originated in Excelsior, Minnesota, by the University of Minnesota Fruit Breeding Farm. Introduced commercially in 1924. Burbank x Wolf; cross made in 1908; selected about 1912. Fruit: large; quality good.

Minnesota 5.--See **Mendota**.

Minnesota 8.--See **Elliot**.

Minnesota 10.--See **Waconia**.

Minnesota 12.--See **Red Wing**

Minnesota 17.--See **Redcoat**.

Minnesota 21.--See **Tonka**.

Minnesota 30.--See **Winona**.

Minnesota 50.--See **Mound**.

Minnesota 83.--See **Ember**.

Minnesota 91.--See **Underwood**.

Minnesota 101.--See **Redglow**.

Minnesota 109.--See **La Crescent**.

Minnesota 116.--See **Newport**.

Minnesota 118.--See **Anoka**.

Minnesota 120.--See **Golden Rod.**

Minnesota 132.--See **Hennepin.**

Minnesota 157.--See **Radisson.**

Minnesota 194.--See **Superior.**

Minnesota 218.--See **Pipestone.**

Monitor.--Originated in Excelsior, Minnesota, by the Minnesota Agricultural Experiment Station (W. H. Alderman). Introduced commercially in 1920. Burbank x a native American plum; first fruited in 1918. Fruit: medium to large; roundish-ovate; dull bronze-red; quality good; clingstone; cracks in rainy weather. Tree: vigorous; very hardy; productive.

Monster.--Originated in Sebastopol, California, by Luther Burbank. Introduced commercially in 1941 by Stark Brothers Nurseries and Orchards Company, Louisiana, Missouri. Parentage unknown; selected in 1936. Fruit: very large; flesh red. Tree: productive.

Morden 101.--See **Norther.**

Morden 105.--See **Bounty.**

Mound *(Minnesota 50).*--Originated in Excelsior, Minnesota, by the University of Minnesota Fruit Breeding Farm. Introduced commercially in 1922. Burbank x Wolf; cross made in 1908. Fruit: medium red; flesh yellow; partly freestone. Tree: vigorous; hardy; very productive.

Mount Royal.--Originated in Outremont, Quebec, Canada, by W. W. Dunlop. Has not been introduced commercially. Parentage unknown; discovered in 1913. Fruit: dark blue skin; size medium; good for canning. Tree: very hardy, being the hardiest domestica plum at Ottawa.

New Jersey 1.--See **Raribank.**

Newport *(Minnesota 116).*--Originated in Excelsior, Minnesota, by the University of Minnesota Fruit Breeding Farm. Introduced commercially in 1923. Omaha x *Prunus pissardi.* An ornamental with purple foliage.

Norther *(Morden 101).*--Originated in Morden, Manitoba, Canada, by the Dominion Experimental Station. Introduced commercially in 1944. Open pollinated seedling of Assiniboine; selected in 1933 from seed originally sent from the Minnesota State Fruit Breeding Farm in 1922. Fruit: medium size; skin bright red, grey bloom; flesh yellowish, juicy, sweet; quality good as dessert, fair for canning; season early to mid-August. Tree: moderately spreading; sturdy; very hardy; suited to northern prairies.

Ottawa 302.--See **Algoma.**

Ox-Heart.--Originated in Mountain Grove, Missouri, by the Missouri State Fruit Experiment Station (Paul H. Shepard). Introduced commercially in 1947. Burbank x Methley; selected in 1947. Fruit: very large; shaped like Burbank, but larger and redder; clingstone; flesh red, firm; flavor good, sweet. Tree: vigorous; resembles Methley in tree growth.

Ozark Premier.--Originated in Mountain Grove, Missouri, by the Missouri State Fruit Experiment Station (Paul H. Shepard). Introduced commercially in 1946. Burbank x Methley; selected in 1943. Fruit: extremely large; firm; red; suture shallow; flesh yellow; clingstone; juicy, tart, flavor good; seed small; skin tough; ripens August 1, with Burbank which it most nearly resembles.

Padre.--Originated in Palo Alto, California, by the United States Department of Agriculture (W. F. Wight). Introduced commercially in 1938. Wickson x Santa Rosa. Fruit: early shipping plum, slightly later than Santa Rosa. Japanese type.

Pipestone *(Minnesota 218)*.--Originated in Excelsior, Minnesota, by the University of Minnesota Fruit Breeding Farm. Introduced for trial in 1928; introduced commercially in 1942. Burbank x *(Prunus salicina* x Wolf); cross made in 1919; fruited in 1926. Fruit: large; skin solid deep red, thin, tough but peeling easily; flesh yellow, somewhat stringy, with excellent quality; for home and commercial use. Tree: vigorous; hardy; performance reliable.

Prinlew *(Lewis)*.--Originated in Portland, Oregon, by H. A. Lewis. Introduced commercially in 1923. Italian prune x Bradshaw plum; selected in 1918. Fruit: large, firm, juicy; flavor good; texture of flesh fine; ships well.

Purple Flame.--Originated in Sebastopol, California, by Luther Burbank. Introduced commercially in 1931 by Stark Brothers Nurseries and Orchards Company, Louisiana, Missouri; trademarked by this company. Parentage unknown; selected about 1922. Fruit: flesh red; quality good. Tree: foliage red; an ornamental variety.

Radiance.--Originated in Mountain Grove, Missouri, by the Missouri State Fruit Experiment Station (Paul H. Shepard). Introduced commercially in 1947. Stanley x President; selected in

1947. Fruit: large; skin light yellow with pink blush; attractive; resembling Yellow Egg in size and shape; freestone; flesh yellow, firm; flavor good, sweet. Tree: vigorous; productive.

Radisson *(Minnesota 157)*.--Originated in Excelsior, Minnesota, by the University of Minnesota Fruit Breeding Farm. Introduced commercially in 1925. *Prunus salicina* x *P. americana*; cross made in 1907 or 1908. Fruit: large; round; skin rich red with heavy bloom; flesh firm, yellow; semifreestone; quality high.

Raribank *(New Jersey 1)*.--Originated in New Brunswick, New Jersey, by the New Jersey Agricultural Experiment Station (J. H. Clarke). Introduced commercially in 1949. Parentage unknown; wild beach plum *(Prunus maritima)* selection. Fruit: purplish red; freestone; good quality; good as jelly or canned; ripens during early September in New Brunswick. Tree: large; vigorous; very resistant to brown rot and Japanese beetle.

Red Ace *(Florida)*.--Originated in Sebastopol, California, by Luther Burbank. Introduced commercially in 1931 by Stark Brothers Nurseries and Orchards Company, Louisiana, Missouri; trademarked by this company. Parentage unknown; selected about 1923. Most nearly resembles Elephant Heart. Fruit: flesh red; freestone; quality excellent. Tree: hardy; growth spreading; very productive.

Redbud.--Originated in Mountain Grove, Missouri, by the Missouri State Fruit Experiment Station (Paul H. Shepard). Introduced commercially in 1947. Burbank x Methley; selected in 1947. Fruit: when the small fruit first appears it is red inside and out; most nearly resembles Methley. Tree: can be used for both ornamental and fruiting purposes; has purple foliage and red blossoms; productive.

Redcoat *(Minnesota 17)*.--Originated in Excelsior, Minnesota, by the University of Minnesota Fruit Breeding Farm. Introduced commercially in April, 1942. Burbank *(Prunus salicina)* x Wolf *(P. americana)*; cross made in 1908. Fruit: freestone; skin crimson overlaid with a heavy bloom, thin, tender; flesh yellow, meaty, medium juicy; flavor sweet to mild, subacid, pleasant; season early, closely following Underwood; good canning and culinary qualities. Tree: productive; hardy; bears early.

Redglow *(Minnesota 101)*.--Originated in Excelsior, Minnesota, by the University of Minnesota Fruit Breeding Farm. Introduced commercially March, 1949. Burbank x Jewell; selected in 1919 from seed planted in 1914. Fruit: large; skin dark red with heavy bloom, thick; flesh orange, juicy, tender, sweet; clingstone; ripening in midseason. Tree: hardy; productive. Most nearly resembles Tonka.

Red Wing *(Minnesota 12)*.--Originated in Excelsior, Minnesota, by the University of Minnesota Fruit Breeding Farm. Introduced commercially in 1920. Burbank x Wolf; cross made in 1908. Fruit: large; quality good; flesh firm, yellow.

Rich Pride.--Originated in Junction City, Oregon, by Chris Rich. Introduced commercially in 1946. Parentage unknown; selected about 1920. Fruit: large; ripens very late; good drying qualities; especially good as fresh fruit.

Sapalta.--Originated in Brooks, Alberta, Canada, by the Canadian Pacific Railway in the spring of 1924. Introduced commercially in 1938. It was one of a lot of 1,000 seedlings secured from the Northwest Nursery Company, Valley City, North Dakota; probably a seedling of Sapa. Varietal name is a contraction of Alberta Sapa. Fruit: sand cherry; similar to Sapa but with tendency toward freestone condition; smaller seed with slight ridge on each side. Tree: bush habit, and difficult to distinguish from Sapa.

South Dakota *(South Dakota 27)*.--Originated in Brookings, South Dakota, by the South Dakota Agricultural Experiment Station (N. E. Hansen). Introduced commercially in March, 1949, by the Minnesota Fruit Breeding Farm, Excelsior, Minnesota, with the approval of the South Dakota Experiment Station. Parentage unknown; selected before 1907. Fruit: medium size; freestone; good quality. Tree: excellent pollinator; very hardy, productive; excellent parent for breeding hardy freestone plums.

South Dakota 27.--See **South Dakota**.

Stanley.--Originated in Geneva, New York, by the New York State Agricultural Experiment Station (Richard Wellington). Introduced for trial in 1926. Agen x Grand Duke; cross made in 1912; seed germinated in 1913. Fruit: appearance attractive; ripens 1 week earlier than Italian; most nearly resembles prune type of fruit; better in fruit and tree than Italian. Tree: more reliable in bearing and more adaptable than Italian.

Star Rosa *(Early Santa Rosa)*.--Originated in Di Giorgio, California, by the Di Giorgio Fruit Corporation (Elmer Stark). Introduced commercially June 14, 1950. Patent no. 995; November 28, 1950; assigned July 15, 1948 to the Di Giorgio Fruit Corporation, 433 California Street, San Francisco, California; trademarked 'Oh Yes' Brand. Bud mutation of Santa Rosa. Fruit: larger and ripens earlier than Santa Rosa which it most nearly resembles; improved keeping quality over its parent.

Superior *(Minnesota 194)*.--Originated in Excelsior, Minnesota, by the University of Minnesota Fruit Breeding Farm. Introduced commercially in January, 1933. Burbank x Kaga; selected in 1925. Fruit: early; large; firm; quality superior. Tree: prolific bearer; vigorous.

Tonka *(Minnesota 21)*.--Originated in Excelsior, Minnesota, by the University of Minnesota Fruit Breeding Farm. Introduced commercially in 1920. Burbank x Wolf; cross made in 1908. Fruit: large; quality high. Tree: heavy and reliable producer, but short-lived.

Twilite.--Originated in Mountain Grove, Missouri, by the Missouri State Fruit Experiment Station (Paul H. Shepard). Introduced commercially in 1947. Open pollinated seedling of Black Beauty; selected in 1947. Fruit: skin red with light blue bloom; clingstone; flesh yellow; flavor good; very late ripening, about September 10; will remain firm and in good shape on tree for three or four weeks after that time.

Underwood *(Minnesota 91)*.--Originated in Excelsior, Minnesota, by the University of Minnesota Fruit Breeding Farm. Introduced commercially in 1920. Shiro x Wyant; cross made in 1911; selected in 1916. Fruit: dull red; quality good. Tree: vigorous; heavy bearer.

Waconia *(Minnesota 10)*.--Originated in Excelsior, Minnesota, by the University of Minnesota Fruit Breeding Farm. Introduced commercially in 1923. Burbank x Wolf; cross made in 1908; selected in 1914. Tree: uniformly productive; hardy; quality fair. This variety is no longer propagated.

Winona *(Minnesota 30)*.--Originated in Excelsior, Minnesota, by the University of Minnesota Fruit Breeding Farm. Introduced commercially in 1922. *Prunus salicina* x *P. americana;* cross made in 1909 or 1910. Fruit: medium large; quality good; sweet. Tree: large; vigorous.

Yakima.--Originated in Bingen, Washington, by Theodore Suksdorf. Introduced commercially about 1925 by Washington Nurseries, Inc., Toppenish, Washington. Seedling of Peach plum; discovered about 1902; Washington Nurseries, Inc., obtained buds of this tree in 1922. Fruit: very large; somewhat oblong; skin bright mahogany red; flesh yellow, tender, sweet; very firm. Tree: very shy bearer unless cross-pollinated with other European plums.

Not named.--Originated in Santa Rosa, California, by Luther Burbank. Not introduced commercially. Patent no. 18; July 19, 1932; assigned to Stark Brothers Nurseries and Orchards Company, Louisiana, Missouri. Fruit: skin yellow, moderately thick, adhering to flesh, with a heavy white bloom; flesh rather firm, yellow, tender, melting, freestone; quality excellent; cordate with unequal sides; large. This variety did not prove to be satisfactory and was never offered for sale.

PLUMCOT

Orange.--Originated in Sebastopol, California, by Luther Burbank. Introduced commercially in 1931 by Stark Brothers Nurseries and Orchards Company, Louisiana, Missouri. Parentage unknown; selected about 1922. Fruit: skin yellow with reddish purple cheek; flesh yellow; quality good; flavor subacid.

Purple.--Originated in Sebastopol, California, by Luther Burbank. Introduced commercially in 1931 by Stark Brothers Nurseries and Orchards Company, Louisiana, Missouri; trademarked by this company. Parentage unknown, discovered about 1922. Fruit: skin purple, slightly pubescent, with heavy bloom; flesh deep purple; clingstone; quality good.

POMEGRANATE

Trauernicht.--Originated in Fort Worth, Texas, by E. C. Trauernicht. Introduced commercially in 1936. Patent no. 184; June 16, 1936; assigned to Baker Brothers Company, Fort Worth, Texas. Parentage unknown; selected in 1934. Plant: flowers all summer; produces heavily; semidwarf; hardy.

PRUNE

Gardner.--Originated in Corvallis, Oregon, by the Oregon Agricultural Experiment Station. Introduced commercially in 1923. Petite d'Agen (French) x self; selected in 1923. Fruit: sugar content high; perhaps not superior to Petite d'Agen. Tree: heavy producer.

Grand Prize.--Originated in Sebastopol, California, by Luther Burbank. Introduced commercially in 1937 by Stark Brothers Nurseries and Orchards Company, Louisiana, Missouri. Parentage unknown; selected in 1932. Fruit: very large, approximately twice the size of Italian prune; quality high.

Lafayette.--Originated in Lafayette, Oregon, by the Lafayette Nursery Company (B. Brooks). Introduced commercially in 1949. Open pollinated seedling of Italian. Fruit: identical in color and shape to Italian, but 50% larger; ripens one week earlier than Italian; higher sugar content than Italian; good canning and drying quality. Tree: annual bearer.

Merton.--Originated in Peach, Washington, by Lynn Tuttle. Introduced commercially in 1950. Bud mutation of Italian; discovered about 1935. Fruit: ripens ten days before Italian; has tendency to crack along suture some years and in some localities; most nearly resembles Italian.

Parson.--Originated in Forest Grove, Oregon, by Peter R. Parson. Introduced commercially in Fall 1947. Patent no. 872; September 13, 1949; assigned to the originator. Parentage unknown; discovered about 1939. Fruit: higher sugar content and ripens earlier than Italian, which it most nearly resembles. Tree: hardier and heavier bearing than Italian.

Richards Early Italian.--Originated in Wapato, Washington, by E. C. Richards. Introduced commercially in 1935. Parentage unknown; selected in 1930. Fruit: ripens 3 days before Demaris. Most nearly resembles Italian.

Weatherspoon.--Originated in Elgin, Oregon, by H. H. Weatherspoon. Introduced commercially about 1920. Parentage unknown. Fruit: large; good shipping quality; ripens a week ahead of Italian; most nearly resembles Italian.

QUINCE

Rich.--Originated in Hillsboro, Oregon, by Chris Rich. Introduced commercially in 1948. Parentage unknown; selected about 1940. Tree: uniform shape; less subject to dry rot than other varieties.

RASPBERRY

Amber.--Originated in Geneva, New York, by the New York State Agricultural Experiment Station (George L. Slate). Introduced commercially in the fall of 1950. Taylor x Cuthbert; cross made in 1936. Fruit: amber; large; flavor good, sweet. Plant: very vigorous. Introduced for home use; not considered of commercial value.

Bonanza.--Originated in Ontario, California, by Armstrong Nurseries, Inc. (Herbert C. Swim). Introduced commercially in 1949. Patent no. 908; December 20, 1949; assigned to Armstrong Nurseries, Inc., Ontario, California. Sunrise x Washington; selected in 1945. Fruit: ripens 2 to 3 weeks earlier than Sunrise, tending to continue fruit production throughout the growing season with heavier crop in the fall. Bush: vigorous; low chilling requirement; heavy fruit production in southern California.

Brant.--Originated in Geneva, New York, by the New York State Agricultural Experiment Station (Richard Wellington). Introduced for trial in 1925. Smith 1 x June; cross made in 1912. Fruit: purple; large; handsome; firm; holds up well; of good quality. Now out of cultivation because of mosaic.

Bristol.--Originated in Geneva, New York, by the New York State Agricultural Experiment Station (Richard Wellington). Introduced for trial in 1934. Watson Prolific x Honeysweet; cross made in 1921. Fruit: black; large; firm; fairly glossy; attractive; quality excellent; season 1 week earlier than Naples. Bush: hardy, vigorous; bears heavy crops. Now widely planted as one of the best varieties.

Cayuga.--Originated in Geneva, New York, by the New York State Agricultural Experiment Station (Richard Wellington). Introduced for trial in 1922. June x Cuthbert; cross made in 1910. Fruit: red; ripens before Cuthbert, which it resembles. Bush: productive; suckers heavily. Variety now superseded by better sorts.

Chief *(Minnesota 223).*--Originated in Excelsior, Minnesota, by the University of Minnesota Fruit Breeding Farm. Introduced commercially in May, 1930. Latham x self; selected in 1920. Fruit: early; quality good. Bush: hardy, vigorous.

Dike.--Originated in Bristol, Vermont, by A. C. Dike. Introduced commercially about 1926. Latham x Cuthbert. Fruit: red; color good; quality good. Bush: hardy; resistant to mosaic.

Dixie.--Originated in Raleigh, North Carolina, by the North Carolina Agricultural Experiment Station (Carlos F. Williams). Introduced commercially in 1938. *Rubus biflorus* x Latham; selected from a cross made in 1928. Fruit: red; size medium; tart. Bush: vigorous, productive; disease resistant; adapted to southeastern states south of the region of American red raspberries thus far produced; most nearly resembles a hybrid with Asiatic species.

Dundee.--Originated in Geneva, New York, by the New York State Agricultural Experiment Station (Richard Wellington). Introduced for trial in 1927. Smith 1 x Palmer; cross made in 1910. Fruit: black; large; glossy; small drupelets attractive, moderately firm, mildly subacid; quality very good. Bush: tall; vigorous; productive; moderately resistant to mosaic.

Durham.--Originated in Durham, New Hampshire, by the New Hampshire Agricultural Experiment Station (A. F. Yeager). Introduced commercially in 1947. Taylor x Nectar blackberry; cross attempted in greenhouse but the seedling is probably a parthenogenetic seed therefrom; selected in 1944. Fruit: red;

firm; medium size; fall bearing, beginning to ripen 2 weeks before the fall crop of Indian Summer, hence a worthwhile crop in autumn.

Evans.--Originated in Geneva, New York, by the New York State Agricultural Experiment Station (Richard Wellington). Introduced for trial in 1936. Watson Prolific x Honeysweet; cross made in 1921. Fruit: black; high quality, very glossy; appearance attractive, only moderately firm. Little grown in New York; considered promising in southern California.

Gatineau *(Ottawa 276).*--Originated in Ottawa, Ontario, Canada, by the Division of Horticulture, Central Experimental Farm. Introduced commercially in 1943. Lloyd George x Newman; selected in 1931. Fruit: red; early ripening.

Honeyking.--Originated in Parkside, Saskatchewan, Canada, by A. J. Porter. Introduced commercially in 1948. Viking x a native raspberry; selected in 1945. Fruit: red; very good quality for canning; fruit too small where standard sorts can be grown. Bush: cold resistant; yields well.

Honeysweet (of New Jersey).--See **Yellow Honeysweet**.

Honeywood.--Originated in Parkside, Saskatchewan, Canada, by Claude Swan. Introduced commercially in 1941. Parentage unknown; discovered in 1936. Fruit: black; medium; quality good. Bush: not entirely winter hardy.

Indian Summer.--Originated in Geneva, New York, by the New York State Agricultural Experiment Station (Richard Wellington). Introduced for trial in 1936. New York 1950 (Empire x Herbert) x Lloyd George; cross made in 1925; seedling first fruited in 1928. Fruit: red; very aromatic; crumbles frequently; useful for jam; superior to Ranere (St. Regis) and Erskine Park; quality good as an autumn-fruiting variety. Bush: very productive; escapes mosaic infection. Planted extensively in home gardens.

Johnson Everbearing.--Originated in Davis, West Virginia, by A. W. Johnson. Introduced commercially in 1945. Parentage unknown; discovered in 1934, supposedly as a wild plant. Fruit: black; large. Plant: pronounced fall-bearing habit; most nearly resembles Cumberland.

Latham *(Minnesota 4).*--Originated in Excelsior, Minnesota by the University of Minnesota Fruit Breeding Farm. Introduced commercially in 1920. King x Louden; cross made in 1908; selected in 1914. Fruit: quality high. Bush: hardy; productive; markedly tolerant of mosaic.

Lloyd George.--Originated as a chance seedling in a wood in Dorsetshire, England. Introduced in England by J. J. Hettle, Corbe Castle, Dorset, England. Introduced for trial in the United States in 1929 by the New York State Agricultural Experiment Station. Parentage unknown. Fruit: red; quality excellent; variety considered very promising in 1928 but now sparingly grown. An outstanding parent in breeding new varieties.

Madawaska *(Ottawa 272)*.--Originated in Ottawa, Ontario, Canada, by the Division of Horticulture, Central Experimental Farm. Introduced commercially in 1943. Lloyd George x Newman; selected in 1931. Fruit: dark red; excellent canner; early ripening. Plant: hardy.

Magnaberry.--Originated in Ontario, California, by Armstrong Nurseries, Inc. (Herbert C. Swim). Introduced commercially in 1949. Patent no. 1,008; March 20, 1951; assigned to Armstrong Nurseries, Inc., Ontario, California. F_3 (Nessberry x Sodus raspberry); selected in 1945. Fruit: combines flavor of the raspberry and blackberry, excellent for jam or jelly with a distinct flavor and fine appearance. Bush: large; vigorous: produces heavy crops.

Marcy.--Originated in Geneva, New York, by the New York State Agricultural Experiment Station (Richard Wellington). Introduced for trial in 1936. Lloyd George x Newman; seedling first fruited in 1928. Fruit: red; extremely large, firm, thick-fleshed; flavor mild; quality good but too dark in color when fully ripe. Bush: lacks hardiness; escapes mosaic.

Marion.--Originated in Geneva, New York, by the New York Agricultural Experiment Station (Richard Wellington). Introduced for trial in 1937. Bristol x New York 2585 (Newman x Herbert); selected in 1930. Fruit: purple; large; moderately juicy; firm; tart; quality good; season late, 1 week after Sodus. Bush: resembles red raspberry in habit.

Milton.--Originated in Geneva, New York, by the New York State Agricultural Experiment Station. Introduced commercially in 1942. Lloyd George x Newburgh; cross made in 1927. Fruit: bright red; large; firm; quality good; ripens late; most nearly resembles Taylor. Plant: vigorous; productive; escapes mosaic.

Minnesota 4.--See **Latham.**

Minnesota 223.--See **Chief.**

Monroe.--Originated in Geneva, New York, by the New York State Agricultural Experiment Station (Richard Wellington). Few sent out for trial in 1932. Newman x Cuthbert; cross made in 1921. Fruit: red; firm; quality and flavor excellent, but more acid than Cuthbert; ripens about 1 week before Cuthbert. Variety never formally introduced and now superseded by better ones.

Morris.--See **Morrison**.

Morrison *(Morris).*--Originated in North Kingsville, Ohio, by Fred Morris. Introduced commercially in 1942. Parentage unknown; discovered about 1925. Fruit: black; large; attractive; season late; most nearly resembles Cumberland.

Mortgage Lifter.--Originated in Berrien County, Michigan, by O. K. White. Introduced commercially in January, 1949. Parentage unknown; discovered in 1946 as a seedling along a fence row. Fruit: good size; black; sweet; early ripening, continuing to bear throughout the season; resembles both Cumberland and Logan.

Naples.--Originated in Geneva, New York, by the New York State Agricultural Experiment Station (Richard Wellington). Introduced for trial in 1932. Honeysweet x Rachel; cross made in 1921. Fruit: black; large, firm, glossy, attractive; quality good; season 1 week later than Bristol. Bush: vigorous, productive, hardy, susceptible to mosaic. Plantings are decreasing.

Newburgh.--Originated in Geneva, New York, by the New York State Agricultural Experiment Station (Richard Wellington). Introduced for trial in 1929. Newman x Herbert; cross made in 1922. Fruit: red; very large and firm; bright, attractive color; keeping and shipping quality very good; ripens 3 to 4 days earlier than Cuthbert. Bush: mosaic is rarely serious. An important commercial variety.

Newman *(Newman 23).*--Originated in Ville La Salle, Quebec, Canada, by C. P. Newman. Introduced commercially in 1924. Parentage unknown; selected about 1918. Fruit: red; large; flavor mild; season with or a little later than Cuthbert. Plant: susceptible to mosaic. Variety now almost obsolete.

New York 17438.--See **September**.

Ontario 2504137.--See **Vandyke**.

Ottawa *(Ottawa 275).*--Originated in Ottawa, Ontario, Canada, by the Division of Horticulture, Central Experimental Farm. Introduced commercially in 1943. Viking x (Logan x Ranere); selected in 1931. Fruit: red; firm; good shipper. Most nearly resembles Viking.

Ottawa 262.--See **Rideau**.

Ottawa 263.--See **Tweed**.

Ottawa 264.--See **Trent**.

Ottawa 272.--See **Madawaska**.

Ottawa 275.--See **Ottawa**.

Ottawa 276.--See **Gatineau**.

Owasco.--Originated in Geneva, New York, by the New York State Agricultural Experiment Station (Richard Wellington). Introduced for trial in 1922. June x Cuthbert; cross made in 1910. Fruit: red; excellent in every way. Bush: poor plant-maker; not too hardy; variable in growth habit. Variety now eliminated by mosaic.

Park Black.--Originated in Des Moines, Iowa, by Charles Park. Introduced commercially in January, 1950, by the Earl Ferris Nursery, Hampton, Iowa. Open pollinated seedling of Cumberland; discovered in 1929. Fruit: long and large; very uniform in size; flavor good. Bush: hardy; vigorous; heavy producer; relatively free from disease.

Potomac.--Originated in Glenn Dale, Maryland, by the United States Department of Agriculture (George F. Waldo). Introduced commercially in 1933. Farmer black raspberry x Newman red raspberry; selected in 1924. Fruit: purple; well suited for canning and preserving. Bush: resistant to fungus disease; free from virus diseases; vigorous; productive.

Rideau *(Ottawa 262)*.--Originated in Ottawa, Ontario, Canada, by the Division of Horticulture, Central Experimental Farm. Introduced commercially in 1943. Lloyd George x Newman; selected in 1931. Fruit: red; firm; good shipper; bright and attractive.

Ruddy.--Originated in Fargo, North Dakota, by the North Dakota Agricultural Experiment Station (A. F. Yeager). Introduced commercially in 1937. Selected F_2 seedling (Plum Farmer x Latham); selected in 1933. Fruit: purple. Bush: produces well; reproduces by suckers as do the red varieties; resistant to red spider; very hardy.

Seneca.--Originated in Geneva, New York, by the New York State Agricultural Experiment Station (Richard Wellington). Introduced for trial in 1922. June x Cuthbert. Fruit: red. Bush: almost identical with Cayuga, but plants not as tall, with fewer prickles; at one time recommended to precede and to take the place of Cuthbert; susceptible to mosaic, which has now eliminated it.

September *(New York 17438)*.--Originated in Geneva, New York, by the New York State Agricultural Experiment Station (George L. Slate). Introduced commercially in the fall of 1947. Marcy x Ranere; cross made in 1934; selected for second test in 1939. Fruit: bright red; firm; size medium; fruitlets do not crumble; quality of summer crop is only fair, but the autumn berries are considered good in quality; summer crop is as early as that of Indian Summer and June or about 5 days earlier than Newburgh; fall crop matures 2 to 4 weeks before that of Indian Summer; principal fault is the tendency of the berries, especially of the summer crop, to cling to the bushes rather more tightly than is desirable in a commercial berry. Bush: vigorous; increases rapidly; hardy at Geneva; crops well; reaction to mosaic not known.

Sodus.--Originated in Geneva, New York, by the New York State Agricultural Experiment Station (George L. Slate). Introduced for trial in 1935. Dundee (black raspberry) x Newburgh (red raspberry); cross made in 1927. Fruit: purple; large, firm, medium color; sprightly; quality good but not equal to Columbian; season shortly after Latham. Bush: very vigorous, very productive, hardy; more resistant to drought than Columbian; free from mosaic, but variety is susceptible to it and verticillium wilt. Now an important commercial variety.

Sunrise.--Originated in Glenn Dale, Maryland, by the United States Department of Agriculture (George M. Darrow). Introduced commercially in 1939. Latham x Ranere; selected in 1923. Fruit: red, matures very early, 2 days before Ranere and nearly 2 weeks before Latham; quality better than Latham; size intermediate between Ranere and Latham; texture fine; does not crumble; picks easily. Bush: resistant to leaf spot and anthracnose; very hardy.

Tahoma.--Originated in Puyallup, Washington, by the Western Washington Experiment Station. Introduced commercially in 1938. Latham x Lloyd George; selected in 1935. Fruit: red; ripens very early; shipping quality good. Plant: hardy; escapes mosaic infection; resistant to western yellow rust.

Taxpayer.--Originated in Sarona, Wisconsin, by Asaph B. Curtis. Introduced commercially in 1934. Patent 113; November 20, 1934. Selected from the wild. Fruit: color cream with a light pink hue; matures in Wisconsin during the period July 4 to 25. Plant: canes almost thornless. No longer grown as fruits too light in color to sell well.

Taylor.--Originated in Geneva, New York, by the New York State

Agricultural Experiment Station (Richard Wellington). Introduced for trial in 1935. Newman x Lloyd George; cross made in
1925. Fruit: red; ripens with Latham; very large; color bright,
attractive; does not crumble, does not cling to bush; withstands handling; quality high. Bush; vigorous, productive,
tall, increases rapidly; more subject to mosaic than Newburgh.

Tennessee Autumn *(Tennessee Y944)*.--Originated in Knoxville,
Tennessee, by the Tennessee Agricultural Experiment Station.
Introduced commercially in 1940. Patent no. 512; April 28,
1942; assigned to the University of Tennessee Research Corporation, Knoxville, Tennessee. Tennessee Seedling 181 x Lloyd
George; selected in 1935. Fruit: red; quality good. Plants:
healthy; production heavy; some southern adaptation; two crops
per year.

Tennessee Luscious *(Tennessee X37)*.--Originated in Knoxville,
Tennessee, by the Tennessee Agricultural Experiment Station
(Brooks D. Drain). Introduced commercially in 1944. Patent no.
653; March 6, 1945; assigned to the University of Tennessee
Research Corporation, Knoxville, Tennessee. Lloyd George x
Tennessee VVF 169 (Van Fleet x Viking). Fruit: large firm;
conic; medium red, glossy; drupelets strongly coherent; sub-
acid; flavor very good; season late; most nearly resembles
Cuthbert.

Tennessee Prolific *(Tennessee X288)*.--Originated in Knoxville,
Tennessee, by the Tennessee Agricultural Experiment Station
(Brooks D. Drain). Introduced commercially in December, 1948.
Lloyd George x Tennessee seedling VVF 169 (Van Fleet x Viking);
cross made in 1935. Fruit: ripens about the same season as
Latham; firm and handles well; good freezing quality; most
nearly resembles Tennessee Luscious; well adapted to Tennessee
and nearby areas.

Tennessee X37.--See **Tennessee Luscious.**

Tennessee X288.--See **Tennessee Prolific.**

Tennessee Y944.--See **Tennessee Autumn.**

Toms.--Originated in Nevada, Iowa, by Lawrence E. Toms. Introduced commercially in 1948. Patent no. 779; January 13, 1948;
assigned to Inter-State Nurseries, Hamburg, Iowa. Chief x Plum
Farmer; discovered in 1927 or 1928. Fruit: red; quality good.
Bush: very disease resistant; bears well over a long period of
time.

Trent *(Ottawa 264)*.--Originated in Ottawa, Ontario, Canada, by
the Division of Horticulture, Central Experimental Farm. Introduced commercially in 1943. Newman x Lloyd George; selected

in 1931. Fruit: red; early maturing. Plant: hardy.

Tweed *(Ottawa 263)*.--Originated in Ottawa, Ontario, Canada, by the Division of Horticulture, Central Experimental Farm. Introduced commercially in 1946. Newman 23 x Lloyd George; selected in 1931. Fruit: red. Plant: heavy early production; very winter hardy at Ottawa.

Ulster.--Originated in Geneva, New York, by the New York State Agricultural Experiment Station (Richard Wellington). Not formally introduced, but plants sent to cooperators for trial in the late 1920's. Herbert x June; cross made in 1921. Fruit: red, large, soft, fair quality. Plant: vigorous, productive. Probably no longer in cultivation.

Vandyke *(Ontario 2504137)*.--Originated in Vineland, Ontario, Canada, by the Ontario Horticultural Experiment Station. Introduced commercially in 1947. Adams 87 x Viking; selected in 1930. Fruit: large; good quality; slightly earlier than Viking. Bush: vigorous; upright; almost spineless; not resistant to virus; yields well.

Van Fleet.--Originated in Chico, California, by the United States Department of Agriculture (Walter Van Fleet). Introduced commercially in 1924. *Rubus kuntzeanus* x Cuthbert; selected in 1911; female parent collected in China. Fruit: red. Plant: very vigorous; highly productive; resistant and hardy in southern states where other raspberry plants do not succeed.

Viking.--Originated in Vineland, Ontario, Canada, by the Ontario Horticultural Experiment Station. Introduced commercially in 1924. Cuthbert x Marlboro; selected in 1918 from 1914 breeding. Fruit: red; ripens in early midseason; large, bright, good market berry; easily picked. Most nearly resembles Cuthbert.

Washington.--Originated in Puyallup, Washington, at the Western Washington Experiment Station. Introduced commercially in 1938. Cuthbert x Lloyd George; selected in 1935. Fruit: red; quality high; canning and freezing adaptability. Plant: definite rest period; production heavy; escapes mosaic infection; resistant to western yellow rust.

Webster.--Originated in Geneva, New York, by the New York State Agricultural Experiment Station (Richard Wellington). Introduced commercially in 1926. Smith 1 black raspberry x a purple raspberry seedling; cross made in 1910. Fruit: size medium; color dark, dull purple; firm; tart; quality fair. Plants: slow growing; not very productive. Plantings are increasing in Erie County, New York.

Willamette.--Originated in Corvallis, Oregon, by the United States Department of Agriculture (George F. Waldo). Introduced commercially in 1943. Newburgh x Lloyd George; selected in 1936. Fruit: red; large; excellent for shipping; firm; most nearly resembles Newburgh, but fruit is darker.

Yellow Honeysweet *(Honeysweet* (of New Jersey)).--An unidentified French variety introduced into the United States about 1925 by Bobbink and Atkins, East Rutherford, New Jersey. Fruit: color golden yellow; flavor good.

STRAWBERRY

Adirondack.--Originated in Glens Falls, New York, by George A. Webster. Introduced commercially April 1, 1948. Fairfax x Howard 17; selected in 1940. Fruit: large, conic; flesh firm, red throughout, aromatic; calyx very showy. Plant: vigorous; deep rooted; heavy bearer over a long season. In quality ranks with Fairfax; in yield with Howard 17.

Alamo *(Texas 21).*--Originated in Texas by the Texas Agricultural Experiment Station. Introduced commercially in 1937. Blakemore x Ettersburg 80?; selected in 1935. Fruit: flavor mild. Plant: yields heavily; large; low plant producer.

Armore.--Originated in Columbia, Missouri, by the University of Missouri (H. G. Swartout). Introduced commercially in January, 1940. Blakemore x Aroma; selected in 1940. Fruit: large size throughout season; more nearly resembles Aroma in southwest Missouri. Plant: productive; sets and matures nearly all the flowers.

Arrowhead *(Minnesota 1118).*--Originated in Excelsior, Minnesota, by the University of Minnesota Fruit Breeding Farm. Introduced commercially in November, 1946. Duluth x Senator Dunlap; selected in 1929. Fruit: firm enough to stand shipping. Plant: hardy; vigorous; forms many runners; flowers perfect.

Beacon.--Originated in Geneva, New York, by the New York State Agricultural Experiment Station (Richard Wellington). Introduced for trial in 1923. President x Marshall; cross made in 1910. Fruit: ripens with Dunlap. Plant: unproductive and blossoms susceptible to frost. Now an obsolete variety.

Bellmar.--Originated in Glenn Dale, Maryland, by the United States Department of Agriculture (George M. Darrow). Introduced commercially in 1932. Missionary x Howard 17; selected in 1925. Fruit: firm; high dessert and shipping quality.

Blakemore.--Originated in Glenn Dale, Maryland, by the United States Department of Agriculture (George M. Darrow). Introduced commercially in 1930. Missionary x Howard 17; selected in 1925. Fruit: matures early; good color; skin tough; firm; flavor tart and excellent; very good for preserving. Adapted to southern states.

Bliss.--Originated in Geneva, New York, by the New York State Agricultural Experiment Station (Richard Wellington). Introduced for trial in 1923. Chesapeake x Atkins Continuity; seed borne in 1911. Fruit: ripens late; quality excellent. Plant: withstands drought well, but lacks vigor and productivity. Almost obsolete.

Boquet.--Originated in Geneva, New York, by the New York State Agricultural Experiment Station (Richard Wellington). Introduced for trial in 1923. Chesapeake x Pan American; cross made in 1911. Fruit: large; light red; ripens in midseason; quality good, but not as good as Bliss. Plant: runner production scanty; flowers perfect. Almost obsolete; superseded by more recent varieties superior in vigor and productivity.

Borden.--Originated in Ottawa, Ontario, Canada, by the Division of Horticulture, Central Experimental Farm. Introduced for trial in 1936. (Nor J x Parsons Beauty) x (*Fragaria* sp. x Jessie); selected in 1934. Plant: very productive; light runnering; subject to drought. Variety grown only to a limited extent.

Branford *(Connecticut 431).*--Originated in New Haven, Connecticut, by the Connecticut Agricultural Experiment Station (D. F. Jones). Introduced commercially in 1939. (Kalicene x Howard 17) x (Progressive x Howard 17); first selected in 1923. Fruit: color light and bright, being excellent in frozen product and in preserves; size and shape even.

Brightmore.--Originated in Corvallis, Oregon, by the United States Department of Agriculture (George M. Darrow and George F. Waldo). Introduced commercially in 1942. Blakemore x Oregon 154; selected in 1934. Fruit: quality excellent for frozen pack; bright red; most nearly resembles Blakemore. Plant: fairly resistant to virus diseases.

Bristol.--Originated in New Haven, Connecticut, by the Connecticut Agricultural Experiment Station (D. F. Jones). Introduced commercially in 1939. (Chesapeake x Marshall) x (Progressive x Howard 17); selected in 1923. Fruit: attractive; quality high. Most nearly resembles Chesapeake.

Brunes Marvel.--Originated in Pequot Lakes, Minnesota, by Charles Brunes. Introduced commercially in 1942. Progressive Gem x Mastadon seedling; selected in 1935. Fruit: sugar content high, acid low; recommended as non-acidic; most nearly resembles Progressive.

Burgundy *(Minnesota 1192)*.--Originated in Excelsior, Minnesota, by the Minnesota Agricultural Experiment Station (A. N. Wilcox). Introduced commercially in 1943. Easypicker x Duluth; selected in 1929. Fruit: late; large; regular; somewhat pubescent; roundish cordate; dark red, evenly colored; rather glossy; achenes medium few and raised; flesh very dark red, firm and meaty; flavor aromatic and subacid; quality very good. Plant: hardy, vigorous, upstanding; very productive; June-bearing; flowers late and pistillate, being 2 weeks later than Howard 17.

Caledonia.--Originated in Geneva, New York, by the New York State Agricultural Experiment Station (Richard Wellington). Introduced commercially in 1931. Marshall x Howard 17; cross made in 1923. Fruit: large; attractive; firm; flesh red; quality good; makes an excellent preserve for which purpose it was introduced. Plant: numerous plant maker; vigorous; productive; eventually proved too susceptible to leaf-spot and is probably out of cultivation.

California 403.8.--See **Shasta**.

California 467.1.--See **Campbell**.

California 537.5.--See **Sierra**.

California 544.2.--See **Lassen**.

California 567.6.--See **Tahoe**.

California 579.4.--See **Donner**.

California 829.9.--See **Cupertino**.

Camden.--Originated in Geneva, New York, by the New York State Agricultural Experiment Station (Richard Wellington). Introduced for trial in 1931. Marshall x Howard 17; cross made in 1923. Fruit: large; holds up well in size; glossy, attractive; flavor mild; quality fairly good; when overripe, color tends to darken. Only sparingly grown.

Campbell *(California 467.1; Riverview)*.--Originated in Davis, California, by the California Agricultural Experiment Station (R. E. Baker and Victor Voth). Introduced commercially in 1949. Parentage: Cal. 177.21 (USDA 543 x Cal. 68.24 (USDA 634 x New York 4626)) x Cal. 103.22 (Cal. A.08 (USDA 253 x F_2 USDA 253) x Nick Ohmer). Fruit: early summer and early fall production precede other University of California varieties (Sierra, Tahoe), thus filling in the slack picking periods.

Canall.--Originated in Brigham City, Utah, by the Larsen Experimental Farm (L. L. Larsen). Introduced for trial in 1950. Catskill x Golden Gate; selected in 1947. Fruit: large; dark red, nearly black; highly flavored; good dessert quality. Plant: heavy cropper.

Cato.--Originated in Geneva, New York, by the New York State Agricultural Experiment Station (Richard Wellington). Introduced for trial in 1931. Marshall x Howard 17; cross made in 1923. Fruit: quality nearly equals Marshall and much superior in plant characters; large; attractive, but bruises very easily. Plant: vigorous and productive; home garden variety. Now superseded by other varieties.

Catskill.--Originated in Geneva, New York, by the New York State Agricultural Experiment Station (Richard Wellington). Introduced for trial in 1934. Marshall x Howard 17; cross made in 1923; selected in 1925. Fruit: large; mid-season; slightly irregular; moderately firm; dark red, glossy, attractive; mildly subacid; quality good. Plant: very vigorous and productive. Widely grown from Maryland north.

Chaska *(Minnesota 801)*.--Originated in Excelsior, Minnesota, by the University of Minnesota Fruit Breeding Farm. Introduced commercially in 1922. (Dunlap x Pocomoke) x Brandywine. Fruit: large; showy; firm; good canner; high yielder. Variety no longer propagated.

Claribel.--Originated in Ottawa, Ontario, Canada, by the Division of Horticulture, Central Experimental Farm. Introduced for trial in 1935. Ettersburg 121 x Cassandra; selected in 1933. Fruit: very firm fleshed; short fruit stalks; season very late; quality poor. Plant: imperfect flowers. Variety grown only to a limited extent.

Clermont.--Originated in Geneva, New York, by the New York State Agricultural Experiment Station (Richard Wellington). Introduced for trial in 1931. Marshall x Howard 17; cross made in 1923; selected in 1925. Fruit: excellent for market and home use; very large, holds up well in size through season; regular in shape; very glossy, attractive, does not bruise easily; quality excellent. Plant: somewhat susceptible to leafspot.

Corvallis *(Oregon State College 12)*.--Originated in Oregon by the Oregon Agricultural Experiment Station (C. E. Schuster). Introduced commercially in 1930. Patent no. 60; April 18, 1933; dedicated, by mesne assignments, to the People of the United States of America. Ettersburg 121 x Marshall; selected in 1922. Fruit: excellent for canning and frozen pack. Plant: vigorous and productive. Most nearly resembles Ettersburg 121

Crimson Glow *(New Jersey 311)*.--Originated in New Brunswick, New Jersey, by the New Jersey Agricultural Experiment Station (J. H. Clark). Introduced under restrictions in 1940; named in 1943. Fairfax x New Jersey 51 (Pearl x Aberdeen); selected in 1933. Fruit: quality high; picking easy, since stem breaks.

Culver.--Originated in Geneva, New York, by the New York State Agricultural Experiment Station (Richard Wellington). Introduced for trial in 1931. Marshall x Howard 17; cross made in 1923; selected in 1925. Fruit: color dark; large; regular in shape; bruises slightly; flavor sprightly; quality very good; ripens early midseason; well adapted for preserves.

Cupertino *(California 829.9)*.--Originated in Davis, California, by the California Agricultural Experiment Station (R. E. Baker and Victor Voth). Introduced commercially in 1949. Parentage: Cal. 611.4 (168.3 x 186.1) x Cal. 468.4 (177.21 x 135. 18); derived from Nich Ohmer, Banner, Fendalcino, USDA 253 and 634 and New York 4626. Fruit: exceptionally glossy; aromatic; flavor good; production peaks follow other University varieties (e.g., Shasta, Tahoe) and thus fills in slack picking periods.

Daybreak.--Originated in Glenn Dale, Maryland, by the United States Department of Agriculture (George F. Waldo). Introduced commercially in 1939. Missionary x Fairfax; selected in 1932. Fruit: matures early; large. Bush: very vigorous; crop large.

Deephaven *(Minnesota 41)*.--Originated in Excelsior, Minnesota, by the University of Minnesota Fruit Breeding Farm. Introduced commercially in 1922. Parentage unknown; selected in 1919. Fruit: large. Plant: everbearing; productive. Variety obsolete.

Donner *(California 579.4)*.--Originated in Wheatland, California, by the California Agricultural Experiment Station (Harold E. Thomas and Earl V. Goldsmith). Introduced commercially in 1945. Cal. 145.52 (Cal. BH-14 (mixed crosses) x Redheart) x Cal. 222 (Cal. 66.2 (USDA 634 x Banner) x Cal. 7.20 (Blakemore x Nich Ohmer)); selected in 1938. Fruit: high dessert quality; good fresh-market berry.

Dorsett.--Originated in Glenn Dale, Maryland, by the USDA (George M. Darrow). Introduced commercially in 1933. Royal Sovereign x Howard 17; selected in 1925. Fruit: dessert quality high; appearance attractive. Bush: very vigorous and productive.

Dresden.--Originated in Geneva, New York, by the New York State Agricultural Experiment Station (George L. Slate). Introduced for trial in 1939. Beacon x Howard 17; cross made in 1929; selected in 1931. Fruit: light red, smooth; maintains size throughout the season; few or no nubbins. Plant: best adapted to northern tier of states and Canada; very productive; crown appears to lack hardiness.

Duluth *(Minnesota 1017).*--Originated in Excelsior, Minnesota, by the University of Minnesota Fruit Breeding Farm. Introduced commercially in 1920. Pan American x Dunlap; cross made in 1909; selected in 1913. Fruit: dark red; quality good. Plant: adapted to heavy soils; vigorous; everbearer.

Earlee.--Originated in Brigham City, Utah, by the Larsen Experimental Farm (L. L. Larsen). Introduced commercially in 1949. Premier x unnamed seedling; selected in 1937. Fruit: medium size. Plant: early; heavy producer; a spring and fall cropper in Utah.

Easy Picker *(Minnesota 775).*--Originated in Excelsior, Minnesota, by the University of Minnesota Fruit Breeding Farm. Introduced commercially in 1922. Dunlap x Crescent. Fruit: quality good; flesh dark red. Plant: productive.

Eleanor Roosevelt.--Originated in Glenn Dale, Maryland, by the United States Department of Agriculture (George F. Waldo). Introduced commercially in 1939. Bellmar x Fairfax; selected in 1933. Fruit: immense; firm; deep red; season long; shipping quality good. Bush: very productive.

Elgin *(Ottawa 271).*--Originated in Ottawa, Ontario, Canada, by the Division of Horticulture, Central Experimental Farm. Introduced commercially in 1944. Ettersburg 214 x Wm. Belt; selected in 1940. Fruit: ripening very late. Plant: resistant to leafspot; perfect flowers. Variety most nearly resembles Ettersburg 214.

Evermore *(Minnesota 1166).*--Originated in Excelsior, Minnesota, by the University of Minnesota Fruit Breeding Farm. Introduced commercially in February, 1945. Duluth x Senator Dunlap; selected in 1929. Plant: everbearer; productive; hardy; drought resistant.

Fairfax.--Originated in Glenn Dale, Maryland, by the United States Department of Agriculture (George M. Darrow). Introduced commercially in 1933. Royal Sovereign x Howard 17; selected in 1925. Fruit: exceptional firmness; dessert quality high; appearance fine; season early and long; large.

Fairland.--Originated in Beltsville, Maryland, by the United States Department of Agriculture (George M. Darrow). Introduced commercially in 1947. Aberdeen x Fairfax; selected in 1938. Fruit: firmer and with better flavor than either Howard 17 or Catskill. Plant: resistant to red stele; very productive.

Fairmore.--Originated in Glenn Dale, Maryland, by the United States Department of Agriculture (George M. Darrow). Introduced commercially in 1939. Blakemore x Fairfax; selected in 1934. Fruit: very firm; shipping quality high; season early; flavor high in southern states. Bush: vigorous growth.

Fairpeake.--Originated in Glenn Dale, Maryland, by the United States Department of Agriculture (George F. Waldo). Introduced commercially in 1944. Chesapeake x Fairfax; selected in 1933. Fruit: highly flavored; firm; matures very late. Plant: productive; very vigorous.

Gemzata.--Originated in Bristol, Indiana, by Victor Judson. Introduced commercially in 1934. Parentage unknown; discovered in 1932. Fruit: large. Plant: produces well; good plant maker. Most nearly resembles Gem and Wayzata.

Glenheart.--Originated in Miami, Manitoba, Canada, by William Oakes. Introduced commercially about 1941. Probable parentage: Gem x Wayzata. Fruit: large; bright, medium red, firm, very attractive coloring and shape; sweet, pleasant. Plant: strong; vigorous; strong plant maker; very hardy; productive; moderately susceptible to leaf spot; perfect flowers.

Green Mountain.--Originated in Putney, Vermont, by George D. Aiken. Introduced commercially in 1935. Patent no. 112; November 20, 1934. Open-pollinated seedling of Superb Everbearing. Fruit: similar to Howard 17 but matures about one week later. Plant: has everbearing characteristics.

Hagerstrom's Everbearing.--See Red Rich.

Hebron.--Originated in New Haven, Connecticut, by the Connecticut Agricultural Experiment Station (D. F. Jones). Introduced commercially in 1939. Inbred Chesapeake x (F_1 cross of inbred Progressive x Howard 17). Fruit: matures late; color light, bright; calyces green on maturing. Most nearly resembles Chesapeake.

Howard 25.--See Howard's Supreme.

Howard's Supreme *(Howard 25).*-- Originated in Belchertown, Massachusetts, by E. C. Howard. Introduced commercially in 1931. Patent no. 71; July 25, 1933; assigned to E. W. Townsend and Sons, Salisbury, Maryland. Howard Seedling 103 x Howard 17; selected in 1909. Fruit: dark rich red; juicy, firm texture; quality good; good shipper. Plant: vigorous, healthy; high production; flowers imperfect, which has taken it out of production commercially.

Howe.--Originated in Ottawa, Ontario, Canada, by the Division of Horticulture, Central Experimental Farm. Introduced for trial in 1936. (Red Sugar x Howard 17) x (Willard x Santiago de Chile); selected in 1934. Fruit: large; appearance attractive; frequently rough. Plant: imperfect flowers. Variety grown only to a limited extent.

Improved Clark *(Ulrich)*.--Originated near The Dalles, Oregon, by Julius Ulrich. Introduced commercially in 1925. Plant found near a field containing Gold Dollar and Clark; discovered in 1920. Plant: seems resistant to strawberry mite in Hood River Valley. Most nearly resembles Clark's Seedling.

Jim.--Originated in Ottawa, Ontario, Canada,by the Division of Horticulture, Central Experimental Farm. Introduced for trial in 1932. Open pollinated seedling of Willard; selected in 1931. Fruit: large; season early; too pale in color; soft fleshed. Variety grown only to a limited extent.

John.--Originated in Ottawa, Ontario, Canada, by the Division of Horticulture, Central Experimental Farm. Introduced for trial in 1933. Open pollinated seedling of Willard; selected in 1931. Fruit: fairly attractive and productive. Variety grown only to a limited extent, giving way to better ones.

Julymorn *(New Jersey 225)*.--Originated in New Brunswick, New Jersey, by the New Jersey Agricultural Experiment Station (J. H. Clark). Introduced under restrictions in 1938; named in 1943. Redheart x New Jersey 5 (Mastodon x Howard 17); selected in 1932. Fruit: very firm; strong inside color; good for processing; most nearly resembles Redheart.

June Rockhill.--Originated in Conrad, Iowa, by Harlow Rockhill. Introduced commercially in 1947 by the Wheelock Wilson Nursery, Marshalltown, Iowa. Patent no. 854; July 19, 1949; assigned to the estate of the late Harlow Rockhill. Progressive x Early Jersey Giant; selected in 1932. Fruit: identical with Rockhill 26 except that June Rockhill fruits in June. Plant: prolific plant producer.

Jupiter.--Originated in Salisbury, Maryland, by Oliver C. Cordrey, Hannah E. Cordrey, and Ernest W. Townsend. Introduced commercially in 1931 by Ernest W. Townsend. Patent no. 46; November 29, 1932; assigned to Ernest W. Townsend. Howard 17 x Gandy; selected in 1925. Fruit: firm; size similar to Blakemore, but somewhat elongated, similar to the last half of a heavy crop of Howard 17; quality poor. Plant: very productive. Apparently identical with Ridgeley as grown in Maryland.

Kanner King,--Originated in Sawyer, Michigan, by Bert W. Keith and Bud H. Keith. Introduced commercially in 1932. Patent no. 26; August 30, 1932. Chance seedling of Glen Mary; discovered in 1926. Fruit: medium to large; conic shape of Dunlap; flesh very firm; canning quality very good; long fruiting season.

Klonmore.--Originated in Baton Rouge, Louisiana, by the Louisiana State University Experiment Station (Julian C. Miller). Introduced commercially in 1940. Blakemore x Klondike; selected in 1935. Fruit: matures over a long season; excellent shipper; good for quick-freezing process. Plant: resistant to leafspot and scorch. Resembles Blakemore.

Konvoy.--Originated in Baton Rouge, Louisiana, by the Louisiana State University Experiment Station (Julian C. Miller). Introduced commercially in 1942. Fairmore x Klondike; selected in 1938. Fruit: yields are high. Plant: resistant to leafspot and scorch. Resembles Klondike.

Lassen *(California 544.2).*--Originated in Wheatland, California, by the California Agricultural Experiment Station (Harold E. Thomas and Earl V. Goldsmith). Introduced commercially in 1945. Cal. 21.9 (Blakemore x Cal. Z9 (Banner x Fendalcino)) x Cal. 161.1 (Nich Ohmer x Cal. 86.6 (USDA 634 x Cal. Z11 (Banner x Fendalicino))); selected in 1938. Plant: long-lived; resistant to virus diseases; high production.

Lindalicious.--Originated in Brigham City, Utah, by the Larsen Experimental Farm (L. L. Larsen). Introduced commercially in 1948. Fairfax x unnamed seedling; selected in 1937. Fruit: medium to large; solid red; turns red on inside before completely colored on outside; no core; no green tip; tough skin; high freezing and shipping quality. Plant: everbearing in some localities; heavy producer.

Louise.--Originated in Ottawa, Ontario, Canada, by the Division of Horticulture, Central Experimental Farm. Introduced commercially in 1942. Ettersburg 80 x self; selected in 1933. Fruit: ripens very late; quality high. Plant: flowers imperfect.

Lustre.--Originated in Merchantville, New Jersey, by Oscar Earle Felten. Introduced commercially in 1949. Patent no. 929; March 28, 1950; assigned to O. E. Felten and W. T. Wilkins, Merchantville, New Jersey. Seedling 3001 (Howard 17 x Marvel) x Seedling 3700 (Seedling 3001 x Fairfax); selected in 1945. Fruit: large; flesh firm; skin fairly tough; seeds in position to protect berry in shipment; most nearly resembles Sparkle. Bush: stems hold berries off ground.

Mackenzie.--Originated in Ottawa, Ontario, Canada, by the Division of Horticulture, Central Experimental Farm. Introduced commercially in 1941. Excelsior x Howard 17; selected in 1934. Fruit: about same season as Howard 17. Plant: flowers perfect;

more productive under certain conditions than Howard 17, which it most nearly resembles.

Majestic.--Originated in Jonesville, Virginia, by E. L.Russell. Introduced commercially in 1940. Patent no. 345; October 24, 1939; assigned to the originator. Seedling of Howard 17; discovered in 1933. Fruit: large; flesh firm, red; ripens in midseason; good shipping quality; tends to dark color when fully ripe. Plant: large; very productive; sets many plants; resistant to drought and leafspot; sturdy and upright stems; more productive and a little more tart than Blakemore or Howard 17.

Marion Bell.-Originated in Baton Rouge, Louisiana, by the Louisiana State University Experiment Station (Julian C. Miller). Introduced commercially in 1946. Fairmore x self; selected in 1942. Fruit: matures over a long period of time; flavor excellent; good shipper; color bright. Plant: resistant to leafspot and scorch. Most nearly resembles Klonmore.

Massey.--Originated in Glenn Dale, Maryland, by the United States Department of Agriculture (George M. Darrow). Introduced commercially in 1940. USDA 634 (Royal Sovereign x Howard 17) x Blakemore; selected in 1934. Fruit: dessert quality high; large; extremely attractive.

Mastodon.--Originated in Peru, Indiana, by George Voer. Introduced commercially in 1921. Superb x Kellogg; selected in 1917. Fruit: large, somewhat variable and irregular; quality good; colors somewhat unevenly. Plant: very vigorous, productive; superior to Progressive and Superb; autumn cropper.

Maytime.--Originated in Glenn Dale, Maryland, by the United States Department of Agriculture (George F. Waldo). Introduced commercially in 1941. Missionary x Fairfax; selected in 1933. Fruit: matures a week earlier than other early varieties; firm; quality good.

McClintock *(Tennessee 6).*--Originated in Knoxville, Tennessee, by the Tennessee Agricultural Experiment Station. Introduced commercially in 1932. Aroma x self; selected in 1924. Fruit: more attractive appearance and larger yield than Klondike, which it resembles.

Midland.--Originated in Glenn Dale, Maryland, by the United States Department of Agriculture (George F. Waldo and George M. Darrow). Introduced commercially in 1944. Howard 17 x Redheart; selected in 1931. Fruit: large, firm, high flavor; matures early. Plant: productive.

Mildred Felten. -- Originated in Merchantville, New Jersey, by Oscar Earle Felten. Patent no. 761; September 16, 1947; assigned to Oscar E. Felten. Fairfax x Seedling 3001 (Premier x Marvel); selected in 1934. Fruit: larger, tarter, lighter colored than Fairfax, which it most nearly resembles; picking season is longer than Fairfax and later berries hold up in size much better. Plant: larger, heavier bearer than Fairfax.

Minnehaha *(Minnesota 935)*. --Originated in Excelsior, Minnesota, by the University of Minnesota Fruit Breeding Farm. Introduced commercially in 1920. Minnesota x Abington; cross made in 1911. Fruit: large; firm; wedge-shaped; ships very well; late season. Variety no longer propagated.

Minnesota *(Minnesota 3)*. --Originated in Excelsior, Minnesota, by the University of Minnesota Fruit Breeding Farm. Introduced commercially in 1920. Dunlap x Pocomoke; cross made in 1907. Fruit: attractive; high quality. Plant: productive; subject to mosaic disease (June yellows).

Minnesota 3. --See **Minnesota.**

Minnesota 41. --See **Deephaven.**

Minnesota 489. --See **Nokomis.**

Minnesota 775. --See **Easy Picker.**

Minnesota 801. --See **Chaska.**

Minnesota 935. --See **Minnehaha.**

Minnesota 1017. --See **Duluth.**

Minnesota 1118. --See **Arrowhead.**

Minnesota 1166. --See **Evermore.**

Minnesota 1192. --See **Burgundy.**

Montana Progressive. --Originated in Bozeman, Montana, by the Montana Experiment Station (H. E. Morris and M. M. Afanasiev). Introduced commercially in 1942. Open pollinated seedling of Progressive; selected in 1935. Fruit: dessert quality good; shipping quality good. Plant: everbearing; resistant to yellows and leaf spot; spring crop fair to good; fall crop heavy.

Narcissa. --Originated in Glenn Dale, Maryland, by the United States Department of Agriculture (George M. Darrow). Introduced commercially in 1933. Royal Sovereign x Howard 17; selected in 1925. Fruit: high dessert quality; early; resistant to fruit rots in the Northwest; yields high.

Nectarena.--Originated in Thornhill, Ontario, Canada, by Matthew James Johnson. Introduced commercially in January, 1947. Patent no. 780; January 20, 1948; assigned to the R. M. Kellogg Company, Three Rivers, Michigan. Howard 17 x Bedarena; selected about 1940. Fruit: flavor sweet and mild, similar to Bedarena. Plant: vigor and productiveness similar to that of Howard 17.

New Jersey 35.--See **Pathfinder.**

New Jersey 225.--See **Julymorn.**

New Jersey 311.--See **Crimson Glow.**

New Jersey 312.--See **Sparkle.**

New Jersey 347.--See **Redwing.**

New Jersey 377.--See **Redcrop.**

Nokomis *(Minnesota 489).*--Originated in Excelsior, Minnesota, by the University of Minnesota Fruit Breeding Farm. Introduced commercially in 1922. Dunlap x Abington; selected in 1918. Fruit: large; flavor good. Plant: drought resistant. Variety no longer propagated.

Northstar.--Originated in Glenn Dale, Maryland, by the United States Department of Agriculture (George F. Waldo and George M. Darrow). Introduced commercially in 1939. Howard 17 x Redheart; selected in 1930. Fruit: quality high; firm; beauty above average; matures very early.

Northwest *(Washington 220).*--Originated in Puyallup, Washington, by the Western Washington Experiment Station (C. D. Schwartze). Introduced for trial September, 1949. Brightmore x a complex hybrid derived from Narcissa, Ettersburg, and Wilson; selected in 1943. Fruit: surface bright crimson with a high gloss; long-conic; flesh firm, light red throughout; size large to very large in early pickings, medium size at end of the season; ripening season late, beginning almost a week after the first picking of Marshall; well adapted to commercial freezing and canning. Plant: high resistance to yellows virus; very productive; single-crop variety, showing no tendency of everbearing habit; not resistant to root rots. Recommended for areas that can no longer grow Marshall because of yellows disease.

Oregon State College 12.--See **Corvallis.**

Ottawa 271.--See **Elgin.**

Pathfinder *(New Jersey 35).*--Originated in New Brunswick, New Jersey, by the New Jersey Agricultural Experiment Station (J. H. Clark). Introduced commercially in 1938. Howard 17 x Aberdeen. Fruit: medium to large; bright red; brisk subacid; quality good; ripens 3 days after Howard 17; very resistant to Aberdeen strain of red stele in New Jersey.

Paymaster.--Originated in Sawyer, Michigan, by B. W. Keith. Introduced commercially in 1942. Howard 17 x Gem Everbearer; selected in 1937. Fruit: firm; good shipper, canner, and for deep freezing. Plant: productive; resistant to red stele disease; spring fruiting.

Pixie.--Originated in Parkside, Saskatchewan, Canada, by A. J. Porter. Introduced commercially in 1947. Open pollinated seedling of August Beauty; selected in 1943. Fruit: high quality for either dessert or canning. Plant: yields heavily; vigorous spring and fall crops.

Ranger *(Texas 68).*--Originated in Winter Haven, Texas, by the Texas Agricultural Experiment Station. Introduced commercially in 1937. Texas x Missionary; selected in 1935. Fruit: colors evenly; ripens earlier than Klondike. Plant: flowers and fruit covered well by foliage; heavy plant producer adapted to southern conditions.

Redcrop *(New Jersey 377).*--Originated in New Brunswick, New Jersey, by the New Jersey Agricultural Experiment Station (J. H. Clark). Introduced under restriction in 1948; introduced commercially in 1949. Aberdeen x Fairfax. Fruit: large; high quality; medium firm; red throughout; attractive calyx; very good for frozen pack. Plant: vigorous; productive; resistant to Aberdeen strain of red stele in New Jersey.

Red-Glo.--See **Red Rich.**

Redheart.--Originated in Glenn Dale, Maryland, by the United States Department of Agriculture (George M. Darrow). Introduced commercially in 1932. Portia x Eureka; selected in 1925. Fruit: very good for canning; quality high; firm; color good.

Red Rich *(Red-Glo, Hagerstrom's Everbearing).*--Originated in Enfield, Minnesota, by Marion Hagerstrom. Introduced commercially in April 1949. Patent no. 993; assigned to Marion and Carl R. Hagerstrom, Nov. 28, 1950. Wayzata x Fairfax; selected in 1940. Fruit: conical-wedge shape; flesh red, firm; good quality for freezing. Plant: everbearer; hardy; good runner formation; productive.

Redstar.--Originated in Glenn Dale, Maryland, by the United States Department of Agriculture (George M. Darrow and George F. Waldo). Introduced commercially in 1940. Chesapeake x Fairfax; selected in 1933. Fruit: latest productive firm variety of high flavor for latitude of Washington, D. C.; attractive; most nearly resembles Fairfax. Plant: leaf-spot resistant; leaves very large.

Redwing *(New Jersey 347)*.--Originated in New Brunswick, New Jersey, by the New Jersey Agricultural Experiment Station (J. H. Clark). Introduced under restrictions in 1940; named in 1943. New Jersey 46 (Pearl x Aberdeen) x Fairfax; selected in 1933. Fruit: very large; firm; good for frozen pack.

Riogrande *(Texas 15)*.--Originated in Winter Haven, Texas, by the Texas Agricultural Experiment Station. Introduced in 1937. Blakemore x Ettersburg 80?; selected in 1935. Fruit: season early; flavor good. Plant: good plant producer; adapted to southern winters. Most nearly resembles Blakemore.

Riverview.--See Campbell.

Shasta *(California 403.8)*.--Originated in Davis, California, by the California Agricultural Experiment Station (Harold E. Thomas and Earl V. Goldsmith). Introduced commercially in 1945. Cal. 67.5 (Nich Ohmer x USDA 634) x Cal. 177.21 (USDA 543 x Cal. 68.24 (USDA 634 x N.Y.4626)). Plant: widely adapted in central coast area of California; fair resistance to virus diseases and verticillium wilt.

Shelton.--Originated in New Haven, Connecticut, by the Connecticut Agricultural Experiment Station (D. F. Jones). (Chesapeake x Marshall) x (F_1 cross of inbred Progressive x Howard 17). Fruit: color attractive, retained after picking. Foliage healthy. Most nearly resembles Chesapeake.

Sierra *(California 537.5)*.--Originated in Davis, California, by the California Agricultural Experiment Station (Harold E. Thomas and Earl V. Goldsmith). Introduced commercially in 1945. Nich Ohmer x Cal. 177.21 (USDA 543 x Cal. 68.24 (USDA 634 x N.Y. 4626)); selected in 1937. Plant: fair resistance to virus disease.

Silva.--Originated in Sebastopol, California, by William E. Silva. Introduced commercially in 1950. Patent no. 890; November 1, 1949. Rockhill x (Gem x Wayzata); selected in 1945. Fruit: large, heart-shaped, everbearer. Plant: produces no runners.

Simcoe.--Originated in Ottawa, Ontario, Canada, by the Division of Horticulture, Central Experimental Farm. Introduced for trial in 1936. (Red Sugar x Howard 17) x (Delecto x Cassandra); selected in 1934. Fruit: large; attractive; loses size after two or three pickings. Plant: imperfect flowered. Variety grown only to a limited extent.

Sioux.--Originated in Cheyenne, Wyoming, and North Platte, Nebraska, by the Horticultural Field Station and the North Platte Experiment Station (Le Roy Powers and Glenn Veihmeyer). Introduced commercially October 11, 1948. (Fairfax x *Fragaria ovalis*) x Fairfax. Fruit: good quality. Plant: extreme winter hardiness.

Southland.--Originated in Washington, D. C., by the United States Department of Agriculture (George M. Darrow). Introduced commercially in 1932. Ettersburg 80 x Howard 17; selected in 1922. Fruit: quality high; beautiful appearance. Plant: very productive; remarkable plant growth; adapted to the South.

Sparkle *(New Jersey 312).*--Originated in New Brunswick, New Jersey, by the New Jersey Agricultural Experiment Station (J. H. Clark). Introduced under restrictions in 1942; named in 1943. Fairfax x Aberdeen; selected in 1933. Fruit: good for frozen pack. Plant: very productive; last flowers on cluster usually set; highly resistant to red stele.

Sparta.--Originated in Parkside, Saskatchewan, Canada, by A. J. Porter. Introduced commercially in 1941. Gem x Fairfax; selected in 1936. Fruit: large, conic; bright red; very firm; good keeping quality; flavor fair to good. Plant: large; vigorous; very resistant to leaf spot and mildew; everbearing.

Starbright.--Originated in Glenn Dale, Maryland, by the United States Department of Agriculture (George M. Darrow and George F. Waldo). Introduced commercially in 1940. Chesapeake x Fairfax; selected in 1933. Fruit: season early; quality high; flavor good; firm; beauty above average.

Streamliner.--Originated in Lostine, Oregon, by Roy C. Edgmand. Introduced commercially in 1944. Parentage unknown; discovered in 1938. Fruit: firm; good keeper for home use. Plant: hardy; heavy spring cropper; everbearer; makes runners freely.

Superfection.--Originated in Farewell, Clare County, Michigan, by Frank J. Keplinger. Introduced commercially in 1946. Open pollinated seedling of Gem; selected in 1937. Fruit: large; high quality. Plant: everbearing type; vigorous.

Suwannee.--Originated in Glenn Dale, Maryland, by the United States Department of Agriculture (George F. Waldo). Introduced commercially in September, 1945. Missionary x Howard 17; cross made in 1931; selected in 1933. Fruit: its ability to develop high flavor and quality under adverse weather conditions when most varieties are quite deficient in these qualities. Plant: resembles Southland in adaptation, uses, and limitations; adapted to home gardens.

Sweetheart.--Originated in Parkside, Saskatchewan, Canada, by A. J. Porter. Introduced commercially in 1947. Open pollinated seedling of August Beauty; selected in 1943. Fruit: highly flavored; somewhat soft for shipping. Plant: everbearer.

Tahoe *(California 567.6)*.--Originated in Wheatland, California, by the California Agricultural Experiment Station (Harold E. Thomas and Earl V. Goldsmith). Introduced commercially in 1945. Cal. 144.21 (Narcissa x Nich Ohmer) x Cal. 143.32 (Narcissa x Cal. BH-14 (mixed crosses)); selected in 1938. Fruit: ripens late. Plant: fair resistance to virus diseases.

Temple.--Originated in Beltsville, Maryland, by the United States Department of Agriculture (George M. Darrow) and the Maryland Agricultural Experiment Station (W. F. Jeffers). Introduced commercially in 1943. Aberdeen x Fairfax; selected in 1939. Fruit: earlier, firmer, and more resistant to leaf-scorch disease than Aberdeen; brighter red color than Fairfax. Plant: very free plant maker; highly resistant to red stele root disease.

Tennessean *(Tennessee 965)*.--Originated in Jackson, Tennessee, by the West Tennessee Experiment Station (Brooks D. Drain). Introduced commercially in 1950. Tennessee Selection 230 x Tennessee Selection 586; selected in December, 1949. Fruit: early; commercial quality good; most nearly resembles Howard 17.

Tennessee 6.--See **McClintock.**

Tennessee 148.--See **Tennessee Shipper.**

Tennessee 260.--See **Tennessee Supreme.**

Tennessee 263.--See **Tennessee Beauty.**

Tennessee 965.--See **Tennessean.**

Tennessee Beauty *(Tennessee 263)*.--Originated in Knoxville, Tennessee, by the Tennessee Agricultural Experiment Station (Brooks D. Drain). Introduced commercially in 1942. Patent no. 629; June 6, 1944; assigned to the University of Tennessee Research Corporation, Knoxville, Tennessee. Missionary x Howard 17; selected in 1935. Fruit: ripens midseason to late; quality good; most nearly resembles Aroma. Plant: healthy; production good.

Tennessee Shipper *(Tennessee 148).*--Originated in Knoxville, Tennessee, by the Tennessee Agricultural Experiment Station (Brooks D. Drain). Introduced commercially in 1941. Patent no. 570; March 2, 1943; assigned to the University of Tennessee Research Corporation. Knoxville, Tennessee. Missionary x Blakemore; selected in 1935. Fruit: an all-purpose variety; very firm; quality high. Plant: healthy; produces heavily. Most nearly resembles Blakemore.

Tennessee Supreme *(Tennessee 260).*--Originated in Knoxville, Tennessee, by the Tennessee Agricultural Experiment Station (Brooks D. Drain). Introduced commercially in 1940. Patent no. 502; February 3, 1942; assigned to the University of Tennessee Research Corporation, Knoxville, Tennessee. Missionary x Howard 17; selected in 1935. Fruit: flavor fine; selected for frozen pack. Adapted south of Howard 17, which it most nearly resembles.

Texas 15.--See **Riogrande**.

Texas 21.--See **Alamo**.

Texas 68.--See **Ranger**.

Tupper.--Originated in Ottawa, Ontario, Canada, by the Division of Horticulture, Central Experimental Farm. Introduced commercially in 1942. Ettersburg 214 x Cassandra; selected in 1934. Fruit: late; valuable for home use and local markets. Plant: flowers imperfect, very productive. Variety most nearly resembles Ettersburg 214.

Twentieth Century Everbearing.--Originated in Cottonwood Height, Utah, by Taijiro Kasuga. Introduced commercially in 1932. Berri-Supreme x Rockhill; selected in 1926. Fruit: ships well; highly flavored. Plant: yields heavily; heavy plant maker. Most nearly resembles Rockhill.

Ulrich.--See **Improved Clark**.

Utah Shipper.--Originated in Brigham City, Utah, by Larsen Experimental Farm (L. L. Larsen). Introduced for trial in 1950. Lindalicious x Catskill; selected in 1947. Fruit: medium red; large to extra large; very firm skin; good shipper; most nearly resembles Lindalicious except color is lighter. Plant: heavy cropper.

Valentine.--Originated in Vineland, Ontario, Canada, by the Ontario Horticultural Experiment Station. Introduced commercially in 1941. Howard 17 x Vanguard; selected in 1930 from 1927 breeding. Fruit: matures very early. Most nearly resembles Parsons.

Vandyke.--Originated in Vineland, Ontario, Canada, by the Ontario Horticultural Experiment Station. Introduced commercially in 1928. Open-pollinated seedling of Ontario Seedling 1467 (Dunlap seedling x Early Ozark); selected in 1922 from 1919 breeding. Fruit: matures early. Variety now lost because of susceptibility to yellows. Most nearly resembled Dunlap.

Vanguard.--Originated in Vineland, Ontario, Canada, by the Ontario Horticultural Experiment Station. Introduced commercially in 1924. Pocomoke x Early Ozark; selected in 1915 from 1913 breeding. Fruit: matures early. Most nearly resembles Early Ozark.

Vanrouge.--Originated in Vineland, Ontario, Canada, by the Ontario Horticultural Experiment Station. Introduced commercially in 1938. Ontario Seedling 180115 (Admiral x Ontario Seedling 1563 (Dunlap x Early Ozark)) x Bliss; selected in 1933 from 1930 breeding. Fruit: flesh deep red throughout; excellent for frozen pack.

Vermilion.--Originated in Urbana, Illinois, by the University of Illinois (A. S. Colby). Introduced commercially in 1950. Redstar x Pathfinder; cross made in 1941; selected in 1943. Fruit: high dessert quality; attractive; most nearly resembles Pathfinder; in season with Howard 17. Plant: resistant to red stele root rot, leaf spot, leaf blight, and leaf scorch; productive.

Washington 220.--See **Northwest.**

Wray Red.--Originated in White Salmon, Washington, by E. P. Wray. Introduced commercially about 1930. Patent no. 101; August 7, 1934. Klickitat x (seedling of Chesapeake x Campbells Early); selected about 1920. Plant: very productive in eastern Washington.

Wright.--Originated in Ottawa, Ontario, Canada, by the Division of Horticulture, Central Experimental Farm. Introduced for trial in 1936. (Portia x Ettersburg 512) x (Santiago de Chile x self); selected in 1934. Fruit: large; sugar content high; flavor flat. Plant: foliage leathery and thick; production poor. Variety grown only to a limited extent.

Wyona.--Originated in Bedford, Virginia, by A. S. Johnson. Introduced commercially about 1923. Perhaps an open-pollinated seedling of Gandy; selected prior to 1922. Fruit: flesh firm; quality good for a subacid berry; long keeper; late maturity. No longer planted.

TANGELO

Broward.--Originated in Eustis, Florida, by the United States Department of Agriculture (F. W. Savage). Introduced commercially in 1939. Bowen grapefruit x Dancy tangerine; selected in 1912. Fruit: medium to large; quality good; ripens during December and January at Eustis.

Lake.--See **Orlando**.

Minneola.--Originated in Eustis, Florida, by the United States Department of Agriculture (E. M. Savage). Introduced commercially in 1931. Bowen grapefruit x Dancy tangerine; selected in 1912. Fruit: juicy; flavor fine; color very attractive; ripens in January and February at Eustis.

Orlando *(Lake)*.--Originated in Eustis, Florida, by the United States Department of Agriculture (E. M. Savage). Introduced commercially in 1931; trademarked Orlando. Bowen grapefruit x Dancy tangerine; selected in 1912. Fruit: matures early, November to February; size small to medium, flavor fine; well colored. One of the best tangelo varieties.

Pearl.--Originated in Riverside, California, by the California Citrus Experiment Station (H. B. Frost). Introduced commercially in 1940. Imperial grapefruit x Willow Leaf mandarin; selected in 1929. Fruit: ripens very early; flesh firm; quality very good; acid and sugar similar to sweet orange; aroma unique.

Sampson.--Originated in Eustis, Florida, by the United States Department of Agriculture (Walter T. Swingle and H. J. Webber). Introduced commercially in 1904; named in honor of F. G. Sampson, Boardman, Florida. Grapefruit x Dancy tangerine; cross made in 1897. Fruit: thin-skinned, bruises easily; good for juice and marmalade; season February to April. Tree: resistant to gummosis; promising as a rootstock for orange and lemon.

San Jacinto.--Originated in Indio, California, by the United States Department of Agriculture (Walter T. Swingle). Introduced commercially in 1931. F_2 hybrid seedling of unknown tangelo; most nearly resembles Orlando; from the same parentage as Thornton. Fruit: quality fair; early ripening; more resistant to handling than Thornton.

Seminole.--Originated in Eustis, Florida, by the United States Department of Agriculture (E. M. Savage). Introduced commercially in 1931. Bowen grapefruit x Dancy tangerine; selected in 1912. Fruit: matures late, February to April; attractive; medium sized; most nearly resembles Orlando, but more acid.

Webber.--Originated in Eustis, Florida, by the United States Department of Agriculture (E. M. Savage). Introduced commercially in 1932. Bowen grapefruit x Dancy tangerine; selected in 1909. Fruit: flavor fine; very juicy; size medium; flat; skin smooth, thin, orange-colored; ripens December to February. Named for H. J. Webber, who deemed it one of the best of the tangelos.

Wekiwa.--Originated in Eustis, Florida, by the United States Department of Agriculture (E. M. Savage). Introduced commercially in 1931. Trademarked Wekiwa. Bowen grapefruit seedling 37 x Sampson tangelo; selected in 1909. Fruit: small; sweet; pink-fleshed; attractive and pleasing taste; ripens during December and January.

TANGERINE

Frua.--Originated in Riverside, California, by the University of California Citrus Experiment Station (Howard B. Frost). Introduced commercially in 1950. King tangor x Dancy tangerine; selected in 1925. Fruit: larger than Dancy, which it most nearly resembles; ripens earlier; few seeds; peels easily.

Kara.--Originated in Riverside, California, by the California Citrus Experiement Station (H. B. Frost). Introduced commercially in 1935. Owari (?) Satsuma x King; selected in 1925. Fruit: size good; quality excellent; high in sugar and acid; flesh color high; aroma unique.

Kinnow.--Originated in Riverside, California, by the California Citrus Experiment Station (H. B. Frost). Introduced commercially in 1935. King x Willow Leaf; selected in 1925. Fruit: matures early; quality and appearance excellent; sugar very high; as acid as the sweet orange; aroma unique.

Pitman's Chinese Ponkan.--Originated in Apopka, Florida, by Robert G. Pitman. Introduced commercially in 1949. Patent no. 863; August 9, 1949. Bud sport of Ponkan. Fruit: larger than Dancy and without the characteristic neck; of light orange color; with few seeds; flesh soft and melting; quality very good. Tree: more upright in growth than Dancy; fair vigor.

Silverhill.--Originated in Mary, Florida, by the United States Department of Agriculture (Walter T. Swingle). Introduced commercially in 1931. Seedling of Owari Satsuma x sweet orange, but apparently not a hybrid; selected in 1909. Fruit: large; quality good. Tree: extra vigorous and hardy.

Wilking.--Originated in Riverside, California, by the California Citrus Experiment Station (H. B. Frost). Introduced commercially in 1935. King x Willow Leaf; selected in 1925. Fruit: flavor very good; maintains firmness in a long season. Not valuable unless the excessive alternate bearing, now usual at Riverside, California, can be obviated.

TANGOR

Altoona.--See Umatilla.

Dweet.--Originated in Riverside, California, by the University of California Citrus Experiment Station (Howard B. Frost). Introduced commercially in 1950. Mediterranean sweet orange x Dancy tangerine; selected in 1930. Fruit: most nearly resembles Dancy in flavor and Valencia in size; juice easily extracted.

Umatilla *(Altoona).*--Originated in Eustis, Florida, by the United States Department of Agriculture (E. M. Savage). Introduced commercially in 1931; trademarked Umatilla. Satsuma mandarin x Ruby orange; selected in 1912. Fruit: a very good late variety, ripening January to March; sweeter than the Seminole tangelo; most nearly resembles the Tangelo group.

TUNG

Cooter *(USDA F-4).*--Originated in Brooker, Florida, by the United States Department of Agriculture. Introduced commercially in 1948. Parentage unknown; original tree was planted in January, 1931, in the orchard of H. W. Bennett near Brooker, Florida. Fruit: size medium; spherical, sometimes slightly oblate; borne in small clusters; oil content intermediate; matures early. Tree: productivity very high; moderately cold resistant.

Gahl *(USDA L-51).*--Originated in Isabel, Louisiana, by the United States Department of Agriculture. Introduced commercially in 1948. Parentage unknown; original tree located in an orchard planted about 1928 by the Great Southern Lumber Company near Isabel, Louisiana. Fruit: large; borne singly or in small clusters; almost spherical except for tip of apex; percentage of kernel medium; oil content medium high; matures early. Tree: productivity very high; resistant to cold injury.

Isabel *(USDA L-2).*--Originated in Isabel, Louisiana, by the United States Department of Agriculture. Introduced commercially in 1948. Parentage unknown; original tree is located in an orchard planted about 1928 by the Great Southern Lumber Company, near Isabel, Louisiana. Fruit: large; borne singly or in small clusters; rather prominently ridged at sutures; kernel percentage high; oil content very high; matures early. Tree: productivity very high; moderately resistant to cold injury.

La Crosse *(USDA F-99)*.--Originated in Brooker, Florida, by the United States Department of Agriculture. Introduced commercially in 1948. Parentage unknown; original tree planted in January, 1931, in the orchard of H. W. Bennett, near Brooker, Florida. Fruit: small; length shorter than breadth; flattened at apical and basal ends; cluster type; matures late; oil content high. Tree: productivity very high; top moderately dense with fruiting wood throughout.

Lamont *(USDA F-542)*.--Originated in Lamont, Florida, by the United States Department of Agriculture. Introduced commercially in 1948. Parentage unknown; original tree located in the Chase orchard near Lamont, Florida, and planted about 19-31. Fruit: size medium to large; slightly flattened at apical end; frequently one fruit in each cluster is small and abnormal in shape; cluster medium type; percentage of kernel high; oil content high; matures in midseason. Tree: productivity very high; moderately resistant to cold injury.

Lampton *(USDA F-578)*.--Originated in Leon County, Florida, by the United States Department of Agriculture. Introduced commercially in January, 1950. Open pollinated seedling of USDA L-14; selected in 1943. Fruit: kernel percentage high; oil content 22% to 23% on a whole fruit basis at 15% moisture content; most nearly resembles Isabel. Tree: highly productive; vigorous growth.

USDA F-4.--See **Cooter.**

USDA F-99.--See **La Crosse.**

USDA F-542.--See **Lamont.**

USDA F-578.--See **Lampton.**

USDA L-2.--See **Isabel.**

USDA L-51.--See **Gahl.**

WALNUT

Firstling.--Originated in the Carpathian Mountains of Poland; nuts collected there by the Rev. Paul C. Crath of Toronto, Canada; Mr. Carl Weschcke of Wisconsin procured some seeds and introduced this variety commercially in 1942. Parentage unknown. Nut: Persian (English); medium to small; shell thin. Tree: hardy; difficult to graft on native black walnut.

Grande.--Originated in Mesilla Park, New Mexico, by the New Mexico Agricultural Experiment Station (Fabian Garcia). Introduced commercially in 1932. Open pollinated seedling of Franquette; selected in 1928. Nut: quality fine; most nearly resembles Mayette; Persian type. Tree: prolific bearer.

Hare.--Originated in Rushville, Schuyler County, Illinois, by F. M. Hare. Seedling of *Juglans nigra;* discovered in 1926. Nut: large kernel; good cracking quality.

Harney.--Originated in Cynthiana, Harrison County, Kentucky, by the United States Department of Agriculture Soil Conservation Service (Cullie Baughn). Seedling of *Juglans nigra;* discovered in 1939. Nut: shell thin; high kernel percentage; excellent cracking quality.

Littlepage.--Originated in Wassaic, New York, by Gilbert L. Smith and Wm. A. Benton. Introduced commercially in 1945. Patent no. 815; December 14, 1948. Parentage unknown; seed planted in 1935; fruited in 1944. Nut: Persian; shell thin; size and quality good; early maturing. Tree: hardy.

Norris.--Originated in Knox County, Tennessee, named by Division of Forestry Relations, Tennessee Valley Authority (Spencer B. Chase). Seedling of *Juglans nigra;* discovered in 1940. Nut: excellent cracking quality; good kernel content.

Schafer.--Originated in Yakima, Washington, by Wilhelm Schafer. Introduced commercially in 1940. Patent no. 494; December 16, 1941; assigned to H. Lynn Tuttle, Clarkston, Washington. Grown from seed brought from Austria or Rumania; selected in 1937. Nut: Persian (English); matures very early in fall; high percentage of kernel. Tree: hardy; productivity high.

WHITE SAPOTE

Dade.--Originated in Homestead, Florida, by the Florida Subtropical Experiment Station. Introduced commercially in 1943. Open-pollinated seedling of the common white sapote; selected in 1939. Fruit: flavor fair; no bitter element; shape and size uniform. Tree: bears well.

Flournoy.--Originated on the Flournoy ranch, El Cajon, California, by James H. Macpherson. Introduced commercially in 1930. Open pollinated seedling of Wilson; selected in 1928. Fruit: quality fine; most nearly resembles Wilson. Tree: bears heavily; hardy.

Hubbell.--See **Suebelle.**

Maltby.--Originated in Carlsbad, California, by Guy Maltby. Introduced commercially about 1933. Parentage unknown; discovered about 1930. Fruit: large, weighing up to one pound; skin, too thin for commercial shipper; prominent protuberances; flavor poor; seeds numerous. Tree: heavy bearer.

May.--Originated in San Diego, California, by L. S. Whitmoyer. Introduced commercially in 1945. Parentage unknown. Fruit: sugar content high; matures in September and October.

Pike.--Originated in Santa Barbara, California, by the United States Department of Agriculture. Introduced commercially in the late 1920's. Parentage unknown; grown from seed secured from the USDA; planted on the Pike ranch. Fruit: large; quality good; skin thin and fragile; matures in fall months. Tree: considered productive.

Suebelle *(Hubbell)*.--Originated in Encinitas, California, by Susan Hubbell, Rancho Leucadia Nursery. Introduced commercially in 1931 as Hubbell by the Rancho Leucadia Nursery; later introduced as Suebelle by Mr. C. Tanner. Fruit: smooth; round; 2 to 6 ounces; flesh custard-like, melting; no ginger taste in skin. Tree: everbearing type.

Wilson.--Originated in Monrovia, California, by W. C. Wilson. Introduced commercially in 1927 by Armstrong Nurseries, Inc., Ontario, California. Fruit: quality good; matures crop in the fall. Tree: produces well.

Wood.--Originated in Encinitas, California, by Winfield M. Wood. Introduced commercially in 1943. Parentage unknown; discovered in 1939. Fruit: large; flesh sweet; skin contains practically no bitterness; ripens in early summer. Tree: bears well.

Patented Varieties

Patent Number	Varietal Name	Species
4	Acme Thornless Young	blackberry
7	Hal-berta Giant	peach
12	June Redskin	plum
13	Great Yellow	plum
14	Flaming Delicious	plum
15	July Elberta	peach
16	Mammoth Cardinal	plum
18	Not named	plum
26	Kanner King	strawberry
29	Montlate	cherry
30	Montearly	cherry
31	White Hale	peach

Patent Number	Varietal Name	Species
39	Kosmos	blackberry
41	Honey Heart	cherry
42	Early Giant	grape
46	Jupiter	strawberry
47	Brake	pecan
51	Candoka	peach
53	Ruby	grapefruit
57	Scarlet Staymared	apple
60	Corvallis	strawberry
61	Newtown Delicious	apple
71	Howard's Supreme	strawberry
73	Humble	pecan
74	Riland	apricot
81	Lucas	peach
82	Bauer Thornless Logan	blackberry
84	Rio Oso Gem	peach
85	Jonared	apple
86	Nectar	peach
88	Bonnet Seedless	grape
90	Shotwell Delicious	apple
92	Garden State	nectarine
94	Sweet September	cherry
100	Gano	avocado
101	Wray Red	strawberry
111	Mariposa	plum
112	Green Mountain	strawberry
113	Taxpayer	raspberry
119	Fragrance	mango
120	Hardee	peach
124	Armstrong Seedless Valencia	orange
125	Yorking	apple
126	Robertson Navel	orange
139	Hass	avocado
142	Lemor	orange
161	Nectar-Florence	peach
164	August Supreme	cherry
166	Elliott Special	peach
168	Colora Red York	apple
173	Kim	nectarine
175	Fertile Hale	peach
184	Trauernicht	pomegranate
186	Sullivan 1	peach
195	Not named	grape
232	Redelberta	peach
233	Howard Fisher	peach
234	Henry's Select	avocado
238	Valmore	apple
247	Olympic	blackberry

Patent Number	Varietal Name	Species
258	York-A-Red	apple
261	Monroe	avocado
262	Plantz	peach
271	Hardy-Berta	peach
278	Red Graham	apple
283	Fairberta	peach
290	Burbank's Orchid	peach
291	Burbank's Santa Rosa	peach
293	Red Striped Graham	apple
306	Tom Thumb	peach
309	Not named	pear
311	Empress	grape
316	Richmorency	cherry
320	Erly-Red-Fre	peach
325	Early Halehaven	peach
327	Almeda	apple
328	Violet	nectarine
342	Armstrong Seedless	lemon
345	Majestic	strawberry
347	Summernavel	orange
351	Early Rochester	peach
380	Royal Red	pear
388	Wrixparent	apple
413	Maglio	plum
418	Sunday	peach
421	York Imperial	cherry
433	Macpherson	avocado
435	Guraly Jr.	pear
444	Idemor	lime
451	Fascell	mango
473	Golden Blush	peach
474	Minnetonka Beauty	apple
476	Harriet	apricot
477	Ragin Seedless Pineapple	orange
479	Fuzzless-Berta	nectarine
494	Schafer	walnut
496	Sequoia	nectarine
498	Brooks	apricot
502	Tennessee Supreme	strawberry
503	Ernie Fehr	apricot
506	Kirkman Gem	peach
507	Wiser	peach
509	Sanger Sweet	grape
510	Select	pecan
512	Tennessee Autumn	raspberry
520	Wahlbert	peach
528	Meadow Lark	peach
529	Robin	peach

Patent Number	Varietal Name	Species
540	Sharon	peach
548	Paradise Navel	orange
549	Le Grand	nectarine
560	Crystal Red	plum
564	Martin	apple
567	Fowler	peach
570	Tennessee Shipper	strawberry
571	Merton Thornless	blackberry
572	Dillon	peach
573	Late President	plum
575	Bim	nectarine
576	Mary Martin	avocado
580	Brandywine	peach
585	Grand Champion	pear
587	Hayes Late	nectarine
588	Herb Hale	peach
592	Glamar	peach
593	Hoffman	peach
604	Bates	peach
608	Empire Red	apple
619	Baxter's Black Winesap	apple
621	Redwing	peach
623	Freeland	peach
624	McGuigan	peach
625	Dream Navel	orange
627	Stark Royal Purple	cherry
628	Tomko	avocado
629	Tennessee Beauty	strawberry
630	Bowers	apricot
635	Bowen	blackberry
642	Stark Earliest	apple
648	Dakota Beauty	apple
651	Curlew	peach
653	Tennessee Luscious	raspberry
656	Ott	cherimoya
657	Cornell	orange
658	Humboldt	apple
659	Etter's Gold	apple
661	Flamingo	peach
662	Graham	avocado
667	Arturo	avocado
670	Stark Sure Crop	peach
674	Earle Orange	apricot
692	Nevermiss	grape
693	Reeves	apricot
699	Alaska	apple
710	Jonwin	apple
720	Redgold	apple

Patent Number	Varietal Name	Species
721	Howard Miracle	plum
722	Frostproof	apple
723	Pink Pearl	apple
724	Wickson	apple
728	Devoe	pear
741	Max-Red Bartlett	pear
751	Sun Glo	apricot
757	Not named	pear
759	Stark Early Flame	nectarine
760	Pearson Hiley	peach
761	Mildred Felten	strawberry
764	Starking Hardy Giant	cherry
765	June Wealthy	apple
773	Gem	avocado
779	Toms	raspberry
780	Nectarena	strawberry
782	Sanderson Special	grape
787	Pioneer	nectarine
793	Giant	plum
794	Jongrimes	apple
795	Royal Fay	peach
798	R. L. Stoner	peach
801	Not named	apple
803	Starking Delicious	peach
808	Franciscan	apricot
813	Albru	peach
814	Hale Harrison Brilliant	peach
815	Littlepage	walnut
816	Elsie	avocado
819	Yakima Newtown	apple
821	Wickersham	peach
833	Royal	pecan
854	June Rockhill	strawberry
863	Pitman's Chinese Ponkan	tangerine
868	Merrill Gem	peach
869	Merrill June	peach
872	Parson	prune
878	Early White Giant	peach
888	Honey Dew Hale	peach
890	Silva	strawberry
904	S-37	peach
905	Merrill Beauty	peach
906	Davey	apple
908	Bonanza	raspberry
920	Late Kirkman	peach
924	Tropico	peach
929	Lustre	strawberry
930	Alamar	peach

Patent Number	Varietal Name	Species
966	Vetter Elberta	peach
969	Rusterholz	avocado
970	Golden Early Bird	peach
971	Evalyn Gem	peach
972	Metzger	apple
974	Sunbrite	nectarine
980	Early Le Grand	nectarine
993	Red Rich	strawberry
995	Star Rosa	plum
1008	Magnaberry	raspberry

Varieties by Place of Origin

C A N A D A

ALBERTA

Apple: Acheson.
Pear: Pioneer 3.
Plum: Sapalta.

BRITISH COLUMBIA

Apple: Blackmack, Empire Red,
Jubilee, Spartan, Stirling.
Apricot: Reliable.

Cherry: Sparkle, Star, Van.
Filbert: Brag, Comet, Craig,
G 2 (see Holder), Holder.
Peach: Glamar, Solo, Spot-
light, Summerland S-11-3
(see Solo), Superior.
Plum: Maglio.

MANITOBA

Apple: Breakey, Godfrey,
Manitoba, Manitoba Spy,
Mantet, Morden 347, Morden
352.

Apricot: Leslie, Morden 604, Robust, Scout.
Cherry: Morden 500 (see Coronation), Coronation.
Cherry Plum: Convoy, Dura, Manor, Mordena.
Plum: Bounty, Mandarin, Morden 101 (see Norther), Morden 105 (see Bounty), Norther.
Strawberry: Glenheart.

ONTARIO

Apple: Geneva, Horace, Lobo, Margaret Pratt, Melred (see Red Melba), Patricia, Red Melba, Rosilda, Trail.
Blackberry: Lowden.
Cherry: Velvet, Vernon, Victor.
Currant: Coronet, Crusader, Ottawa 381 (see Crusader), Ottawa 393 (see Coronet), Stephens, Stephens 9 (see Stephens).
Peach: Erlyvee, Howard Fisher, McGuigan, Ontario 290159 (see Vesper), Ontario 350113 (see Erlyvee), Valiant, Vanguard, Vaughan, Vedette, Veefreeze, Vesper, Veteran, Viceroy.
Plum: Algoma, Crystal Red, Grenville, Ottawa 302 (see Algoma).
Pear: Tait-Dropmore.
Raspberry: Gatineau, Madawaska, Ontario 2504137 (see Vandyke), Ottawa, Ottawa 262 (see Rideau), Ottawa 263 (see Tweed), Ottawa 264 (see Trent), Ottawa 272 (see Madawaska, Ottawa 275 (see Ottawa), Ottawa 276 (see Gatineau), Rideau, Trent, Tweed, Vandyke, Viking.
Strawberry: Borden, Claribel, Elgin, Howe, Jim,

John, Louise, MacKenzie, Nectarena, Ottawa 271 (see Elgin), Simcoe, Tupper, Valentine, Vandyke, Vanguard, Vanrouge, Wright.
Plum: Mount Royal.
Raspberry: Newman, Newman 23 (see Newman).

SASKATCHEWAN

Apple: Heyer 12, Rescue, Scott 1 (see Rescue).
Cherry Plum: Heaver.
Raspberry: Honeyking, Honeywood.
Strawberry: Pixie, Sparta, Sweetheart.

ENGLAND

Blackberry: John Innes, Merton Thornless.
Cherry: Noble, St. Margaret (see Noble), Tradescant Heart (see Noble).
Raspberry: Lloyd George.

FRANCE

Peach: Tom Thumb.
Raspberry: Honeysweet (of New Jersey) (see Yellow Honeysweet), Yellow Honeysweet.

GUATEMALA

Avocado: Itzamna, Nabal, P. I. 43486 (see Itzamna), P. I. 55736 (see Itzamna).

ITALY

Grape: Italia.

M E X I C O

Avocado: Schmidt.
Cherimoya: Ott.

N O R T H A F R I C A

Date: Medjhool, Talfilalet
(see Medjhool).

N O R W A Y

Currant: Holländische Rote
(see Viking), Rød Hol-
ländsk Druerips (see Vik-
ing), Viking.

P O L A N D

Walnut: Firstling.

R U S S I A

Nectarine: Ferganensis 0932
(see Krasvynos), Krasvynos,
P. I. 119844 (see Kras-
vynos).

U N I T E D S T A T E S
O F A M E R I C A

ALABAMA

Apple: Atha, Red Hackworth.
Nectarine: Stark Early Flame.
Peach: Jubilant.

ARIZONA

Date: Desert Dew, Sphinx.
Grape: Sanderson Special
Orange: Diller.

ARKANSAS

Apricot: Hardy.
Cherry: Unark.
Grape: Early Giant.
Peach: Early White Giant,
Golden Elberta Cling, Jun-
berta, Starking Delicious.

CALIFORNIA

Almond: Harpareil, Jordanolo.
Apple: Alaska, Beverly Hills,
Cal-King, Etter's Gold,
Humboldt, Jonwin, Pink
Pearl, Valmore, Western
Giant, Wickson.
Apricot: Earligold, Early
Bee, Franciscan, Reeves.
Avocado: Arturo, Coit, Dar-
win, Edranol, Elsie, Gano,
Gem, Graham, Hass, Hellen,
Henry Select (see Henry's
Select), Henry's Select,
Jalna, Leucadia, Macpher-
son, Mary Martin, Middle-
ton, Rusterholz, Ryan,
Summer Fuerte (see Ryan),
Tomko, Zutano.
Blackberry: Acme Thornless
Young, Bauer Thornless
Logan, Bowen, Nectar,
Nectarberry (see Nectar),
Thornless Boysen.
Carissa: Chesley, Serena.
Carob: Santa Fe.
Cherimoya: Bays, Booth,
Carter, Chaffey, Dr. White
(see White), McPherson, P.
I. 44841 (see Chaffey),
Ryerson, Sallmon, Whaley,
White.
Cherry: Black Giant, Bur-
bank's Hearthoney (see
Honey Heart), Honey Heart.
Chestnut: Mayseptjan.
Fig: Beall, Kearney, King,
USDA Rixford 2630 (see
Kearney).
Grape: Almission, Bonnet

Seedless, Bonnet Seedless Muscat, Cardinal, Christmas, Delight, Emerald Riesling, Empress, Perlette, Ruby Cabernet, Sanger Sweet, Scarlet, Seedless Emperor (see Empress).

Lemon: Armstrong Seedless, Frost Eureka, Pink-Fleshed, Variegated (see Pink-Fleshed).

Mango: Macpherson.

Nectarine: Bim, Burbank's Fuzzless (see Flaming Gold), California 27-12 (see Philp), California 27-12a (see Mabel), California 27-13 (see Mabel), Early Le Grand, Flaming Gold, Fuzzless (see Flaming Gold), Hayes Late, Kim, Le Grand, Mabel, Philp, Pioneer, Sequoia, Sunbrite, Tioga, Violet.

Orange: Armstrong Seedless Valencia, Lemor, Robertson Navel, Summernavel, Trovita, Workman Navel (see Summernavel).

Peach: Alamar, Amador, Andora, Anza, Babcock, Babdon, Bates, Bonita, Brentwood Beauty (see July Elberta), Burbank's Elberta (see July Elberta), Burbank's Orchid, Burbank's Santa Rosa, Burton, C. O. Smith, Carolyn, Chadon, Chaffey, Corona, Coronado, Cortez, Curlew, Deberard, Dillon, Donwel, Early Babcock, Early Elberta (see July Elberta), Elliott Special, Ellis, Evalyn Gem, Farida, Flamingo, Floretta, Fontana, Fortuna, Gloribloom, Gold Dust, Golden Blush, Golden State, Gomes, Halford 1, Halford 2, Hermosa, Hiraoka Flame, Hoffman, Honeyberta, Hutchison,

Impon, J. L. Ames, Jewell (see July Elberta), July Elberta, July Gold, Kim Early Elberta (see July Elberta), Kirkman Gem, Late Kirkman, Late Rio Oso Gem (see Kirkman Gem), Leeton, Lovell Cling (see Wiser), Lucas, Lyman Late, Maxine, Maydon, Maywel, McKnight (see Halford 1), Meadow Lark, Merrill 49'er, Merrill Beauty, Merrill Brilliant, Merrill Dandy, Merrill Delicious, Merrill Gem, Merrill Gold Rush, Merrill Home Canner, Merril June, Merrill Late Canner, Merrill Late Gold, Merrill Necta-Heath, Merril Schooldays, Merrill Surprise, Merrill Yellow King, Nectar, Nectar Florence, Nestor, Pedersen, Penryn, Plantz, Pomeroy, Ramona, Redwing, Rio Oso Gem, Robin, Rosy, Royal Fay, Rubidoux, S-37, Shannon, Sharon, Shasta, Socala, Stanford, Stribling S-37-18 (see S-37), Stribling S-47-4 (see Gold Dust), Stuart, Sullivan 1, Sullivan 4, Sunglow, Taylor, Tropico, Tudor, USDA W21-19C (see Vivian), USDA W38-39B (see Coronado), Vetter Elberta, Vivian, Welberta, Weldon, Williams, Wiser, Yelo.

Pear: Christmas Holiday, Orient, P. I. 64224 (see Orient), Royal Red.

Pecan: Royal, Select.

Persimmon: Jumbo.

Plum: Burbank's Flaming Delicious (see Flaming Delicious), Burbank's Great Yellow (see Great Yellow), Burbank's June Redskin (see June Redskin), Bur-

bank's Mammoth Cardinal
(see Mammoth Cardinal),
Early Santa Rosa (see Star
Rosa), Elephant Heart,
Eugene, Flaming Delicious,
Florida (see Red Ace),
Great Yellow, Hollywood,
Honeymoon, Howard Miracle,
Improved Satsuma (see
Mariposa), June Redskin,
Late President, Mammoth
Cardinal, Mariposa, Mon-
ster, Padre, Purple Flame,
Red Ace, Star Rosa.
Plumcot: Orange, Purple.
Prune: Grand Prize.
Raspberry: Bonanza, Magna-
berry, Van Fleet.
Strawberry: California 403.8
(see Shasta), California
467.1 (see Campbell), Cal-
ifornia 537.5 (see Sier-
ra), California 544.2 (see
Lassen), California 567.6
(see Tahoe), California
579.4 (see Donner), Cali-
fornia 829.9 (see Cuper-
tino), Campbell, Cupertino,
Donner, Lassen, Riverview
(see Campbell), Shasta,
Sierra, Silva, Tahoe.
Tangelo: Pearl, San Jacinto.
Tangerine: Frua, Kara, Kinnow, Wilking.
Tangor: Dweet.
White Sapote: Flournoy, Hubbell (see Suebelle), Maltby, May, Pike, Suebelle,
Wilson, Wood.

COLORADO

Apricot: Golden Giant.
Peach: Giant Elberta.

CONNECTICUT

Chestnut: Connecticut Yankee (see Yankee), Yankee.

Plum: Giant.
Strawberry: Branford, Bris-
tol, Connecticut 431 (see
Branford), Hebron, Shelton.

DELAWARE

Apple: Wrixparent.

DISTRICT OF
COLUMBIA

Orangequat: Nippon.
Strawberry: Southland.

FLORIDA

Avocado: Avon, Blair, Bonita,
Booth 1, Booth 3, Booth 7,
Booth 8, Choquette, Col-
linred Seedling B, Col-
linson, Courtright, Ed-
monds, Fairchild 106941
(see Collinred Seedling B),
Fuchsia, Hall, Harris,
Herman, Hickson, Kilgore
Special, Lindgren, Lula,
Major, Marfield, Mitchell,
Monroe, Simpson, Tonnage,
Winter Mexican, Yon.
Grape: Myakka, Seminole.
Guava: Hart, Red Indian,
Redland, Ruby, Supreme.
Lemon: Perrine.
Lime: Eustis, Idemor, Lake-
land, Newell, Newell's
Thornless Key (see Newell).
Mango: Brooks, Brooks Late
(see Brooks), Fascell,
Fragrance, Kent, Simmonds,
Springfels, Zill.
Orange: Cornell, Dream Na-
vel, Paradise Navel, Seed-
less Pineapple, Zellwood
Satin.
Papaya: Betty.
Tangelo: Broward, Lake (see

Orlando), Minneola, Orlando, Sampson, Seminole, Webber, Wekiwa.

Tangerine: Pitman's Chinese Ponkan, Silverhill.

Tangor: Altoona (see Umatilla), Umatilla.

Tung: Cooter, La Crosse, Lamont, Lampton, USDA F-4 (see Cooter), USDA F-99 (see La Crosse), USDA F-542 (see Lamont), USDA F-578 (see Lampton).

White Sapote: Dade.

GEORGIA

Blackberry: Brainerd.

Blueberry: Callaway, Coastal, Ethel, Satilla, Walker.

Chestnut: Hobson, Kuling, Meiling, Nanking.

Grape: Brownie, Creek, Dawn, Dulcet, Howard, Hunt, Irene, Lucida, Nevermiss, November, Qualitas, Spalding, Stuckey, Yuga.

Peach: Dixigem, Dixigold, Dixired, Early Hiley, Pearson Hiley, Southland, Sullivans Early Elberta.

HAWAII

Mango: Schobank.

IDAHO

Apple: Idagold, Idajon, Idared, Payette, Stark Earliest.

Apricot: Brooks, Ernie Fehr.

Cherry: Ebony, Lamida, Spalding.

ILLINOIS

Apple: Baxter's Black Winesap, Lizakowsky (see Saint Clair), Saint Clair, Willow Twig Double Red.

Grape: Black Beauty.

Peach: Golden Early Bird, Hal-Berta Giant, Hardy-Berta, Illinois K40 (see Prairie Schooner), Illinois K43 (see Prairie Rambler), Illinois K47 (see Prairie Clipper), Illinois K69 (see Prairie Daybreak), Illinois K73 (see Prairie Dawn), Illinois K74 (see Prairie Sunrise), Illinois K80 (see Prairie Rose), Prairie Clipper, Prairie Dawn, Prairie Daybreak, Prairie Rambler, Prairie Rose, Prairie Schooner, Prairie Sunrise.

Pecan: Fisher.

Persimmon: Creggs, Spencer.

Strawberry: Vermilion.

Walnut: Hare.

INDIANA

Apple: Hoosier Seedling (see Jongrimes), Jongrimes, Turley.

Peach: Giant Snowball.

Strawberry: Gemzata, Mastodon.

IOWA

Apple: Secor, Sharon.

Hickory: Weschcke.

Peach: Freeland, Polly, Sungold.

Raspberry: Park Black, Toms.

Strawberry: June Rockhill.

KENTUCKY

Walnut: Harney.

LOUISIANA

Apple: Martin.
Strawberry: Klonmore, Konvoy, Marion Bell.
Tung: Gahl, Isabel, USDA L-2 (see Isabel), USDA L-51 (see Gahl).

MARYLAND

Apple: Colora Red York, Red York Imperial (see Colora Red York).
Cranberry: Beckwith, Stevens, Wilcox.
Peach: Colora, Redskin.
Raspberry: Potomac, Sunrise.
Strawberry: Bellmar, Blakemore, Daybreak, Dorsett, Eleanor Roosevelt, Fairfax, Fairland, Fairmore, Fairpeake, Jupiter, Massey, Maytime, Midland, Narcissa, Northstar, Redheart, Redstar, Starbright, Suwannee, Temple.

MASSACHUSETTS

Apple: Davey, Galbraith Baldwin.
Blueberry: Wareham.
Strawberry: Howard 25 (see Howard's Supreme), Howard's Supreme.

MICHIGAN

Apple: Red Graham, Red Striped Graham, Superior.
Cherry: Early Montmorency (see Richmorency), Late Lambert (see Stark Royal Purple), Montearly, Montlate, Richmorency, Stark Royal Purple.
Cherry Plum: Red Cortland.
Grape: Jumbo Red.
Peach: Early Halehaven, Fairhaven, Fertile Hale, Halehaven, Kalhaven, Redhaven, South Haven, Sunday, Sunday Elberta (see Sunday), Sun Glo (see South Haven).
Raspberry: Mortgage Lifter.
Strawberry: Kanner King, Paymaster, Superfection.

MINNESOTA

Almond-Peach: Manitou, Minnesota 7 (see Manitou).
Apple: Beacon, Chestnut, Erickson, Fireside, Flame, Folwell, Haralson, Lakeland, Minjon, Minnehaha, Minnesota 90 (see Haralson), Minnesota 207 (see Wedge), Minnesota 237 (see Folwell), Minnesota 240 (see Chestnut), Minnesota 300 (see Minnehaha), Minnesota 396 (see Victory), Minnesota 423 (see Beacon), Minnesota 635 (see Flame), Minnesota 638 (see Redwell), Minnesota 700 (see Minjon), Minnesota 714 (see Oriole), Minnesota 978 (see Lakeland), Minnesota 993 (see Fireside), Minnesota 1007 (see Prairie Spy), Minnetonka Beauty, Oriole, Prairie Spy, Redwell, Victory, Wedge.
Apricot: Harriet.
Cherry: Minnesota 58 (see Northstar), Minnesota 63 (see Orient), Northstar, Orient.
Cherry Plum: Minnesota 144

(see Nicollet), Minnesota 145 (see St. Anthony), Nicollet, St. Anthony, Zumbra.

Currant: Cascade, Minnesota 70 (see Cascade), Red Lake.

Gooseberry: Como, Minnesota 43 (see Como).

Grape: Bluebell, Blue Jay, Minnesota 45 (see Red Amber), Minnesota 66 (see Moonbeam), Minnesota 69 (see Blue Jay), Minnesota 158 (see Bluebell), Moonbeam, Red Amber.

Pear: Bantam, Cashman, Golden Spice, Mendel, Minnesota 1 (see Parker), Minnesota 3 (see Bantam), Minnesota 4 (see Golden Spice), Parker.

Plum: Anoka, Elliot, Ember, Fiebing, Golden Rod, Hennepin, La Crescent, Mendota, Minnesota 5 (see Mendota), Minnesota 8 (see Elliot), Minnesota 10 (see Waconia), Minnesota 12 (see Red Wing), Minnesota 17 (see Redcoat), Minnesota 21 (see Tonka), Minnesota 30 (see Winona), Minnesota 50 (see Mound), Minnesota 83 (see Ember), Minnesota 91 (see Underwood), Minnesota 101 (see Redglow), Minnesota 109 (see La Crescent), Minnesota 116 (see Newport), Minnesota 118 (see Anoka), Minnesota 120 (see Golden Rod), Minnesota 132 (see Hennepin), Minnesota 157 (see Radisson), Minnesota 194 (see Superior), Minnesota 218 (see Pipestone), Monitor, Mound, Newport, Pipestone, Radisson, Redcoat, Redglow, Red Wing, Superior, Tonka, Underwood, Waconia, Winona.

Raspberry: Chief, Latham, Minnesota 4 (see Latham), Minnesota 223 (see Chief).

Strawberry: Arrowhead, Brunes Marvel, Burgundy, Chaska, Deephaven, Duluth, Easy Picker, Evermore, Hagerstrom's Everbearing (see Red Rich), Minnehaha, Minnesota, Minnesota 3 (see Minnesota), Minnesota 41 (see Deephaven), Minnesota 489 (see Nokomis), Minnesota 775 (see Easy Picker), Minnesota 801 (see Chaska), Minnesota 935 (see Minnehaha), Minnesota 1017 (see Duluth), Minnesota 1118 (see Arrowhead), Minnesota 1166 (see Evermore), Minnesota 1192 (see Burgundy), Nokomis, Red-glo (see Red Rich), Red Rich.

MISSISSIPPI

Apple: Cauley.

Pecan: Desirable, USDA 7191 (see Desirable).

MISSOURI

Apple: Conard, Delcon, Faurot, Fyan, Grove, Whetstone, Wright, Young-Bearing Jonathan.

Grape: Beaver, Blue Eye, Bokay, Bryant, Eleven Point, Gasconade, North Fork, Ozark Prize, Piney, Roubidoux, St. Francis, Tetra.

Peach: Elberta Queen, Halate, Loring, Missouri, Osage, Ozark, Poppy, Romance, Stark Sure Crop, Tulip.

Pecan: Stark Hardy Paper Shell.

Plum: Bluebell, Bluefre, Bonnie, Brilliant, Marvel, Ox-Heart, Ozark Premier, Radiance, Redbud, Twilite.
Strawberry: Armore.

MONTANA

Strawberry: Montana Progressive.

NEW HAMPSHIRE

Apple: Double-Red Baldwin.
Raspberry: Durham.

NEW JERSEY

Apple: Double-Red Delicious (see Starking), Starking.
Blueberry: Atlantic, Berkeley, Burlington, Cabot, Catawba, Concord, Coville, Dixi, Greenfield, Jersey, June, Katharine, Pemberton, Pioneer, Rancocas, Redskin, Scammell, Stanley, Weymouth.
Cherry: Black Sour.
Gooseberry: Glendale.
Nectarine: Garden State, Nectacrest, Nectaheart, Nectalate, Nectarose.
Peach: Afterglow, Ambergem, Autumn, Buttercup, Cherryred, Constitution, Cumberland, Delicious, Early East, Eclipse, Envoy, Fallate, Fireglow, Frostqueen, Goldeneast, Golden Globe, Golden Jubilee, Goldfinch, Goodcheer, Honeygem, Jerseyland, Laterose, Marigold, Massasoit, Maybelle, Meteor, Midway, Newcheer, Newday, New Jersey 41SD, New Jersey 66 (see Sixty-six), New Jer-

sey 79 (see Newday), New Jersey 87 (see Goldeneast), New Jersey 99 (see Pacemaker), New Jersey 101 (see Summerrose), New Jersey 102 (see Envoy), New Jersey 109 (see Laterose), New Jersey 118 (see Wildrose), New Jersey 126 (see Redcrest), New Jersey 129 (see Cherryred), New Jersey 134 (see Early East), New Jersey 135 (see Jerseyland), New Jersey 145 (see Autumn), New Jersey 152 (see Goodcheer), New Jersey 159 (see Frostqueen), New Jersey 161 (see Constitution), New Jersey 164 (see Maybelle), New Jersey 183 (see Fallate), New Jersey 185 (see Frostqueen), New Jersey E (see Rutgers Green Leaf), New Jersey Low Acid 5 (see Newcheer), New Jersey Low Acid 8 (see Honeygem), Oriole, Pacemaker, Pioneer, Primrose, Radiance, Raritan Rose, Redcrest, Redrose, Rosebud, Rutgers Green Leaf, Rutgers Red Leaf, Sixty-six, Summercrest, Summerrose, Sunbeam, Sunhigh, Triogem, White Hale, Wildrose.
Plum: New Jersey 1 (see Raribank), Raribank.
Raspberry: Honeysweet (of New Jersey) (see Yellow Honeysweet), Yellow Honeysweet.
Strawberry: Crimson Glow, Julymorn, Lustre, Mildred Felten, New Jersey 35 (see Pathfinder), New Jersey 225 (see Julymorn), New Jersey 311 (see Crimson Glow), New Jersey 312 (see Sparkle), New Jersey 347 (see Redwing), New Jersey

377 (see Redcrop), Path-
finder, Redcrop, Redwing,
Sparkle.

NEW MEXICO

Walnut: Grande.

NEW YORK

Apple: Alton, Astrachan 2391
(see Carlton), Carlton,
Cortland, Double-Red Duch-
ess (see Red Duchess),
Dunning, Early McIntosh,
Greendale, Kendall, Lodi,
Macoun, Medina, Milton,
Monroe, Newfane, New York
1546 (see Monroe), Ogden,
Orleans, Red Duchess, Red-
field, Redford, Redhook,
Red McIntosh, Red Sauce,
Red Spy, Sweet Delicious,
Sweet McIntosh, Van Buren
(see Red Duchess), Wealthy
Double Red, Webster.
Apricot: Doty, Henderson.
Blackberry: Bailey, Hedrick.
Cherry: Gil Peck, Seneca,
Sodus.
Elderberry: Adams.
Gooseberry: Fredonia.
Grape: Athens, Brocton,
Bronx Seedless, Buffalo,
Dunkirk, Eden, Fredonia,
Golden Muscat, Hanover,
Hector, Interlaken Seed-
less, Kendaia, Keuka, Mel-
ton, Pontiac, Ruby, Schuy-
ler, Seneca, Sheridan,
Steuben, Stout Seedless,
Urbana, Van Buren, Watkins,
Wayne, Westfield, Yates.
Hickory: Murdock.
Nectarine: Hunter, Hunter 1
(see Hunter), New York 50
(see Hunter).
Peach: Fowler.
Pear: Cayuga, Caywood, Cha-
pin, Clyde, Covert, Devoe,
Early Seckel, Gorham, Ovid,
Phelps, Pulteney, Willard.
Plum: Albion, American Mira-
belle, Hall, Stanley.
Raspberry: Amber, Brant,
Bristol, Cayuga, Dundee,
Evans, Indian Summer, Mar-
cy, Marion, Milton, Mon-
roe, Naples, Newburgh, New
York 17438 (see September),
Oswasco, Seneca, September,
Sodus, Taylor, Ulster,
Webster.
Strawberry: Adirondack, Bea-
con, Bliss, Boquet, Cale-
donia, Camden, Cato, Cat-
skill, Clermont, Culver,
Dresden.
Walnut: Littlepage.

NORTH CAROLINA

Blackberry: Cameron.
Blueberry: Murphy, North
Carolina 255 (see Wolcott),
North Carolina 262 (see
Murphy), Wolcott.
Chestnut: Carr, Carrissima
(see Carr).
Grape: Burgaw, Cape Fear,
Creswell, Duplin, Kilgore,
Morrison, New River, On-
slow, Orton, Pender, Stan-
ford, Tarheel, Topsail,
Wallace, Willard.
Pecan: Brake.
Persimmon: Penland, Penn-
land's Seedless (see Pen-
land).
Raspberry: Dixie.

NORTH DAKOTA

Gooseberry: Pixwell.
Raspberry: Ruddy.

OHIO

Apple: Delawine, Franklin, June Wealthy, Melrose, Miami, Warder.
Cherry: August Supreme, Sweet September.
Peach: Albru, Hardee, R.L. Stoner.
Pear: Ewart, Guraly Jr.
Raspberry: Morris (see Morrison), Morrison.

OKLAHOMA

Peach: Brandywine.

OREGON

Blackberry: Cascade, Chehalem. Kosmo (see Kosmos), Kosmos, Olallie, Oregon 609 (see Olallie), Oregon 731 (see Chehalem), Pacific.
Chestnut: Abundance, Honan.
Cranberry: Stankavich.
Filbert: Royal, Woodford.
Pear: Grand Champion.
Plum: Lewis (see Prinlew), Prinlew, Rich Pride.
Prune: Gardner, Lafayette, Weatherspoon.
Quince: Rich.
Raspberry: Willamette.
Strawberry: Brightmore, Corvallis, Improved Clark, Oregon State College 12 (see Corvallis), Streamliner, Ulrich (see Improved Clark).

PENNSYLVANIA

Apple: Red York Imperial (see Yorking), Red Yorking (see Yorking), Yorking.
Cherry: York Imperial.

Chestnut: Zimmerman.
Filbert: Bixby, Jones 200 (see Bixby).
Peach: Honey Dew Hale.
Pear: Richard Peters.

SOUTH CAROLINA

Peach: Goldray.

SOUTH DAKOTA

Apple: Dakota Beauty.
Apricot: Anda, Manchu, Ninguta, Sing, Sunshine, Tola.
Cherry Plum: Honey Dew.
Plum: South Dakota, South Dakota 27 (see South Dakota).

TENNESSEE

Apple: Almeda.
Peach: Davidson, Redleaf (see Davidson), Tennessee Redleaf (see Davidson), World's Earliest.
Raspberry: Tennessee Autumn, Tennessee Luscious, Tennessee Prolific, Tennessee X37 (see Tennessee Luscious), Tennessee X288 (see Tennessee Prolific), Tennessee Y944 (see Tennessee Autumn).
Strawberry: McClintock, Tennessean, Tennessee 6 (see McClintock), Tennessee 148 (see Tennessee Shipper), Tennessee 260 (see Tennessee Supreme), Tennessee 263 (see Tennessee Beauty), Tennessee 965 (see Tennessean), Tennessee Beauty, Tennessee Shipper, Tennessee Supreme.
Walnut: Norris.

TEXAS

Apricot: Improved Cluster.
Blackberry: Big-Ness, Earli-Ness, Regal-Ness, Texas R40-4 (see Earli-Ness), Texas R40-51 (see Big-Ness), Texas R40-202 (see Regal-Ness).
Grape: Favorite, La Pryor.
Grapefruit: Henninger's Ruby (see Ruby), John Garner, Red Blush (see Ruby), Ruby, Ruby Red (see Ruby).
Peach: Fairberta, Frankie, Improved Pallas (see Melba), Melba, Texaberta.
Pecan: Humble, John Garner, Texhan.
Pomegranate: Trauernicht.
Strawberry: Alamo, Ranger, Riogrande, Texas 15 (see Riogrande), Texas 21 (see Alamo), Texas 68 (see Ranger).

UTAH

Peach: Christensen Early Elberta, Johnson Early Elberta, Klondyke Early Elberta.
Strawberry: Canall, Earlee, Lindalicious, Twentieth Century Everbearing, Utah Shipper.

VERMONT

Raspberry: Dike.
Strawberry: Green Mountain.

VIRGINIA

Apple: Close, Dark-Red Staymared, Frostproof, Staymared, USDA 57 (see Close), Vance Delicious.

Chestnut: Reliable, Stoke, Stoke Hybrid (see Stoke).
Nectarine: Fuzzless-Berta.
Peach: All-Red-Free (see Erly-Red-Fre), Erly-Red-Fre, Hale Harrison Brilliant.
Pear: USDA 66131 (see Waite), Waite.
Strawberry: Majestic, Wyona.

WASHINGTON

Apple: Blackjon, Improved Blaxtayman 201, Jonared, Metzger, Newtown Delicious, Nu-Jon, Red Delicious (see Redwin), Redgold, Red Gravenstein, Redwin, Red Winesap, Richard Delicious, Rome Beauty Double Red, Scarlet Staymared, SeeandO Red Rome 262, See andO Winesap, Shotwell Delicious, Yakima Newtown.
Apricot: Bowers, Earle Orange, Perfection, Phelps, Riland, Sun Glo.
Blackberry: Kayberry, Olympic.
Cherry: Rainbow Stripe.
Filbert: Fitzgerald, Nonpareil.
Peach: Candoka, Early Rochester, Halo, Herb Hale, Lawrence, Pacific Gold, Redelberta, Wahlbert, Wickersham.
Pear: Max-Red Bartlett.
Plum: Yakima.
Prune: Merton, Parson, Richards Early Italian.
Raspberry: Tahoma, Washington.
Strawberry: Northwest, Washington 220 (see Northwest), Wray Red.
Walnut: Schafer.

WEST VIRGINIA

Apple: York-A-Red.
Raspberry: Johnson Everbearing.

WISCONSIN

Butternut: Weschcke.
Cherry: Meyer (see Starking Hardy Giant), Starking Hardy Giant.

Filbert: Carlola, Dolores, Magdalene.
Raspberry: Taxpayer.

WYOMING

Strawberry: Sioux.

Index

Glamar peach, 91
Glendale gooseberry, 57
Glenheart strawberry, 151
Gloribloom peach, 91
Godfrey apple, 8
Gold Dust peach, 91
Golden Blush peach, 92
Golden Early Bird peach, 92
Goldeneast peach, 92
Golden Elberta Cling peach, 92
Golden Giant apricot, 25
Golden Globe peach, 92
Golden Jubilee peach, 92
Golden Muscat grape, 62
Golden Rod plum, 127
Golden Spice pear, 119
Golden State peach, 92
Goldfinch peach, 92
Goldray peach, 93
Gomes peach, 93
Goodcheer peach, 93
Gorham pear, 119
Graham avocado, 31
Grand Champion pear, 119
Grande walnut, 167
Grand Prize prune, 135
Great Yellow plum, 127
Greendale apple, 8
Greenfield blueberry, 40
Green Mountain strawberry, 151
Grenville plum, 127
Grove apple, 8
Guraly Jr. pear, 119

Hagerstrom's Everbearing (See Red Rich) strawberry, 157
Halate peach, 93
Hal-Berta Giant peach, 93
Hale Harrison Brilliant peach, 93
Halehaven peach, 93
Halford 1 peach, 94
Halford 2 peach, 94
Hall avocado, 31
Hall plum, 127
Halo peach, 94
Hanover grape, 63
Haralson apple, 8

Hardee peach, 94
Hardy apricot, 25
Hardy-Berta peach, 94
Hare walnut, 167
Harney walnut, 167
Harpareil almond, 1
Harriet apricot, 25
Harris avocado, 31
Hart guava, 72
Hass avocado, 31
Hayes Late nectarine, 77
Heaver cherry plum, 49
Hebron strawberry, 151
Hector grape, 63
Hedrick blackberry, 37
Hellen avocado, 31
Henderson apricot, 25
Hennepin plum, 127
Henninger's Ruby (See Ruby) grapefruit, 72
Henry Select (See Henry's Select) avocado, 32
Henry's Select avocado, 32
Herb Hale peach, 94
Herman avocado, 32
Hermosa peach, 94
Heyer 12 apple, 8
Hickson avocado, 32
Hiraoka Flame peach, 94
Hobson chestnut, 51
Hoffman peach, 95
Holder filbert, 56
Holländische Rote (See Viking) currant, 54
Hollywood plum, 127
Honan chestnut, 51
Honeyberta peach, 95
Honey Dew cherry plum, 49
Honey Dew Hale peach, 95
Honeygem peach, 95
Honey Heart cherry, 45
Honeyking raspberry, 138
Honeymoon plum, 127
Honeysweet (of New Jersey) (See Yellow Honeysweet) raspberry, 145
Honeywood raspberry, 138
Hoosier Seedling (See Jongrimes) apple, 9
Horace apple, 8
Howard grape, 63